# National 4 Maths

The cover photograph shows circles, curves and reflections at a road bridge over the River Aray at Inveraray. The central hole provides additional relief for flood waters.

## David Alcorn

**Consultant Editors**
**Robert Barclay and Mike Smith**

HODDER
GIBSON

The author and publisher would like to extend grateful thanks to Robert Barclay and Mike Smith for assistance offered at the manuscript stage of this book, as well as for further guidance and editorial advice during the production process.

The rights of David Alcorn to be identified as the author of this work have been asserted by him in accordance with the Copyright, Designs and Patents Act, 1998.

Every effort has been made to trace all copyright holders, but if any have been inadvertently overlooked, the Publishers will be pleased to make the necessary arrangements at the first opportunity.

Although every effort has been made to ensure that website addresses are correct at time of going to press, Hodder Gibson cannot be held responsible for the content of any website mentioned in this book. It is sometimes possible to find a relocated web page by typing in the address of the home page for a website in the URL window of your browser.

Hachette UK's policy is to use papers that are natural, renewable and recyclable products and made from wood grown in sustainable forests. The logging and manufacturing processes are expected to conform to the environmental regulations of the country of origin.

Orders: please contact Bookpoint Ltd, 130 Park Drive, Abingdon, Oxon OX14 4SE. Telephone: (44) 01235 827720. Fax: (44) 01235 400454. Lines are open 9.00-5.00, Monday to Saturday, with a 24-hour message answering service. Visit our website at www.hoddereducation.co.uk. Hodder Gibson can be contacted direct on: Tel: 0141 848 1609; Fax: 0141 889 6315; email: hoddergibson@hodder.co.uk

© David Alcorn 2013
First published in 2013 by
Hodder Gibson, an imprint of Hodder Education
An Hachette UK Company
2a Christie Street
Paisley PA1 1NB

Impression number  5  4  3  2  1
Year                      2017  2016  2015  2014  2013
ISBN                     978 1 444 19783 9

Cover photo © Copyright David Hawgood (http://www.geograph.org.uk/photo/1883428) and licensed for reuse under this Creative Commons Licence (http://creativecommons.org/licenses/by-sa/2.0/)
Illustrations by David Alcorn
Proof readers: Stuart Burns and Barbara Alcorn
Typeset in 11 point Times New Roman by Billy Johnson, San Francisco, California, USA
Printed in Italy

A catalogue record for this title is available from the British Library

# PREFACE

*National 4 Maths* has been specifically written to meet the requirements of the SQA Mathematics Course and provides full coverage of the specifications of the **SQA Mathematics (National 4) Course**.

In preparing the text, full account has been made of the requirements for students to develop a range of mathematical, operational and reasoning skills that can be used to solve mathematical and real-life problems. Solving problems both with and without a calculator is also encouraged throughout the text.

To provide efficient, yet flexible, coverage of the specifications, the topics within each unit of the course have been split into chapters.

Chapters  1 -  8   Expressions *and* Formulae
Chapters 11 - 17   Relationships
Chapters 18 - 28   Numeracy

The Expressions *and* Formulae Unit and Relationships Unit may be studied sequentially, with the Numeracy Unit being studied throughout.

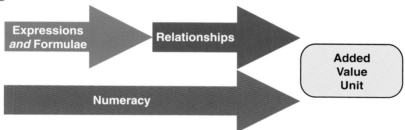

Alternatively, you may wish to study material from different chapters across all three units.

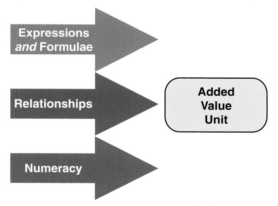

The chapters within each unit have been organised to facilitate either approach.
You can best decide the approach to use depending on the individual needs of the students.

Each chapter consists of fully worked examples with explanatory notes and commentary, carefully graded questions, a summary of key points and a review exercise.
The review exercises provide the opportunity to consolidate topics introduced in the chapter and an efficient method of monitoring progress through the course.

Further opportunities to consolidate skills acquired over a number of chapters are provided with section reviews.

Concise answers are given in this book. Full answers, including all diagrams, are contained in
*National 4 Maths: Teacher's Book, Answers and Assessment Practice*.
It also includes a bank of Assessment Tests and record-keeping suggestions that can be used to record evidence of, manage and monitor, the progress of students.

# CONTENTS

## Expressions *and* Formulae
**Chapters 1 - 10**

## Relationships
**Chapters 11 - 17**

# Numeracy

# 1 Algebraic Expressions

**Algebra** is sometimes called the language of Mathematics.
Algebra uses letters in place of numbers.

## Expressions and terms

A class of children line up.
We cannot see how many children there are
altogether because of a tree.
We can say there are $n$ children in the line.
The letter $n$ is used in place of an unknown number.

Three more children join the line.
There are now $n + 3$ children in the line.

This picture shows two lines of $n$ children.
So, there are $n + n$ or $2 \times n$ children altogether.
The simplest way to write this is $2n$.

Both $n + 3$ and $2n$ are examples of **algebraic expressions**, or simply **expressions**.
Notice that: $1 \times n$ is written as $n$, not as $1n$.

### Example 1

$2n$ students start an IT course.
3 of the students leave the course.
How many students remain on the course?

$2n - 3$ students remain.

> A term includes the sign, $+$ or $-$.
> $2n$ has the same value as $+2n$.

### Example 2

Four apples cost $x$ pence.
What is the cost of one apple?

One apple costs $x \div 4$ pence.
This is written as $\frac{x}{4}$ pence.

An **expression** is just a mathematical sentence made up of letters and numbers.
$+2n$ and $-3$ are **terms** of the expression.

## Practice Exercise 1.1

1. There are $n$ children in a queue. 4 more children join the queue.
   How many children are in the queue now?

2. There are $n$ children in a queue. 3 children leave the queue.
   How many children are left in the queue?

3. There are 3 classes with $n$ children in each class.
   How many children are there altogether?

4. I have $m$ marbles in a bag. I put in another 6 marbles.
   How many marbles are now in the bag?

5. I have $m$ marbles. I lose 12 marbles.
   How many marbles do I have left?

6. I have 8 bags of marbles. Each bag contains $m$ marbles.
   How many marbles do I have altogether?

7. There are $p$ pencils in a pencil case. I take one pencil out.
   How many pencils are left in the pencil case?

8. There are $p$ pencils in a pencil case. I put in another 5 pencils.
   How many pencils are now in the pencil case?

9. I have 25 pencil cases. There are $p$ pencils in each pencil case.
   How many pencils do I have altogether?

10. I have 6 key rings. There are $k$ keys on each key ring.
    How many keys do I have altogether?

11. What is the cost of $b$ biscuits costing 5 pence each?

12. Three cakes cost a total of $c$ pence.
    What is the cost of one cake?

13. Five kilograms of apples cost $a$ pence.
    What is the cost of one kilogram of apples?

14. A group of 36 students are split into $g$ groups.
    How many students are in each group?

15. There are $t$ toffees in a tin.
    (a) How many toffees are there in 2 tins?
    (b) How many toffees are there in 10 tins?

## Simplifying expressions

### Adding and subtracting terms

You can add and subtract terms with the same letter.
This is sometimes called **simplifying an expression** or **collecting like terms**.

$x + x = 2x$     $x + x + x + x = 4x$
$6x - 2x = 4x$     $6x - 5x = x$
$4x - 4x = 0$
$5x - 6x = -x$
$3x + 5 + x - 1 = 4x + 4$

$6 + a$   cannot be simplified.
$5p - 2q$   cannot be simplified.

> A simpler way to write $1x$ is just $x$.
> $-1x$ can be written as $-x$.
> $0x$ is the same as 0.
> Just as with ordinary numbers,
> you can add terms in any order.
> $x - 2x + 5x = x + 5x - 2x = 4x$

**Example 3**

Write down an expression for the perimeter of this shape.
Give your answer in its simplest form.

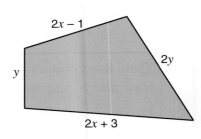

Perimeter is the total distance round the outside of the shape.

$$y + 2x - 1 + 2y + 2x + 3$$

Imagine that each term is written on a separate card.

| $+y$ | $+2x$ | $-1$ | $+2y$ | $+2x$ | $+3$ |

The cards can be arranged in any order.

| $+2x$ | $+2x$ | $+y$ | $+2y$ | $+3$ | $-1$ |

$+2x + 2x = 4x$
$+y + 2y = 3y$
$+3 - 1 = 2$

Simplify this expression to get: $4x + 3y + 2$.
The perimeter of the shape is: $4x + 3y + 2$.

## Practice Exercise 1.2

1. Write simpler expressions for the following.
   (a) $y + y$
   (b) $c + c + c$
   (c) $x + x + x + x + x$
   (d) $p + p + p + p + p + p + p$
   (e) $t + t + t - t$
   (f) $d + d + d - d + d$

2. Simplify where possible.
   (a) $2n + n$
   (b) $2y + 3y$
   (c) $3p - 2p$
   (d) $5r - 3r$
   (e) $7t + 2y$
   (f) $5y - y$
   (g) $5q - 4q$
   (h) $3d - 3d$
   (i) $3x - 4x$
   (j) $4a - a$
   (k) $3b - 2a$
   (l) $5t - 6t$

3. Write simpler expressions for the following.
   (a) $5g + g + 4g$
   (b) $2m + 5m + m$
   (c) $5z + 4z + z + 3z$
   (d) $9c - 2c - 3c$
   (e) $3x - x + 5x$
   (f) $12w - 7w - 4w$
   (g) $5d + 7d - 12d$
   (h) $-2y - 3y$
   (i) $3x - 8x$
   (j) $2a - 5a - 12a + a$
   (k) $3b + 5b - 4b + 2b$
   (l) $m - 2m + 3m$

4. Write an expression for the perimeter of each shape.
   Give each answer in its simplest form.
   (a)            (b)            (c)            (d)

 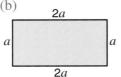  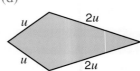

5. Which of these expressions cannot be simplified?
   Give a reason for each of your answers.
   (a) $v + v$
   (b) $v + 4$
   (c) $2v + v + 4$
   (d) $v + w$

6. Simplify where possible.
   (a) $5x + 3x + y$
   (b) $w + 3v - v$
   (c) $2a + b - 3b$
   (d) $2x + 3y + 3x$
   (e) $5 + 7u - 2$
   (f) $p + 3q + q$
   (g) $3d - 5c - 2c$
   (h) $3y + 1 - y$
   (i) $-a + b + 2a$
   (j) $3m + n + m$
   (k) $5c + 4c - d$
   (l) $2x + y - x$
   (m) $-p + 4p + 3p$
   (n) $5 - 9k + 4k$
   (o) $2a - a + 3$

**7.** Simplify where possible.

(a) $3a + 5a + 2b + b$     (b) $p + 2q + 2p + q$     (c) $m + 2m - n + 3n$

(d) $2x + 3y - x - 5y$     (e) $3x - x + 5y - 2y$     (f) $2d + 5 - d - 2$

(g) $3a - 5a + 2b + b$     (h) $a - 2a + 7 + a$     (i) $2a - b + 3b - a$

(j) $-f + g - f - g$     (k) $2v - w - 3w - v$     (l) $7 - 2t - 9 - 3t$

(m) $-p + 3q - 3p + q$     (n) $5 - 9k - 4 + 2k$     (o) $2c + d + 4 - c - 2d + 7$

**8.** Write down an expression for the perimeter of each shape.
Give each answer in its simplest form.

(a) 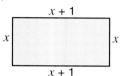     (b) 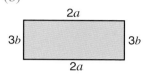     (c)     (d)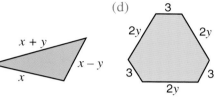

**9.** Show that the perimeter of this triangle is given by the expression: $3x + 5y + 2$.

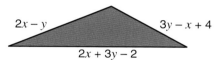

## Multiplying terms

You will need to know these rules for multiplying terms.

$$6 \times a = 6a$$

This is the same as $(+6) \times (+a) = +6a$.

$$4 \times 2y = 8y$$

This is the same as $2y + 2y + 2y + 2y = 8y$.

> When multiplying:
> $+ \times + = +$
> $- \times - = +$
> $+ \times - = -$
> $- \times + = -$

### Example 4

Simplify the following expressions.

(a) $2 \times (-x)$    | This is the same as $(+2) \times (-x)$. |

Deal with the signs first: $+ \times - = -$.
Then, $2 \times x = 2x$.
So, $2 \times (-x) = -2x$.

(b) $(-y) \times (-3)$

Deal with the signs first: $- \times - = +$.

$y \times 3 = 3y$    | $y \times 3$ is the same as $3 \times y$. |

So, $(-y) \times (-3) = 3y$.

(c) $-2 \times p$     (d) $x \times 4$     (e) $(-q) \times (-5)$

$- \times + = -$        $+ \times + = +$       $- \times - = +$

$2 \times p = 2p$       $x \times 4 = 4x$       $q \times 5 = 5q$

$-2 \times p = -2p$     $x \times 4 = 4x$     $(-q) \times (-5) = 5q$

## Brackets

Some expressions contain brackets. $2(x + 3)$ means $2 \times (x + 3)$.

You can multiply out brackets in an expression either by using a diagram or by expanding.

To multiply out $2(x + 3)$ using the **diagram method**:

$2(x + 3)$ means $2 \times (x + 3)$.
This can be shown using a rectangle.
The areas of the two parts are $2x$ and 6.
The total area is $2x + 6$.
$2(x + 3) = 2x + 6$

To multiply out $2(x + 3)$ by **expanding**:

$2(x + 3) = 2 \times x + 2 \times 3$
$2(x + 3) = 2x + 6$

### Example 5

Multiply out $3(2x - 1)$.

**Diagram method**

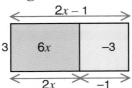

**Expanding**

$3(2x - 1) = 3 \times 2x - 3 \times 1$
This is the same as $(+3) \times (+2x)$ and $(+3) \times (-1)$.
$3(2x - 1) = 6x - 3$

The areas of the two parts are $6x$ and $-3$.
$3(2x - 1) = 6x - 3$

## Practice Exercise 1.3

1. Write these expressions in a simpler form.
   (a) $3 \times a$   (b) $7 \times b$   (c) $e \times 4$   (d) $f \times 8$   (e) $3 \times 2p$   (f) $3q \times 5$
   (g) $y \times 6$   (h) $x \times 1$   (i) $2 \times 5a$   (j) $3 \times 4b$   (k) $6c \times 3$   (l) $3d \times 7$

2. Simplify.
   (a) $3 \times (-x)$      (b) $x \times (-5)$      (c) $(-2) \times (-x)$
   (d) $3 \times (-2x)$     (e) $(+5) \times (-2a)$   (f) $(-5) \times (-2a)$
   (g) $(-3) \times (+c)$   (h) $4 \times (-3c)$     (i) $(-2d) \times (4)$
   (j) $(-3f) \times (-1)$   (k) $(-3p) \times 4$     (l) $(-1) \times (-y)$

   > **Remember:**
   > $2 \times (-x) = -2x$
   > $(-2) \times (-x) = 2x$

3. Write an expression for the area of each shape.
   (a)      (b)      (c)      (d)

4. Draw your own diagrams to multiply out these brackets.
   (a) $3(x + 2)$      (b) $2(y + 5)$      (c) $2(2x + 1)$      (d) $3(p + q)$

**5.** Use the diagrams to multiply out the brackets.

(a)
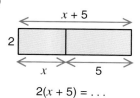
$2(x + 5) = \ldots$

(b)
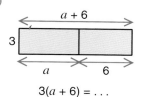
$3(a + 6) = \ldots$

(c)
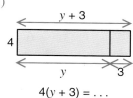
$4(y + 3) = \ldots$

**6.** Use the diagrams to multiply out the brackets.

(a)
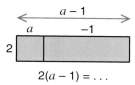
$2(a - 1) = \ldots$

(b)
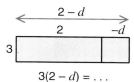
$3(2 - d) = \ldots$

(c)
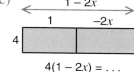
$4(1 - 2x) = \ldots$

**7.** Match the pairs of cards.

| $2(q + 2)$ | $2(q - 1)$ | $2(2q + 1)$ | $2(2 - q)$ |
|---|---|---|---|
| $4q + 2$ | $4 - 2q$ | $2q + 4$ | $2q - 2$ |

**8.** Multiply out the brackets by expanding.

(a) $2(x + 4)$  (b) $3(t - 2)$  (c) $2(3a + b)$  (d) $5(3 - 2d)$
(e) $3(a + b)$  (f) $2(3c + 4)$  (g) $6(b + 2c)$  (h) $3(2m - 5a)$

**9.** Multiply out the brackets.

(a) $-3(x + 2)$  (b) $-3(x - 2)$
(c) $-2(y - 5)$  (d) $-2(3 - x)$
(e) $-3(5 - y)$  (f) $-4(1 + a)$
(g) $-1(-3 + 2a)$  (h) $-2(-d - 3)$
(i) $-2(-b + 3)$  (j) $-3(2p + 3)$

> **Remember:**
>
> $(-2) \times (+3) = -6$
> $(-2) \times (-3) = +6$
>
> so, $-2(x + 3) = -2x - 6$
> and $-2(x - 3) = -2x + 6$

> **To simplify an expression involving brackets:**
> - Remove the brackets.
> - Simplify by collecting like terms together.
>
> $3(t + 4) + 2$ ⎤
> $= 3t + 12 + 2$ ⎦ Remove the brackets
> $= 3t + 14$ ← Simplify

**10.** Multiply out the brackets and simplify.

(a) $2(x + 1) + 3$  (b) $3(a + 2) + 5$  (c) $6(w - 4) + 7$
(d) $4 + 2(p + 3)$  (e) $3 + 3(q - 1)$  (f) $1 + 3(2 - t)$
(g) $4(z + 2) + z$  (h) $5(t + 3) + 3t$  (i) $3(c - 2) - c$
(j) $2a + 3(a - 3)$  (k) $y + 2(y - 5)$  (l) $5x + 3(2 - x)$
(m) $5 - 2(a + 1)$  (n) $5d - 3(d - 2)$  (o) $4b - 2(3 + b)$
(p) $-3(2p + 3)$  (q) $5m - 2(3 + 2m)$  (r) $2(3d - 1) - d + 3$

## Factorising

**Factorising** is the opposite operation to removing brackets.

For example: to remove brackets $2(x + 5) = 2x + 10$

To factorise $3x + 6$ we can see that $3x$ and 6 have a **common factor** of 3 so,

$$3x + 6 = 3(x + 2)$$

> **Common factors:**
> The **factors** of a number are all the numbers that will divide exactly into the number.
> Factors of 8 are: 1, 2, 4 and 8.   Factors of 4 are: 1, 2, and 4.
> A **common factor** is a factor which will divide into two or more terms.
> When factorising, you **must** use the **highest** common factor.

### Example 6

Factorise $4x - 6$.

Each term has a factor of 2.
So, the common factor is 2.
$4x - 6 = 2(2x - 3)$

### Example 7

Factorise $3x + 15$.

Each term has a factor of 3.
So, the common factor is 3.
$3x + 15 = 3(x + 5)$

### Example 8

Factorise $8a - 4b$.

The **highest** common factor
of 8 and 4 is 4.
$8a - 4b = 4(2a - b)$

> You can check that you have factorised an expression
> correctly by multiplying out the brackets.

## Practice Exercise 1.4

1.  Copy and complete.
    (a) $2x + 2 = 2(\ldots + \ldots)$
    (b) $3a - 6 = 3(\ldots - \ldots)$
    (c) $6m + 8 = 2(\ldots + \ldots)$
    (d) $5 - 10y = 5(\ldots - \ldots)$
    (e) $8p - 2 = 2(\ldots - \ldots)$
    (f) $16r - 12 = 4(\ldots - \ldots)$

2.  Copy and complete.
    (a) $3p + 6q = 3(\ldots + \ldots)$
    (b) $8u - 10v = 2(\ldots - \ldots)$
    (c) $2x + 2y = 2(\ldots + \ldots)$
    (d) $8a - 12b = 4(\ldots - \ldots)$
    (e) $16r + 10s = 2(\ldots + \ldots)$
    (f) $3 - 6p = 3(\ldots - \ldots)$

3.  Factorise.
    (a) $2a + 2b$
    (b) $5x - 5y$
    (c) $3d + 6e$
    (d) $4m - 2n$
    (e) $6a + 9b$
    (f) $6a - 8b$
    (g) $8t + 12$
    (h) $5a - 10$
    (i) $4d - 2$
    (j) $3 - 9g$
    (k) $5 - 20m$
    (l) $4k + 4$

## Key Points

▶ $n - 3$ is an **algebraic expression**, or simply an **expression**.
An **expression** is just a mathematical sentence made up of letters and numbers.
$+n$ and $-3$ are **terms** of the expression $n - 3$.

> A term includes the sign,
> $+$ or $-$.
> $n$ has the same value as $+n$.

▶ You can add and subtract terms with the same letter.
This is sometimes called **simplifying an expression**
or **collecting like terms**.   E.g. $2d + 3d = 5d$ *and* $3x + 2 - x + 4 = 2x + 6$

▶ You should be able to **multiply out brackets**, either by using a diagram or by expanding.
Multiply out the bracket $3(4a + 5)$.

**Diagram method**

$3(4a + 5) = 12a + 15$

$$4a + 5$$

| 3 | $12a$ | 15 |

$4a$ ✕ $5$

**Expanding**

$3(4a + 5) = 3 \times 4a + 3 \times 5$
$$= 12a + 15$$

▶ **Factorising** is the opposite operation to removing brackets.

▶ A **common factor** is a factor which divides into two, or more, numbers (or terms).
For example: $4x - 12 = 4(x - 3)$.
When factorising, you **must** use the **highest** common factor.

## Review Exercise 1

1. A lollipop costs $t$ pence. Write an expression for the cost of 6 lollipops.

2. Tom is $x$ years old. Naomi is 3 years older than Tom. How old is Naomi in terms of $x$?

3. Simplify (a) $w + w + w$, (b) $2w + 5 - w - 3$.

4. Write down an expression for the perimeter of each shape.
   Give each answer in its simplest form.
   (a)
   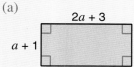
   (b)
   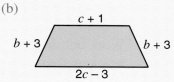
   (c)
   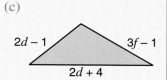

5. Use the diagrams to multiply out the brackets.
   (a)
   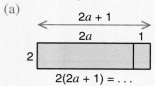
   $2(2a + 1) = \ldots$
   (b)
   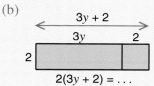
   $2(3y + 2) = \ldots$
   (c)
   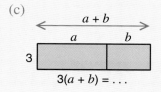
   $3(a + b) = \ldots$

6. Match the pairs of cards.

| $12a + 8$ | $4a - 12$ | $12 - 4a$ | $8 - 12a$ |

| $4(2 - 3a)$ | $4(3 - a)$ | $4(3a + 2)$ | $4(a - 3)$ |

7. Multiply out and simplify where possible. (a) $5(y - 4)$ (b) $4(3y + 1) - 5y$

8. (a) Factorise. (i) $6x - 15$ (ii) $14 + 7y$
   (b) Multiply out and simplify. $3(y + 2) - 2(y - 3)$

9. Remove the brackets and simplify. (a) $2(x + 1) + 3(x + 2)$ (b) $4b - 2(3 + b)$

10. Factorise. (a) $15t - 10a$ (b) $8 - 6x$ (c) $16x - 20y$

# 2 Formulae *and* Patterns

Most people at some time make use of **formulae** to carry out routine calculations.
A **formula** represents a rule written using numbers, letters and mathematical signs.
When using a formula you will need to **substitute** your own values for the letters in order to
carry out your calculation.

## Substituting whole numbers into expressions

### Example 1

Find the value of the following expressions when $a = 4$.

(a) $a + 5$      (b) $a - 3$      (c) $3a$      (d) $\frac{a}{2}$      (e) $a^2$

| (a) $a + 5$ | (b) $a - 3$ | (c) $3a$ | (d) $\frac{a}{2}$ | (e) $a^2$ |
|---|---|---|---|---|
| $= 4 + 5$ | $= 4 - 3$ | $= 3 \times 4$ | $= 4 \div 2$ | $= 4 \times 4$ |
| $= 9$ | $= 1$ | $= 12$ | $= 2$ | $= 16$ |

### Example 2

If $x = 2$, $y = 3$ and $z = 5$, find the value of
(a) $3x + 4y - z$,        (b) $3(y - x)$.

**Alternative method.**

(a) $3x + 4y - z$
$= 3(2) + 4(3) - (5)$
$= 6 + 12 - 5$
$= 13$

> $3x$ means $3 \times x$
> $3(2)$ means $3 \times 2$
> $-z$ means $-1 \times z$
> $-(5)$ means $-1 \times 5$

(b) $3(y - x)$
$= 3(3 - 2)$
Work out the
brackets first.
$3 - 2 = 1$
$= 3(1)$
$= 3$

$3(y - x)$
Expand the brackets.
$3(y - x) = 3y - 3x$
Substitute $y = 3$ and $x = 2$.
$= 3(3) - 3(2)$
$= 9 - 6$
$= 3$

Choose the method you find easiest to use.

## Practice Exercise 2.1      Do not use a calculator.

1. $m = 3$. Find the value of
   (a) $m + 2$      (b) $m - 1$      (c) $4m$      (d) $m \times m$

2. $t = 5$. Find the value of
   (a) $5 + t$      (b) $3 - t$      (c) $2t$      (d) $t^2$

3. $x = 4$. Find the value of
   (a) $x + x$      (b) $x - 4$      (c) $3x$      (d) $x \times x \times 2$

4. $a = 6$ and $b = 3$. Find the value of
   (a) $3a + 2b$      (b) $b - a$      (c) $\frac{a}{b}$      (d) $a \times b$      (e) $2(a + b)$

5. $p = 10$ and $q = 5$. Find the value of
   (a) $p + q$      (b) $p - 2q$      (c) $\frac{p}{q}$      (d) $p \times q$      (e) $3(p - q)$

## Substituting negative numbers into expressions

### Example 3

Find the value of the following expressions when $a = -4$.
(a) $a + 5$ (b) $a - 3$ (c) $3a$

(a) $a + 5$ (b) $a - 3$ (c) $3a$
$\quad = -4 + 5$ $\quad = -4 - 3$ $\quad = 3 \times -4$
$\quad = 1$ $\quad = -7$ $\quad = -12$

Remember:
$(+3) \times (-4) = -12$

### Example 4

Find the value of $5(x + y)$ when $x = 7$ and $y = -3$.

$+ (-3)$ is the same as $(+1) \times (-3) = -3$

$5(x + y)$
$= 5(7 + (-3))$
$= 5(7 - 3)$
$= 5(4)$
$= 20$

Try this example by expanding the brackets, then substituting.

### Practice Exercise 2.2 Do not use a calculator.

1. $m = -3$. Find the value of
   (a) $m + 2$ (b) $m - 1$ (c) $4m$ (d) $2m + 9$

2. $t = -5$. Find the value of
   (a) $5 + t$ (b) $t - 3$ (c) $2t$ (d) $3t - 1$

3. $x = -4$. Find the value of
   (a) $x + x$ (b) $x - 4$ (c) $3x$ (d) $10 + 2x$

4. $a = 6$ and $b = -3$. Find the value of
   (a) $3a + 2b$ (b) $b - a$ (c) $2(a + b)$

5. $p = -10$ and $q = 5$. Find the value of
   (a) $p + q$ (b) $p - 2q$ (c) $3(p - q)$

## Expressions and formulae

Most people at some time make use of **formulae** to carry out routine calculations.
A **formula** represents a rule written using numbers, letters and mathematical signs.

### Example 5

A hedge is $l$ metres long.
A fence is 50 metres longer than the hedge.
Write an **expression**, in terms of $l$,
for the length of the fence.
The fence is $(l + 50)$ metres long.

### Example 6

Boxes of matches each contain 48 matches.
Write down a **formula** for the number of
matches, $m$, in $n$ boxes.
$m = 48 \times n$
This could be written as $m = 48n$.

An **expression** is just a mathematical sentence using letters and numbers.
A **formula** is an algebraic rule. It always has an equals sign.

## Using formulae

The formula for the perimeter of a rectangle is $P = 2L + 2W$.
By **substituting** values for the length, $L$, and the width, $W$, you can calculate the value of $P$.
For example.
To find the perimeter of a rectangle 5 cm in length and 3 cm in width,
substitute $L = 5$ and $W = 3$ into $P = 2L + 2W$.

$$P = 2 \times 5 + 2 \times 3$$
$$P = 10 + 6$$
$$P = 16$$

Multiplication is done before addition.

The perimeter of the rectangle is 16 cm.

### Example 7

$C = \frac{1}{2}x + 3y + 4z$

Find the value of $C$ when
$x = 10$, $y = 2$ and $z = -3$.

$C = \frac{1}{2}(10) + 3(2) + 4(-3)$
$C = 5 + 6 - 12$
$C = -1$

### Example 8

$H = 3(4x - y)$

Find the value of $H$ when $x = 5$ and $y = 7$.

$H = 3(4x - y)$
$H = 3(4 \times 5 - 7)$
$H = 3(20 - 7)$
$H = 3(13)$
$H = 39$

## Practice Exercise 2.3

Do not use a calculator for questions 1 to 6.

1. The number of points scored by a soccer team can be worked out using this formula.

   **Points scored = 3 × games won + games drawn**

   A team has won 5 games and drawn 2 games. How many points have they scored?

2. This formula is used to work out the profit, in £s, made on a coach journey.

   **Profit (£) = 12 × number of passengers − 50**

   How much profit is made on a coach journey with 20 passengers?

3. Here is a formula for the perimeter of a rectangle.

   **Perimeter = 2 × (length + width)**

   A rectangle is 9 cm in length and 4 cm in width.
   Use the formula to work out the perimeter of this rectangle.

4. $T = 5a - 3$. Find the value of $T$ when $a = 20$.

5. $X = 3y + 5$. Work out the value of $X$ when $y = 1$.

6. $M = 4n + 1$. (a) Work out the value of $M$ when $n = -2$.
   (b) Work out the value of $n$ when $M = 21$.

7. $H = 3g - 5$. (a) Find the value of $H$ when $g = 2.5$.
   (b) Find the value of $g$ when $H = 13$.

8. $F = 5(v + 6)$. What is the value of $F$ when
   (a) $v = 1$, (b) $v = 9$, (c) $v = -9$?

9. $V = 2(7 + 2x)$. What is the value of $V$ when
   (a) $x = 3$,    (b) $x = -3$,    (c) $x = 5$?

10. The number of matches, $M$, needed to make a pattern of $P$ pentagons is given by the formula: $M = 4P + 1$.
    Find the number of matches needed to make 8 pentagons.

11. The distance, $d$ metres, travelled by a lawn mower in $t$ minutes is given by the formula: $d = 24t$.
    Find the distance travelled by the lawn mower in 4 minutes.

12. Convert 30° Centigrade to Fahrenheit using the formula: $F = C \times 1.8 + 32$

13. $T = 45W + 30$ is used to calculate the time in minutes needed to cook a joint of beef weighing $W$ kilograms.
    How many minutes are needed to cook a joint of beef weighing 2.4 kg?

## Number patterns

A **number pattern**, or **sequence**, is a list of numbers made according to some rule.
For example: 5, 9, 13, 17, 21, …

The first term is 5.
To find the next term in the sequence, add 4 to the last term.
The next term in this sequence is $21 + 4 = 25$.
*What are the next three terms in the sequence?*

> The numbers in a sequence are called **terms**.
> The start number is the **first term**, the next is the second term, and so on.

> **To continue a sequence:** 1. Work out the rule to get from one term to the next.
> 2. Apply the same rule to find further terms in the sequence.

### Example 9

Find the next three terms in each of these sequences.

(a) 5, 8, 11, 14, 17, …
   To find the next term in the sequence, add 3 to the last term.
   $17 + 3 = 20$,    $20 + 3 = 23$,    $23 + 3 = 26$.
   The next three terms in the sequence are: 20, 23, 26.

(b) 2, 4, 8, 16, …
   To find the next term in the sequence, multiply the last term by 2.
   $16 \times 2 = 32$,    $32 \times 2 = 64$,    $64 \times 2 = 128$.
   The next three terms in the sequence are: 32, 64, 128.

(c) 1, 1, 2, 3, 5, 8, …
   To find the next term in the sequence, add the last two terms.
   $5 + 8 = 13$,    $8 + 13 = 21$,    $13 + 21 = 34$.
   The next three terms in the sequence are: 13, 21, 34.
   This is a special sequence called the **Fibonacci sequence**.

1. Find the next three terms in these sequences.
   (a) 1, 5, 9, 13, ...      (b) 6, 8, 10, 12, ...
   (c) 28, 25, 22, 19, ...      (d) 3, 8, 13, 18, 23, ...
   (e) 3, 6, 12, 24, ...      (f) 10, 8, 6, 4, ...

2. Find the missing terms from these sequences.
   (a) 2, 4, 6, —, 10, 12, —, 16, ...
   (b) 2, 6, —, 14, 18, —, 26, ...
   (c) 1, 2, 4, —, 16, —, 64, ...
   (d) 28, 22, —, 10, 4, —, ...

3. Write down the rule, in words, used to get from one term to the next for each sequence.
   Then use the rule to find the next two terms.
   (a) 2, 9, 16, 23, 30, ...    (b) 3, 5, 7, 9, 11, ...
   (c) 1, 5, 9, 13, 17, ...    (d) 31, 26, 21, 16, ...

4. A sequence begins 1, 4, 7, 10, ...
   (a) What is the 10th number in this sequence?
   (b) Explain how you found your answer.

5. Here is part of a number sequence: 3, 9, 15, 21, ...
   Is the number 50 in this sequence?
   Explain your answer.

6. Find the next three terms in these number patterns.
   (a) 32, 16, 8, 4, ...      (b) 0.5, 0.6, 0.7, 0.8, ...
   (c) 80, 40, 20, 10, ...      (d) 1, 3, 4, 7, 11, 18, ...

7. Write down the rule, in words, used to get from one term to the next for each sequence.
   Then use the rule to find the next three terms.
   (a) 10, 7, 4, 1, −2, ...    (b) 128, 64, 32, 16, 8, ...

## Using rules

Sometimes you will be given a rule and asked to use it to find the terms of a sequence.
For example, a sequence begins: 1, 4, 13, ...

The rule for the sequence is:   | Multiply the last number by 3 then add 1 |

The next term in the sequence is given by:   $13 \times 3 + 1 = 39 + 1 = 40$
The following term is given by:          $40 \times 3 + 1 = 120 + 1 = 121$
So, the sequence can be extended to: 1, 4, 13, 40, 121, ...
*Use the rule to find the next two terms in the sequence.*

The **same rule** can be used to make different sequences.
For example, another sequence begins: 2, 7, 22, ...
Using the same rule, the next term is given by:   $22 \times 3 + 1 = 66 + 1 = 67$
The following term is given by:          $67 \times 3 + 1 = 201 + 1 = 202$
So, the sequence can be extended to: 2, 7, 22, 67, 202, ...
*Use the rule to find the next two terms in the sequence.*

## Example 10

This rule is used to find each number in a sequence from the number before it.

> Subtract 3 and then multiply by 4

Starting with 5 we get the following sequence:  5,  8,  20,  68,  …

(a)  Write down the next number in the sequence.
(b)  Using the same rule, but a different starting number, the second number is 16.
      Find the starting number.

(a)  $(68 - 3) \times 4 = 65 \times 4 = 260$
      Notice that, following the rule, 3 is subtracted first and the result is then multiplied by 4.
      The next number in the sequence is 260.
(b)  Imagine the first number is $x$.

Working backwards.

The starting number is 7.

---

## Practice Exercise 2.5          Do not use a calculator for questions 1 to 3.

1.  Write down the first five terms of these sequences.

   (a)  First term: 1        Rule:  | Add 4 to the last term |

   (b)  First term: 1        Rule:  | Double the last term |

   (c)  First term: 40       Rule:  | Subtract 5 from the last term |

   (d)  First term: 4        Rule:  | Double the last term and then subtract 3 |

   (e)  First term: 2        Rule:  | Add the last two terms and then halve the result |
        Second term: 6

2.  This rule is used to get each number from the number before it:

   > Multiply by 2

   Use the rule to find the next three numbers when the first number is:
   (a)  1,        (b)  3,        (c)  −1.

3.  This rule is used to find each term of a sequence from the one before it:

   > Add 5 then multiply by 3

   (a)  The first term is 7.
        (i)   What is the **second** term?        (ii)  What is the **third** term?
   (b)  Using the same rule, but a different starting number, the second term is 45.
        What is the starting number for the sequence?

**4.** A sequence begins: 1, −3, …

The sequence is continued using the rule:

> Add the previous two numbers and then multiply by 3

Use the rule to find the next two numbers in the sequence.

**5.** A sequence begins: 4, 7, 13, 25, …

The next number in the sequence can be found using the rule:

> Multiply the last term by 2 then subtract 1

(a) Write down the next **two** terms in the sequence.

(b) The 11th term in the sequence is 3073.
   Use this information to find the 10th term in the sequence.

## Sequences of numbers from shape patterns

### Activity

These patterns are made using squares.

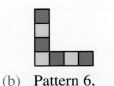

How many squares are used to make:  (a) Pattern 4,   (b) Pattern 6,   (c) Pattern 10?

The number of squares used to make each pattern forms a **sequence**.

Pattern 4 is made using 9 squares.
You could have answered this: by drawing Pattern 4 or,
by continuing the sequence of numbers   3,   5,   7,   …

It is possible to do the same for Pattern 10, though it would involve a lot of work, but it would be unreasonable to use either method for Pattern 100.
Instead we can investigate how each pattern is made.

Each pattern is made using a **rule**.
The rule can be **described in words**.
To find the number of squares used
to make a pattern use the rule:
"Double the pattern number and add 1."

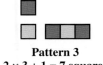

| | Pattern 1 | Pattern 2 | Pattern 3 |
|---|---|---|---|
| | 2 × 1 + 1 = 3 squares | 2 × 2 + 1 = 5 squares | 2 × 3 + 1 = 7 squares |

| Pattern number | Rule | Number of squares |
|---|---|---|
| 4 | 2 × 4 + 1 | 9 |
| 10 | 2 × 10 + 1 | 21 |
| 100 | 2 × 100 + 1 | 201 |

The same rule can be **written using symbols**.
We can then answer a very important question:   How many squares are used to make Pattern $n$?

Pattern $n$ will have   $2 \times n + 1$ squares.
This can be written as   $2n + 1$ squares.

## Special sequences of numbers

### Square numbers

1      4      9      16

The sequence starts: 1, 4, 9, 16, …
The numbers in this sequence are called **square numbers**.

### Triangular numbers

1      3      6      10

The sequence starts: 1, 3, 6, 10, …
The numbers in this sequence are called **triangular numbers**.

## Practice Exercise 2.6

1. These patterns are the start of a sequence.

    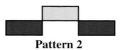   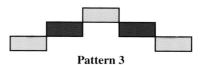

    **Pattern 1**        **Pattern 2**        **Pattern 3**

    Draw the next pattern in the sequence.

2. A sequence of patterns is made using equilateral triangles.

           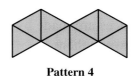

    **Pattern 1**     **Pattern 2**     **Pattern 3**     **Pattern 4**

   (a) Draw the next pattern in the sequence.
   (b) Copy and complete the table.

| Pattern number | 1 | 2 | 3 | 4 | 5 | 6 |
|---|---|---|---|---|---|---|
| Number of equilateral triangles | | | | | | |

   (c) Explain why a pattern in this sequence cannot have 27 triangles.
   (d) Write an expression, in terms of $p$, for the number of triangles in Pattern $p$.
   (e) How many triangles are used to make Pattern 12?

3. A sequence of patterns is made using black and white counters.

         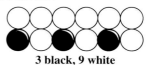

   **1 black, 3 white**     **2 black, 6 white**     **3 black, 9 white**

   (a) How many white counters are there in a pattern with
      (i) 5 black counters,    (ii) 10 black counters,    (iii) 100 black counters?
   (b) How many white counters are there in a pattern with $n$ black counters?

**4.** A sequence of patterns is made using sticks.

Pattern 1          Pattern 2                    Pattern 3

(a) Draw Pattern 4.
(b) How many **more** sticks are used to make Pattern 5 from Pattern 4?
(c) Copy and complete the table.

| Pattern number | 1 | 2 | 3 | 4 | 5 |
|---|---|---|---|---|---|
| Number of sticks | | | | | |

(d) Write an expression, in terms of $n$, for the number of sticks used to make Pattern $n$.
(e) How many sticks are used to make Pattern 20?

**5.** A sequence of patterns is made using matches.

Pattern 1          Pattern 2          Pattern 3
6 matches          10 matches         14 matches

(a) How many matches are used to make
   (i) Pattern 4,          (ii) Pattern 20?
(b) Which pattern in the sequence uses 30 matches?
(c) Explain why any pattern in the sequence will use an even number of matches.
(d) Pattern $n$ uses $T$ matches. Write a formula for $T$ in terms of $n$.
(e) Use your formula to find the number of matches used to make Pattern 50.

**6.** Fences are made by placing fence posts 1 m apart and using 2 horizontal bars between them.

The fence above is 4 m long. It has 5 posts and 8 horizontal bars.
(a) A fence is 50 m long.
   (i) How many posts does it have?   (ii) How many horizontal bars does it have?
(b) A fence is $x$ metres long. It has $P$ posts and $H$ horizontal bars.
   Write down formulae for the number of
   (i) posts,          (ii) bars.
(c) Use your formula to find the number of posts and horizontal bars needed to make a fence which is 100 m long.

**7.** These patterns are made using matches.
(a) How many matches are used to make Pattern 5?
(b) Which pattern uses 15 matches?
(c) How many matches are used to make Pattern 10?
(d) Find a formula for the number of matches, $m$, in Pattern $p$.
(e) Use your formula to find the number of matches used to make Pattern 30.

Pattern 1          Pattern 2

Pattern 3

**8.** A sequence of patterns is made using sticks.

   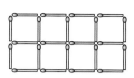

      **Pattern 1**      **Pattern 2**      **Pattern 3**      **Pattern 4**

   (a) How many sticks are used to make Pattern 5?

   (b) Describe a rule, in words, to find the number of matches to make the next pattern.

   (c) One pattern uses 32 sticks. What is the pattern number?

## Key Points

▶ An **expression** is just a mathematical sentence using letters and numbers.
A **formula** is an algebraic rule. It always has an equals sign.

▶ You should be able to **substitute** values into expressions and formulae.

▶ A **number pattern**, or **sequence**, is a list of numbers made according to some rule.
The numbers in the pattern (or sequence) are called **terms**.

▶ You should be able to continue a sequence by following a given rule.

▶ You should be able to draw and continue number sequences represented by patterns
of shapes.

▶ Special sequences   **Square numbers**:   1,  4,  9,  16,  25,  …
                          **Triangular numbers**: 1,  3,  6,  10,  15,  …
                          **Fibonacci sequence**:  1,  1,  2,  3,  5,  8,  13,  …

## Review Exercise 2      Do not use a calculator for questions 1 to 6.

**1.** What is the value of $2g + 3h$ when $g = 5$ and $h = 2$?

**2.** What is the value of $5m + 2n$ when $m = 2$ and $n = -3$?

**3.** $P = 3(m + n)$. Find the value of $P$ when $m = -4$ and $n = -2$.

**4.** (a) What is the value of $3(d - 2) + d$ when $d = 7$?
   (b) Multiply out and simplify $3(d - 2) + d$.

**5.** Bret organises a quiz league.
He uses the formula $m = 2 \times (n - 1)$ to work out the number of matches, $m$,
if $n$ teams play each other twice.
   (a) Work out the number of matches if there are 7 teams in the quiz league.
   (b) The following year, 3 more teams apply to enter the quiz league.
       How many **more** matches will be needed?

**6.** Find the next three terms in each of these sequences.
   (a) 1, 4, 9, 16, …      (b) 1, 1, 2, 3, 5, 8, …

**7.** (a) Write down the next two terms in this sequence.

$$3, \quad 7, \quad 11, \quad 15, \quad 19, \quad \ldots, \quad \ldots$$

(b) What is the first number in the sequence which is greater than 40?

**8.** Find the missing numbers in each of these number patterns.

(a) —, 8, 14, —, —, 32, 38, ...

(b) 56, 51, —, 41, —, —, 26, ...

**9.** This rule is used to find each term of a sequence from the one before:

> Subtract 3 then divide by 2

(a) The first term is 45.
  (i) What is the second term?
  (ii) What is the **fourth** term?

(b) Using the same rule, but a different starting number, the second term is 17. What is the starting number for the sequence?

**10.** A sequence is formed from this rule:

> Add together the last two terms to find the next term

Part of the sequence is ... 5, 9, 14, 23, ...

(a) Write down the next two terms after 23 in the sequence.

(b) Write down the two terms that come before 5 in the sequence.

**11.** A number sequence begins 1, 2, 4, ...
Gregor says that the next number is 8.
Fraser says that the next number is 7.

(a) Explain why they could both be correct.

(b) Find the 10th number in Gregor's sequence.

(c) Find the 10th number in Fraser's sequence.

**12.** A sequence of patterns is shown.

  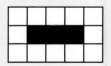

| Pattern 1 | Pattern 2 | Pattern 3 |

(a) Draw the next pattern in the sequence.

(b) Copy and complete the table.

| Number of black squares | 1 | 2 | 3 | 4 | 5 |
|---|---|---|---|---|---|
| Number of white squares | | | | | |

(c) Pattern $n$ uses $W$ white squares and $B$ black squares. Find a formula connecting $W$ and $B$.

(d) Use your formula to find which pattern in the sequence uses 24 white squares.

**13.** A sequence of numbers begins: 1, 3, 6, 10, 15, ...

(a) Write down the next three terms in this sequence.

(b) Describe, in words, the rule to make this pattern.

# 3 Gradient of a Straight Line

## Gradient of a straight line

The gradient of a straight line is found by drawing a right-angled triangle.

$$\text{Gradient} = \frac{\text{vertical height}}{\text{horizontal distance}}$$

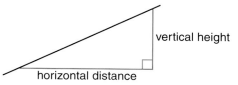
vertical height
horizontal distance

Line (**1**) has **positive gradient**.
As you go from left to right along the line it slopes **up**.

$$\text{Gradient} = \frac{\text{vertical height}}{\text{horizontal distance}} = \frac{2}{3}$$

Line (**1**) has a gradient $\frac{2}{3}$.

Line (**2**) has **negative gradient**.
As you go from left to right along the line it slopes **down**.

$$\text{Gradient} = \frac{\text{vertical height}}{\text{horizontal distance}} = -\frac{4}{2} = -2$$

Line (**2**) has a gradient $-2$.

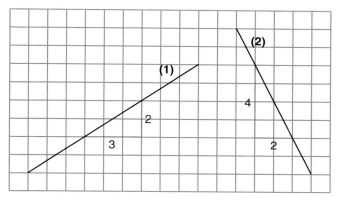

Line (**3**) has **zero gradient**.
The line is **horizontal**.

$$\text{Gradient} = \frac{\text{vertical height}}{\text{horizontal distance}} = \frac{0}{8} = 0$$

Line (**4**) has **undefined gradient**.
The line is **vertical**.

$$\text{Gradient} = \frac{\text{vertical height}}{\text{horizontal distance}} = \frac{7}{0} = \text{undefined}$$

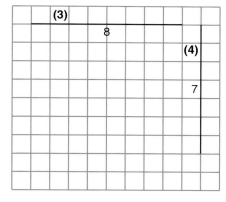

> If you are finding the gradient of lines drawn on a grid, choose points on the line so that distances up and along are whole numbers.

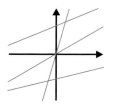
**Positive gradients go "uphill"**

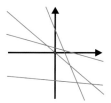
**Negative gradients go "downhill"**

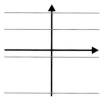
**Zero gradients are "horizontal"**

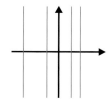
**Undefined gradients are "vertical"**

> Lines which are **parallel** have the **same gradient**.

1. Which lines have positive, negative, zero and undefined gradient?

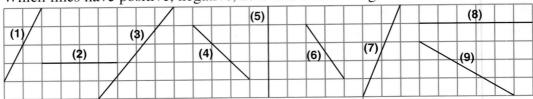

2. Find the gradients of the lines numbered **(1)** to **(6)**.

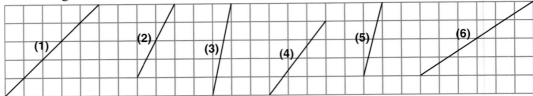

3. Find the gradients of the lines numbered **(1)** to **(6)**.

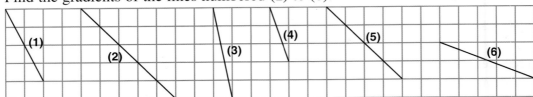

4. Which of the lines in this diagram are parallel to
   (a) line **(A)**, (b) line **(B)**, (c) line **(C)**?

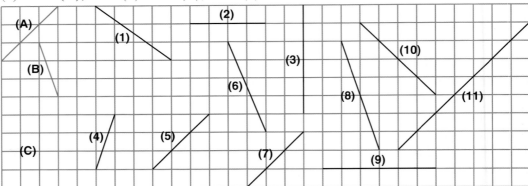

5.

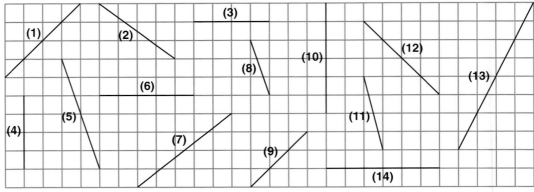

   (a) Find the gradients of the lines numbered **(1)** to **(14)**.
   (b) Which line is parallel to line **(1)**?
   (c) Which line is parallel to line **(8)**?

## Gradient of a straight line graph

The gradient of a **straight line graph** is found by drawing a right-angled triangle.

$$\text{Gradient} = \frac{\text{vertical height}}{\text{horizontal distance}}$$

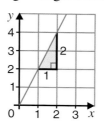

On the graph: vertical height = 2, horizontal distance = 1.
The graph has positive gradient.

$$\text{Gradient} = \frac{2}{1} = 2$$

### Example 1

Find the gradient of this straight line graph.

First, draw a suitable right-angled triangle.
Choose points on the line so that the
distances up and along are whole numbers.

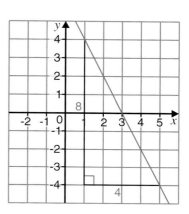

On the graph: vertical height = 8, horizontal distance = 4.
The graph has negative gradient.

$$\text{Gradient} = -\frac{8}{4} = -2$$

## Practice Exercise 3.2

1. Calculate the gradient of these straight line graphs.

(a)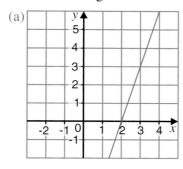

(b)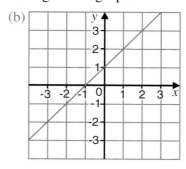

(c)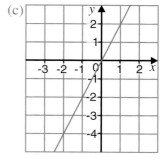

2. Calculate the gradient of these straight line graphs.

(a)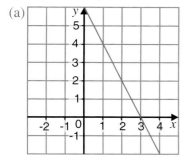

(b)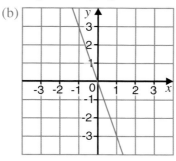

(c)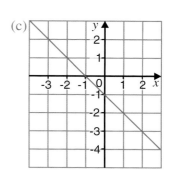

To find the gradient of a line drawn on a grid, you must:
- read the scale on the vertical axis to find the distance up,
- read the scale on the horizontal axis to find the distance along.

3. Calculate the gradient of these straight line graphs.

(a)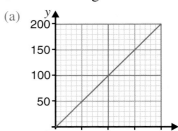

(b)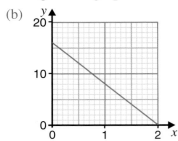

(c)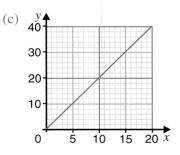

4. Look at this diagram.

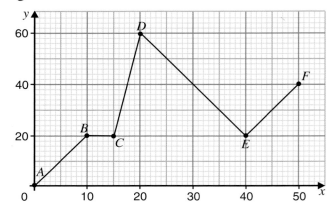

(a) Between which two points is the gradient zero?

Calculate the gradient of the line between points:

(b) *A* and *B*,     (c) *C* and *D*,     (d) *D* and *E*,     (e) *E* and *F*.

## Key Points

▶ The **gradient** of a line can be found by drawing a right-angled triangle.

$$\text{Gradient} = \frac{\text{vertical height}}{\text{horizontal distance}}$$

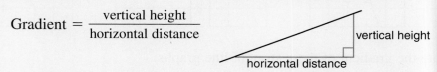

Gradient can be positive, negative, zero or undefined.

▶ To find the gradient of a straight line graph.
First draw a suitable right-angled triangle.
Choose points on the line so that the distances up and along are whole numbers.

▶ To find the gradient of a line drawn on a grid, you must:
- read the scale on the vertical axis to find the distance up,
- read the scale on the horizontal axis to find the distance along.

## Review Exercise 3

**1.**

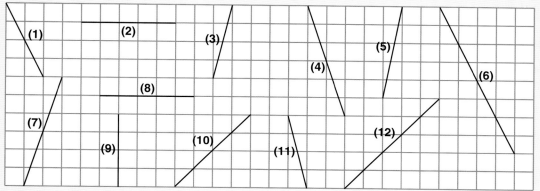

(a) Find the gradient of the lines numbered **(1)** to **(12)**.

(b) Which line is parallel to line **(10)**?

(c) Which line is parallel to line **(1)**?

**2.** Calculate the gradients of these straight line graphs.

(a)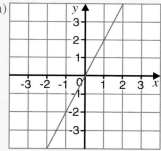

(b)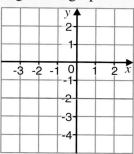

(c)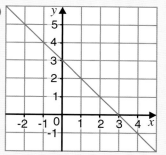

**3.** Look at this diagram.

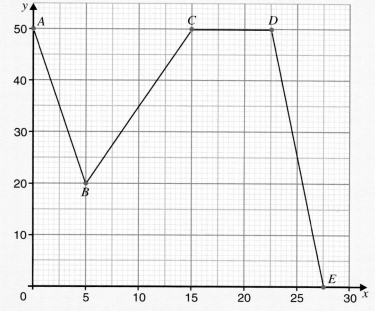

Calculate the gradient of the line joining points:

(a) *A* and *B*,　　(b) *B* and *C*,　　(c) *C* and *D*,　　(d) *D* and *E*.

# 4 Circles

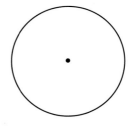

A **circle** is the shape drawn by keeping a pencil the same distance from a fixed point on a piece of paper. Compasses can be used to draw circles accurately.

It is important that you understand the meaning of the following words:

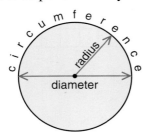

**Circumference** – special name used for the perimeter of a circle.

**Radius** – distance from the centre of the circle to any point on the circumference. The plural of radius is **radii**.

**Diameter** – distance right across the circle, passing through the centre point. Notice that the diameter is twice as long as the radius.

## Activity

Draw a circle with radius 2 cm.
Use thread or the edge of a strip of paper to measure the circumference of your circle.
Draw circles with radii 3 cm, 4 cm and so on.
Measure the circumference of each circle and write your results in a table.

| Radius (cm) | 2 | 3 | 4 | 5 | 6 | 7 | 8 |
|---|---|---|---|---|---|---|---|
| Diameter (cm) | | | | | | | |
| Circumference (cm) | | | | | | | |

*What do you notice?*

## The Greek letter $\pi$

The circumference of any circle is just a bit bigger than three times the diameter of the circle. The Greek letter $\pi$ is used to represent this number.
We use an approximate value for $\pi$, such as 3, $3\frac{1}{7}$, 3.14, or the $\pi$ key on a calculator, depending on the accuracy we require.

## Circumference of a circle

The diagram shows a circle with radius $r$ and diameter $d$.

The **circumference** of a circle can be found using the formulae:

$$C = \pi d$$

Remember: $d = 2 \times r$

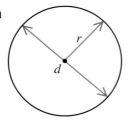

We sometimes use letters in place of words.
$C$ is short for circumference.
$r$ is short for radius.
$d$ is short for diameter.

### Example 1

Find the circumference of a circle with diameter 80 cm. Take $\pi$ to be 3.14.
Give your answer to the nearest centimetre.

$C = \pi d$
$C = 3.14 \times 80 \text{ cm}$
$C = 251.2 \text{ cm}$
Circumference is 251 cm to the nearest centimetre.

### Practice Exercise 4.1

Do not use a calculator for questions 1 and 2.

1. Estimate the circumference of these circles.
   Use the approximate rule:  Circumference = 3 × diameter.

   (a)  4 cm

   (b) 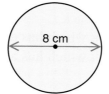 8 cm

   (c) 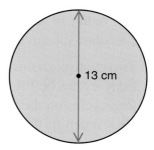 13 cm

2. Use the approximate rule to estimate the circumference of these circles.

   (a)  2.5 cm

   (b) 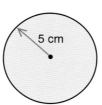 5 cm

   (c) 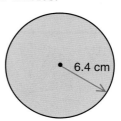 6.4 cm

In questions 3 to 11, take $\pi$ to be 3.14 or use the $\pi$ key on your calculator.

3. Calculate the circumference of these circles.

   (a) 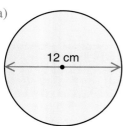 12 cm

   (b) 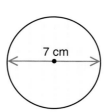 7 cm

   (c) 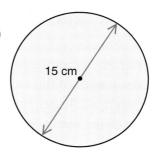 15 cm

4. Calculate the circumference of these circles.

   (a)  4.5 cm

   (b) 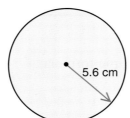 5.6 cm

   (c) 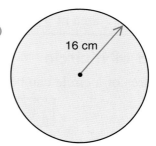 16 cm

5. A circle has a diameter of 9 cm. Calculate the circumference of the circle.
   Give your answer correct to the nearest whole number.

6. A circular biscuit tin has a diameter of 24 cm. What is the circumference of the tin?

7. A dinner plate has a radius of 13 cm. Calculate the circumference of the plate.
   Give your answer to an appropriate degree of accuracy.

8. A circle has a radius of 6.5 cm. Calculate the circumference of the circle.
   Give your answer correct to one decimal place.

9. Stan marks the centre circle of a football pitch.
   The circle has a radius of 9.15 m.
   What is the circumference of the circle?

10. The radius of a tractor wheel is 0.8 m.
    Calculate the circumference of the wheel.

11. Two cyclists go once round a circular track.
    Eddy cycles on the inside of the track which has a radius of 20 m.
    Reg cycles on the outside of the track which has a radius of 25 m.
    How much further does Reg cycle?

## Area of a circle

### Activity

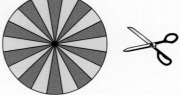

Cut out the 20 sectors.
Arrange them like this.

Draw a circle. Divide it into 20 equal **sectors**.
Colour the sectors using two colours.

The circumference of a circle is given by $2 \times \pi \times r$.
Half of the circumference is $\pi \times r$.
So, the length of the rectangle is $\pi \times r$.
The width of the rectangle is the same as the
radius of the circle, $r$.

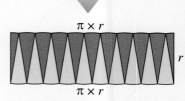

Take the end sector and cut it in half.
Place one piece at each end of the pattern

Using area of a rectangle = length × breadth
area of a circle = $\pi \times r \times r$
area of a circle = $\pi \times r^2$

### Area of a circle

The area of a circle can be found using the formula:

$$A = \pi r^2$$

$$r^2 = r \times r$$

**Example 2**

Estimate the area of a circle with radius of 6 cm. Take $\pi$ to be 3.

$A = \pi r^2$
$A = 3 \times 6 \times 6$
$A = 108\,\text{cm}^2$
Area is approximately $108\,\text{cm}^2$.

**Example 3**

Calculate the area of a circle with diameter 9 cm. Use the $\pi$ key on your calculator.
Give your answer correct to the nearest whole number.

$A = \pi r^2$
$A = \pi \times 4.5 \times 4.5$       **Remember:**   $r = \dfrac{d}{2}$
$A = 63.617\ldots\,\text{cm}^2$
Area is $64\,\text{cm}^2$, to the nearest whole number.

**Practice** Exercise **4.2**     Do not use a calculator for questions 1 and 2.

1.   Estimate the areas of these circles.   Use the approximate rule:   Area $= 3 \times$ (radius)$^2$.
   (a)                          (b)                          (c)

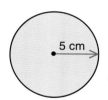  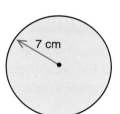  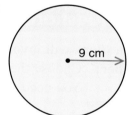

2.   Estimate the areas of these circles.    **Remember:**  Radius $= \dfrac{\text{diameter}}{2}$
   Take $\pi$ to be 3.

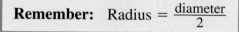

   (a)                          (b)                          (c)

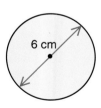  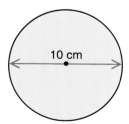  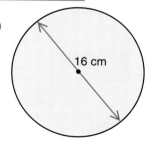

In questions 3 to 8, take $\pi$ to be 3.14 or use the $\pi$ key on your calculator.

3.   Calculate the areas of these circles. Give your answers to the nearest whole number.
   (a)                          (b)                          (c)

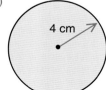  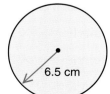  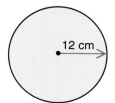

4. Calculate the areas of these circles. Give your answers correct to one decimal place.

(a)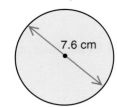
6.4 cm

(b)
7.6 cm

(c)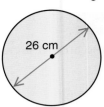
26 cm

5. The lid on a tin of paint is a circle of radius 72 mm.
Calculate the area of the lid.

6. A circular table has a diameter of 1.2 m.
Calculate the area of the table.
Give your answer correct to one decimal place.

7. A circular rug has a radius of 0.5 m.
Calculate the area of the rug.
Give your answer correct to two decimal places.

8. A mug has a diameter of 8 cm.
Calculate the area of the base of the mug.
Give your answer to an appropriate degree of accuracy.

## Mixed questions involving circumferences and areas of circles

Some questions will involve finding the area and some the circumference of a circle.
**Remember:** Choose the correct formula for area or circumference.
You need to think about whether to use the radius or the diameter.

### Example 4

Gina's bicycle wheel has a radius of 24 cm.
How many complete rotations of the wheel are needed to cycle 500 cm? Take $\pi = 3.14$.

Find the circumference of the wheel.   Radius = 24 cm, so diameter = 48 cm.

$C = \pi d$                  | Number of rotations = 500 cm ÷ circumference
$C = 3.14 \times 48$ cm      | Number of rotations = 500 cm ÷ 150.72 cm
$C = 150.72$ cm             | Number of rotations = 3.317…

So, 4 complete rotations of the wheel are needed.

### Example 5

Find the area of a semicircle with radius 4 cm. Take $\pi = 3.14$.
Give your answer to the nearest whole number.

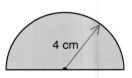
4 cm

Begin by finding the area of a circle with radius 4 cm.

$A = \pi r^2$                      | Area of semicircle = $\frac{1}{2} \times$ area of circle
$A = 3.14 \times 4 \times 4$ cm²   | Area of semicircle = $\frac{1}{2} \times 50.24$ cm²
$A = 50.24$ cm²                   | Area of semicircle = 25.12 cm²

Area of semicircle is 25 cm², to the nearest whole number.

## Practice Exercise 4.3

In this exercise take $\pi$ to be 3.14 or use the $\pi$ key on your calculator.

1. A tea plate has a radius of 9 cm.
   (a) What is the circumference of the plate?
   (b) What is the area of the plate?

2. The top of a tin of cat food is a circle of diameter 8.4 cm.
   (a) Calculate the circumference of the tin.
       Give your answer correct to the nearest whole number.
   (b) Calculate the area of the top of the tin.
       Give your answer correct to one decimal place.

3. 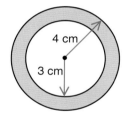 The front wheel on Nick's tricycle has a diameter of 18 cm.
   (a) Calculate the circumference of the front wheel.
   (b) How far does Nick have to cycle for the front wheel to make 20 complete turns?

4. The letter O is cut from card.
   The inside radius of the letter is 3 cm.
   The outside radius of the letter is 4 cm.
   Calculate the area of the letter.

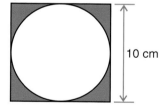

5. Which has the greater area:
   **a circle with radius 4 cm, or a semicircle with diameter 11 cm?**
   You must show all your working.

6. A circle is drawn inside a square, as shown.
   The square has sides of length 10 cm.
   Calculate the area of the shaded region.

7. Thirty students join hands to form a circle.
   The diameter of the circle is 8.5 m.
   (a) Find the circumference of the circle.
       Give your answer to the nearest metre.
   (b) What area is enclosed by the circle?
       Give your answer to an appropriate degree of accuracy.

8. Find the perimeter of a semicircle with radius 6 cm.
   Give your answer to the nearest whole number.

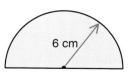

9. A circular flower bed has diameter 12 m.
   (a) How much edging is needed to go right round the bed?
   (b) The gardener needs one bag of fertiliser for each 7 m².
       How many bags of fertiliser are needed for this bed?

## Key Points

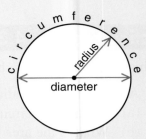

▶ A **circle** is the shape drawn by keeping a pencil the same distance from a fixed point on a piece of paper.

▶ Words associated with circles:
  **Circumference** – perimeter of a circle.
  **Radius** – distance from the centre of the circle to any point on the circumference. The plural of radius is **radii**.
  **Diameter** – distance right across the circle, passing through the centre point.

▶ Diameter = 2 × radius

▶ The **circumference** of a circle is given by: $C = \pi d$

▶ The **area** of a circle is given by: $A = \pi r^2$

## Review Exercise 4

In this exercise take $\pi$ to be 3.14 or use the $\pi$ key on your calculator.

1. (a) Find the circumference of a circle with radius 7 cm.
   (b) A circle has diameter 18 cm. Find the circumference of the circle.

2. (a) A circle has radius 8 cm. Find the area of the circle.
   (b) Find the area of a circle with diameter 20 cm.

3. The diagram shows two pulleys.
   The larger pulley has radius 5 cm.
   The smaller pulley has diameter 8 cm.
   (a) What is the area of the larger pulley?
   (b) What is the circumference of the smaller pulley?

4. The minute hand on the town hall clock is 2.5 m long. How far does the tip of the minute hand travel in an hour?

5. The diagram shows a cardboard ring.
   The inner radius is 9 cm.
   The outer radius is 11 cm.
   Calculate the area of the ring.

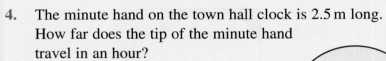

6. A rail for the track of a toy train is a quarter circle of radius 15 cm.

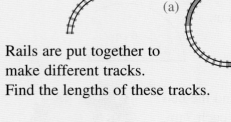

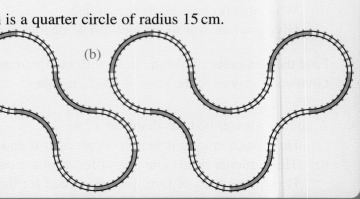

   (a)   (b)

   Rails are put together to make different tracks.
   Find the lengths of these tracks.

# 5 Areas *and* Volumes

## Area

**Area** is the amount of surface covered by a shape. The standard unit for measuring area is the square centimetre, cm². Small areas are measured using square millimetres, mm². Large areas are measured using square metres, m², or square kilometres, km².

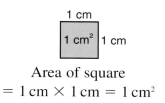

Area of square
= 1 cm × 1 cm = 1 cm²

## Area of a triangle

Imagine a rectangle with a diagonal drawn.
The area of the rectangle is given by   Area = base × height.
The area of the triangle is half the area of the rectangle.

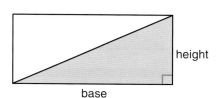

> The area of a triangle is given by:
> Area = $\frac{1}{2}$ × base × perpendicular height.  $A = \frac{1}{2}bh$

In these triangles, *b* is the base and *h* is the perpendicular height.

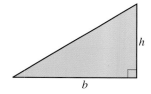
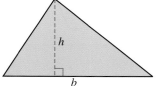
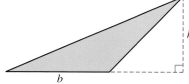

> **Base and perpendicular height**
> The **base** is the side of the shape from which the height is measured.
> The base does not have to be at the bottom of the shape. The height of a shape, measured at right angles to the base, is called the **perpendicular height**.

### Example 1

Calculate the area of this triangle.   $A = \frac{1}{2}bh$

$A = \frac{1}{2} \times 12 \times 7$

$A = 42\,cm^2$

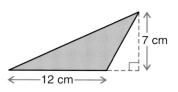

## Practice Exercise 5.1

1.   Calculate the areas of these triangles.

(a)

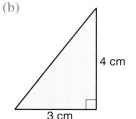

(b)

(c)

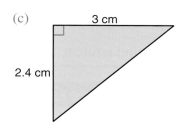

**2.** Work out the areas of these triangles.

(a)

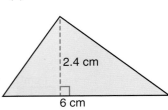
2.4 cm
6 cm

(b)

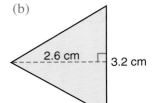
2.6 cm
3.2 cm

(c)

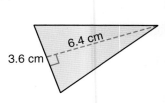
6.4 cm
3.6 cm

**3.** Find the areas of the shaded triangles.

(a)

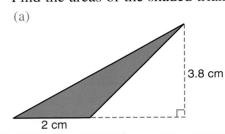
3.8 cm
2 cm

(b)

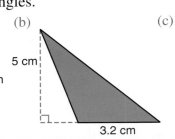
5 cm
3.2 cm

(c)

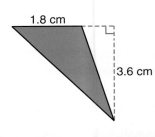
1.8 cm
3.6 cm

## Area of a parallelogram

A **parallelogram** is a special quadrilateral.
The opposite sides of a parallelogram are:
- equal in length
- parallel

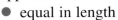

> In a **sketch diagram**:
> Sides of equal length are marked with the same number of **dashes**.
> Lines which are parallel are marked with the same number of **arrowheads**.

### Activity

Look at the following diagram.
It shows a rectangle and a parallelogram drawn on centimetre-squared paper.

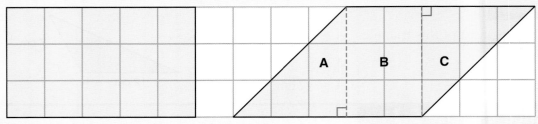

A    B    C

Find the area of the rectangle.
Find the area of the parallelogram by splitting it into two triangles and a rectangle.
*What do you notice?*

Can you find a rule to find the area of a parallelogram?

## Area of a trapezium

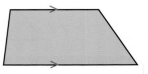

A **trapezium** is a special quadrilateral.
A trapezium has one pair of parallel sides.

**Activity** A trapezium has been drawn on centimetre-squared paper.

Find the area of the trapezium by splitting it into three parts.
Can you find a rule to find the area of the trapezium?

## Area of a kite

A **kite** is a special quadrilateral.
Two pairs of adjacent sides are equal.
The diagonals cross at 90°.

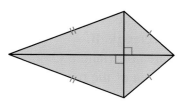

**Activity** A kite has been drawn on centimetre-squared paper.

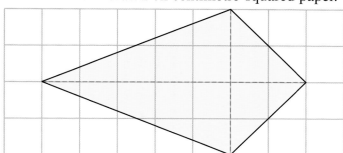

Find the area of the kite by splitting into four triangles.
Show that the area of the kite can be found by splitting the shape into two triangles.
Can you find a rule to find the area of the kite?

## Area formulae

**Parallelogram**

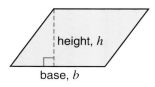

Area = base × height
$A = bh$

**Trapezium**

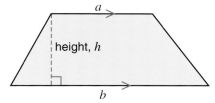

Area = half the sum of the parallel
sides × perpendicular height
$A = \frac{1}{2}(a + b)h$

**Kite**

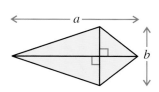

Area = $\frac{1}{2}$ × product of
diagonals
$A = \frac{1}{2}ab$

**Remember:** The area of a parallelogram, a trapezium and a kite can be found
by splitting the original shape into triangles and rectangles.
The total area is found by adding together the areas of the parts.

**Example 2**

Find the area of this trapezium.

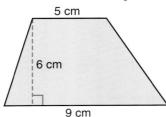

The area of a trapezium is given by

$A = \frac{1}{2}(a + b)h$

Substitute $a = 9$, $b = 5$ and $h = 6$.

$A = \frac{1}{2}(5 + 9)6$

$A = \frac{1}{2} \times 14 \times 6$

$A = 42 \text{ cm}^2$

## Practice Exercise 5.2

1. The diagram shows a parallelogram split into three parts.
   (a) Find the area of triangle **A**.
   (b) Find the area of rectangle **B**.
   (c) Write down the area of triangle **C**.
   (d) What is the total area of the parallelogram?

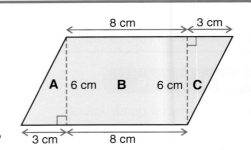

2.

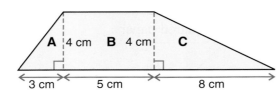

The diagram shows a trapezium.
   (a) Find the area of triangle **A**.
   (b) Find the area of rectangle **B**.
   (c) Find the area of triangle **C**.
   (d) What is the total area of the trapezium?

3. The diagram shows a kite, *ABCD*.
   (a) Find the area of triangle *ABC*.
   (b) Find the area of triangle *ADC*.
   (c) What is the area of the kite, *ABCD*?

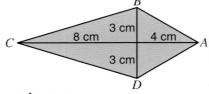

4. These shapes have been drawn on 1 cm squared paper.
   Find the area of each shape.

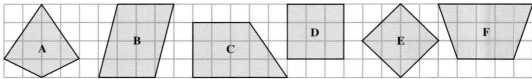

5. Calculate the areas of these parallelograms.
   (a)            (b)            (c)

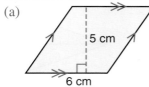
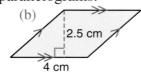
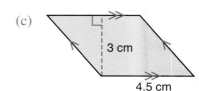

6. Calculate the areas of these trapeziums.
   (a)            (b)            (c)

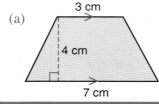
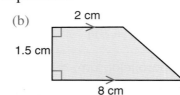
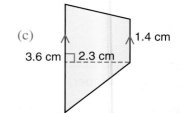

7. Calculate the areas of these kites.

(a)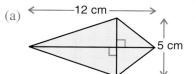

(b)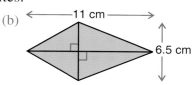

(c)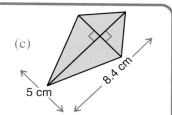

8. The parallelogram has the same area as the square.
   Calculate the height of the parallelogram.

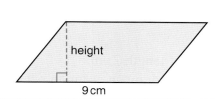

## Making and drawing 3-dimensional shapes

3-dimensional shapes can
be made using **nets**.

This is the net of a cube.

The net can be folded
to make a cube.

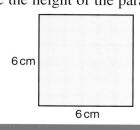

### Example 3

This prism is 6 cm long.

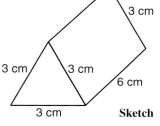

**Sketch**

The ends are equilateral triangles with sides of 3 cm.
Draw an accurate net of the prism.

**Step 1:**
Draw the rectangular faces of the prism.
Each rectangle is 6 cm long and 3 cm wide.

**Step 2:**
The ends of the prism are equilateral triangles.
The length of each side of the triangles is 3 cm.
Use your compasses to construct the equilateral triangles.

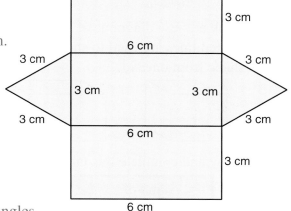

## Naming parts of a solid shape

Each flat surface is called a **face**.
Two faces meet at an **edge**.
Edges of a shape meet at a corner, or point, called a **vertex**.
The plural of vertex is **vertices**.

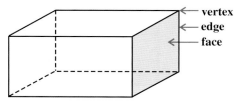

1. This is a cuboid.

   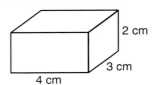

   2 cm
   3 cm
   4 cm

   Sarah has started to draw a net of the
   cuboid on squared paper.

   (a) Copy the diagram.
   (b) Complete the net of the cuboid.

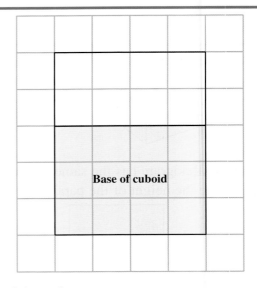

Base of cuboid

2. A cube has edges of length 2 cm.
   Use squared paper to draw an accurate net of the cube.

3. (a) The diagram shows part of a net of a cube.
      In how many different ways can you complete the net?
      Draw each of your nets.

   (b) Explain why this diagram
       is **not** the net of a cube.

4. Draw an accurate net for each of these 3-dimensional shapes.
   (a)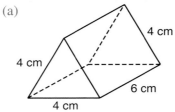

   4 cm
   4 cm
   6 cm
   4 cm

   (b)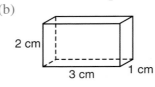

   2 cm
   3 cm   1 cm

5. Look at these diagrams of 3-dimensional shapes.
   Dotted lines are used to show the edges which cannot be seen when you look at the
   shape from one side.

   (a) 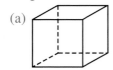   (b) 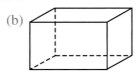   (c) 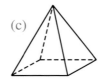   (d)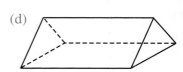

   Copy and complete this table.

| | Name of shape | Number of faces | Number of vertices | Number of edges |
|---|---|---|---|---|
| (a) | | | | |
| (b) | | | | |
| (c) | | | | |
| (d) | | | | |

## Prisms

If you make a cut at right angles to the length of a prism, you will always get the same cross-section.

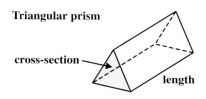

Triangular prism
cross-section
length

These shapes are all **prisms**.

 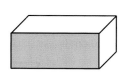   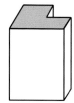

## Surface area of a prism

> To find the surface area of a prism, find the area of the net used to make the prism.

A **cuboid** is a prism.
Opposite faces of a cuboid are the same shape and size.
To find the surface area of a cuboid find the areas of the six rectangular faces and add the answers.

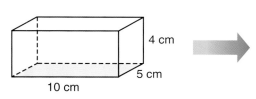

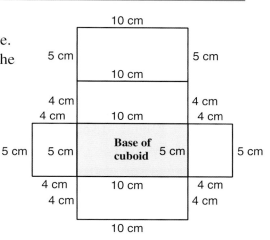

10 cm
5 cm · 5 cm
10 cm
4 cm · 4 cm
4 cm · 10 cm · 4 cm
5 cm · 5 cm · Base of cuboid 5 cm · 5 cm
4 cm · 10 cm · 4 cm
4 cm · 4 cm
10 cm

The surface area of a cuboid can also be found by finding the area of its net.

## Volume

**Volume** is the amount of space occupied by a three-dimensional shape.

This **cube** is 1 cm long, 1 cm wide and 1 cm high.
It has a volume of **1 cubic centimetre**.
The volume of this cube can be written as 1 cm³.

1 cm
1 cm
1 cm
**Volume = 1 cm³**

Volume of cube = 1 cm × 1 cm × 1 cm = 1 cm³

Small volumes can be measured using cubic millimetres (mm³).
Large volumes can be measured using cubic metres (m³).

### Volume of a prism

The formula for the volume of a **prism** is:

> Volume = area of cross-section × length
> $V = Al$ or $V = Ah$

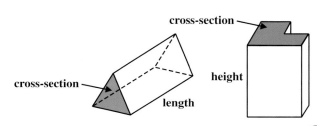

cross-section
cross-section
height
length

# Volume of a cuboid

A **cuboid** is a prism.
The formula for the volume of a **cuboid** is:

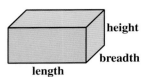

> Volume = length × breadth × height
> $V = lbh$

## Example 4

A cuboid measures 30 cm by 15 cm by 12 cm.

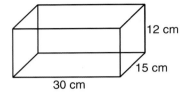

(a) Find the surface area of the cuboid.
(b) Find the volume of the cuboid.

(a)

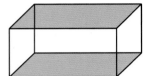
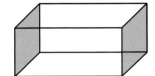
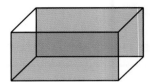

**Top and bottom faces.** | **Two side faces.** | **Front and back faces.**
Each 30 cm × 15 cm. | Each 15 cm × 12 cm. | Each 30 cm × 12 cm.

Surface area = $(2 \times 30 \times 15) + (2 \times 15 \times 12) + (2 \times 30 \times 12)$
Surface area = $900 + 360 + 720$
Surface area = $1980 \, cm^2$

> Try finding the surface area of the cuboid by drawing a net.

(b) Volume = length × breadth × height
Volume = $30 \, cm \times 15 \, cm \times 12 \, cm$
Volume = $5400 \, cm^3$

## Volume of a cylinder

A **cylinder** is a prism.
The **volume of a cylinder** can be written as:

> Volume = area of cross-section × height
> $V = \pi r^2 h$

> Notice that length has been replaced by height.

## Example 5

Find the volumes of these prisms.

(a)

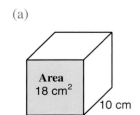

Area 18 cm²
10 cm

Volume = area of cross-
section × length
Volume = $18 \times 10$
Volume = $180 \, cm^3$

(b)

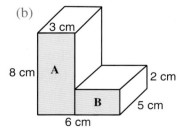

3 cm
8 cm A
2 cm
B 5 cm
6 cm

Area A = $8 \times 3 = 24 \, cm^2$
Area B = $3 \times 2 = 6 \, cm^2$
Total area = $30 \, cm^2$
Volume = $30 \times 5 = 150 \, cm^3$

(c)

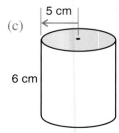

5 cm
6 cm

$V = \pi r^2 h$
$V = \pi \times 5^2 \times 6$
$V = 471.238...$
$V = 471 \, cm^3$, to nearest $cm^3$.

## Practice Exercise **5.4**

1. These cuboids are made using one-centimetre cubes.
   What is the volume of each cuboid?

   (a)   (b) 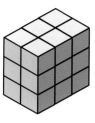  (c)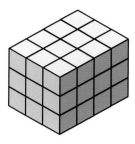

2. Large cubes are made from small cubes of edge 1 cm.

   (i)   (ii) 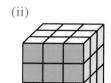  (iii) 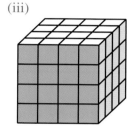  (iv)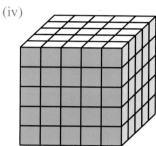

   (a) How many small cubes are in each of the large cubes?
   (b) What is the surface area of each large cube?

3. Calculate the volumes and surface areas of these cubes and cuboids.

   (a) 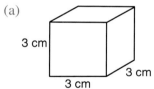  (b) 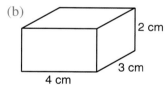  (c)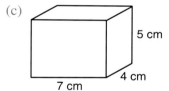

4. Find the volumes of these prisms.

   (a) 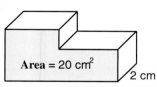  (b) 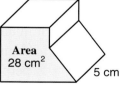  (c)

   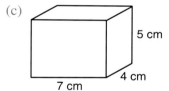

5. Calculate the shaded areas and the volumes of these prisms.
   Take $\pi$ to be 3.14.

   (a) 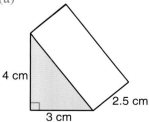  (b) 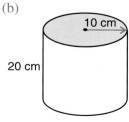  (c)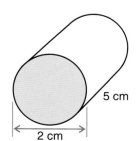

**6.** The diagram shows a plastic wedge.

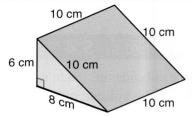

(a) Calculate the total surface area of the wedge.

(b) Calculate the volume of the wedge.

**7.** Which tin holds more cat food?
Show your working.

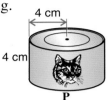 

**8.** Sylvia says,

*"A cylinder with a radius of 5 cm and a height of 10 cm has the same volume as a cylinder with a radius of 10 cm and a height of 5 cm."*

Is she right? Explain your answer

## Key Points

▶ **Area** is the amount of surface covered by a shape.

▶ Area of a triangle $= \dfrac{\text{base} \times \text{perpendicular height}}{2}$

$$A = \tfrac{1}{2} bh$$

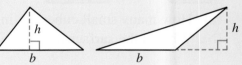

▶ You should be able to find the area of these shapes.

**Parallelogram**

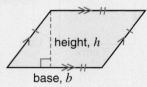

The opposite sides of a parallelogram are:
- equal in length
- parallel

Area = base × height

$$A = bh$$

**Trapezium**

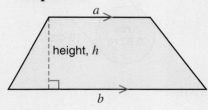

A trapezium has one pair of parallel sides.

Area = half sum of the parallel sides
× perpendicular height

$$A = \tfrac{1}{2}(a + b)h$$

**Kite**

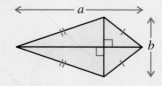

A kite has two pairs of sides equal.
The diagonals cross at 90°.

Area $= \tfrac{1}{2} \times$ product of diagonals

$$A = \tfrac{1}{2} ab$$

▶ The area of a shape can be found by splitting the shape into triangles and rectangles.
Find the area of each part and add the answers together to get the total area.

▶ **Faces**, **vertices** (corners) and **edges**.
   For example, a cube has 6 faces, 8 vertices and 12 edges.

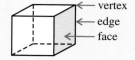

▶ A **net** can be used to make a solid shape.

▶ If you make a cut at right angles to the length of a **prism** you will always get the same cross-section.

▶ To find the **surface area** of a prism, find the area of the net used to make the prism.

▶ Volume of a prism = area of cross-section × length

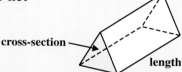

▶ **Volume** is the amount of space occupied by a 3-dimensional shape.

▶ The formula for the volume of a **cuboid** is:
   Volume = length × breadth × height
   $V = lbh$

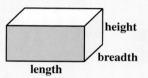

▶ A **cylinder** is a prism.
   Volume of a cylinder is: $V = \pi r^2 h$

## Review Exercise 5

1.  The diagram shows three triangles,
    *BAE*, *BED* and *BDC*.
    (a) Calculate the perimeter of triangle *BAE*.
    (b) Calculate the area of triangle *BED*.
    (c) The areas of triangles *BED* and *BDC* are equal.
        Calculate the length of *DC*.

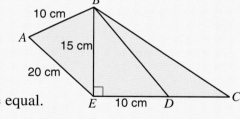

2.  Find the area of these shapes by splitting each shape into triangles and rectangles.
    (a)

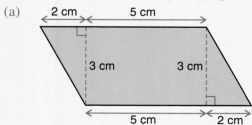

    (b)

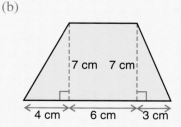

3.  This shape is a triangular prism.
    How many faces, edges and vertices does a triangular prism have?

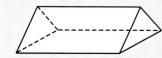

4. Which of these shapes is the net of a cube?

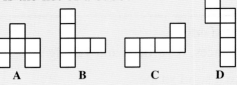

A  B  C  D

5. The diagram shows the shape of a building plot.
   Calculate the area of the plot.

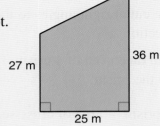

36 m
27 m
25 m

6.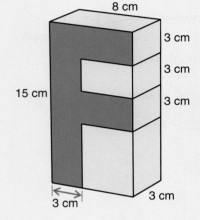

8 cm
3 cm
3 cm
15 cm
3 cm
3 cm
3 cm

Harry uses blocks of wood to make letters that are used in signs.
A block of wood measures 15 cm by 8 cm by 3 cm.
A letter F is cut out of the block of wood, as shown.

(a) Calculate the shaded area.
(b) Calculate the volume of the letter F.

7. The diagram shows a block of wood.
   The block is a cuboid measuring 8 cm by 13 cm by 16 cm.
   A cylindrical hole of radius 5 cm is
   drilled through the block of wood.
   Find the volume of wood remaining.
   Give your answer to the nearest 10 cm³.

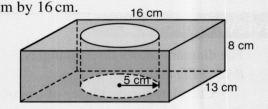

16 cm
8 cm
5 cm
13 cm

8. Sophie makes cushions.
   This cushion is in the shape of a prism.
   The end of the prism is a right-angled triangle.

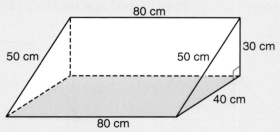

80 cm
50 cm
30 cm
50 cm
40 cm
80 cm

(a) Draw a sketch of a net that Sophie could use to cut the material to make the cushion.
(b) Find the total length of the edges of the cushion.
(c) Calculate the area of the triangular end of the cushion.
(d) Find the total surface area of the cushion.
(e) What is the volume of the cushion?

 # Rotational Symmetry

These shapes are **symmetrical**.

When each shape is folded along the dashed line one side will fit exactly over the other side. The dashed line is called a **line of symmetry**.

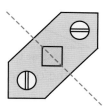

Some shapes have more than one line of symmetry.

A rectangle has two lines of symmetry.

## Rotational symmetry

*Is this shape symmetrical?*

The shape does not have line symmetry.

*Try placing a copy of the shape over the original and rotating it about the centre of the circle.*

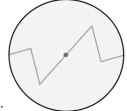

After 180° (a half-turn) the shape fits into its own outline. The shape has **rotational symmetry**.

The point about which the shape is rotated is called the **centre of rotation**.
The **order of rotational symmetry** is 2. When rotating the shape through 360° it fits into its own outline twice (once after a half-turn and again after a full-turn).

> A shape is only described as having rotational symmetry if the order of rotational symmetry is 2 or more.

A shape can have both line symmetry and rotational symmetry.

### Example 1

State the order of rotational symmetry for each shape.

(a)

Order of rotational symmetry 5.

(b)

Order of rotational symmetry 4.
4 lines of symmetry.

(c)

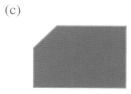

Order of rotational symmetry 1.
The shape is **not** described as having rotational symmetry.

1. What is the order of rotational symmetry for each of these shapes?

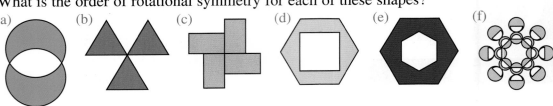

   (a)    (b)    (c)    (d)    (e)    (f)

2. Look at these triangles.

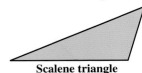    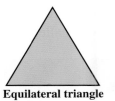

   **Scalene triangle**    **Isosceles triangle**    **Equilateral triangle**

   What is the order of rotational symmetry of each triangle?

3. Copy each of these diagrams.

   **A**     **B** 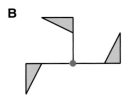    **C**

   (a) Add **one** more flag to each of your diagrams so that the final diagrams have rotational symmetry.
   (b) What is the order of rotational symmetry for each of your diagrams?

4. Look at these letters of the alphabet.

   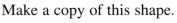

   J M N O P X Y Z

   (a) Which letters have rotational symmetry?
   (b) Which letters have rotational symmetry of order 2?

5. Make a copy of this shape.
   (a) Colour one more square so that your shape has rotational symmetry of order 2.
   (b) Mark the centre of rotational symmetry on your shape.

   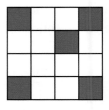

6. Make a copy of this shape.
   (a) Colour one more triangle so that your shape has rotational symmetry of order 3.
   (b) How many lines of symmetry does your shape have?

7. For each shape state the order of rotational symmetry.
   (a)    (b)    (c)    (d)    (e)

## Symmetry of quadrilaterals

> **Remember:**
> ● A two-dimensional shape has rotational symmetry if it fits into a copy of its own outline as it is rotated through 360°.
> ● A shape is only described as having rotational symmetry if the order of rotational symmetry is 2 or more.

In the following diagrams, the centre of rotation is shown by a dot.

| Parallelogram | Isosceles trapezium | Rectangle |
|---|---|---|
|  |  |  |
| Order of rotational symmetry 2. | No rotational symmetry. | Order of rotational symmetry 2. |
| **Square** | **Rhombus** | **Kite** |
|  | 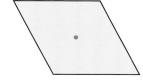 | 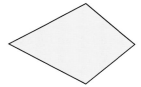 |
| Order of rotational symmetry 4. | Order of rotational symmetry 2. | No rotational symmetry. |

### Example 2

The diagram shows a rectangle, $ABCD$, drawn on a grid.

(a) Write down the coordinates of the centre of rotation, $X$.

(b) When point $A$ is rotated about $X$, through 180° (half-turn),
$A(2, 3) \rightarrow A'(6, 1)$
We say that $A$ is **mapped** to $A'$. $A'$ is the **image** of $A$.
Write mapping statements for $B$, $C$ and $D$.

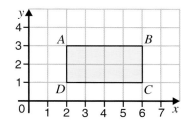

(a) $X(4, 2)$

(b) $B(6, 3) \rightarrow B'(2, 1)$; $C(6, 1) \rightarrow C'(2, 3)$; $D(2, 1) \rightarrow D'(6, 3)$

## Practice Exercise 6.2

1. The diagram shows a parallelogram, $ABCD$.
   (a) State the order of rotational symmetry for a parallelogram.
   (b) Write down the coordinates of the centre of rotation, $X$.
   (c) Copy and complete the following mapping statements when the parallelogram, $ABCD$, is rotated through 180° about $X$.
   (i) $A(1, 3) \rightarrow A'(\text{---}, 7)$
   (ii) $B(3, 7) \rightarrow B'(9, \text{---})$
   (iii) $C(11, \text{---}) \rightarrow C'(\text{---}, 3)$
   (iv) $D(\text{---}, \text{---}) \rightarrow D'(\text{---}, \text{---})$

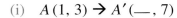

**2.** The diagram shows a square, *PQRS*.

(a) State the order of rotational symmetry for a square.

(b) Write down the coordinates of the centre of rotation.

(c) The square is rotated through 180° (half-turn) about the centre of rotation.
Copy and complete the following mapping statements.

(i) $P(1, 6) \rightarrow P'(7, —)$

(ii) $Q(4, 9) \rightarrow Q'(—, 3)$

(iii) $R(—, 6) \rightarrow R'(—, 6)$

(iv) $S(—, —) \rightarrow S'(—, —)$

(d) The original square, *PQRS*, is to be rotated through 90° (quarter-turn) **clockwise**.
Copy and complete the following mapping statements.

(i) $P(1, 6) \rightarrow P'(4, —)$

(ii) $Q(4, 9) \rightarrow Q'(—, 6)$

(iii) $R(—, 6) \rightarrow R'(—, 3)$

(iv) $S(—, —) \rightarrow S'(—, —)$

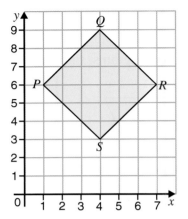

**3.** Draw *x* and *y* axes each labelled from 0 to 8.
*WXYZ* is a rhombus with corners at:
$W(4, 3)$,  $X(4, 8)$,  $Y(8, 5)$  and  $Z(8, 0)$

(a) Plot the points *W*, *X*, *Y* and *Z*. Draw the rhombus.

(b) Find the coordinates of the centre of rotation for the rhombus.

(c) What is the order of rotational symmetry of the rhombus, *WXYZ*?

(d) The rhombus is rotated through 180° about the centre of rotation.
$W \rightarrow W'$,  $X \rightarrow X'$,  $Y \rightarrow Y'$  and  $Z \rightarrow Z'$
Find the coordinates of *W'*, *X'*, *Y'* and *Z'*.

## Key Points

▶ A two-dimensional shape has **line symmetry** if the line divides the shape so that one side fits exactly over the other.

▶ A two-dimensional shape has **rotational symmetry** if it fits into a copy of its outline as it is rotated through 360°.

> A shape is only described as having rotational symmetry if the order of rotational symmetry is 2 or more.

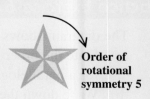

Order of rotational symmetry 5

▶ The number of times a shape fits into its outline in a single turn is the **order of rotational symmetry**.

▶ **Mapping notation** is an efficient method of recording the movement of points.
For example, *A* **mapped** to *A'* can be written as:

$A \rightarrow A'$.

*A'* is the **image** of *A*.

**Review** Exercise **6**

1. What is the order of rotational symmetry for each of these shapes?

   (a)     (b)     (c)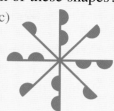

2. What is the order of rotational symmetry for each of these shapes?

   (a) 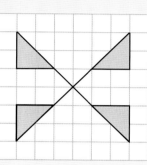    (b) 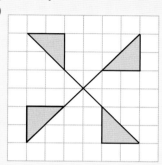    (c)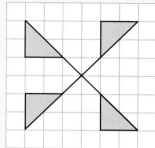

3. Copy the diagram.

   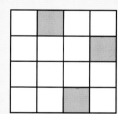

   Shade one more square, so that your diagram has order of rotational symmetry 4.

4. These diagrams show simplified molecular patterns for some chemicals.
   Write down the order of rotational symmetry for each pattern.

   (a)     (b)     (c)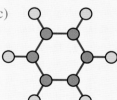

5. The diagram shows a rhombus drawn on a grid.

   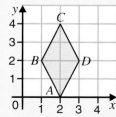

   (a) What is the order of rotational symmetry of the rhombus?
   (b) Give the coordinates of the centre of rotation, $X$.
   (c) When the shape is rotated through 180° (half-turn) about $X$, $C \rightarrow C'$.
       What are the coordinates of $C'$?

# 7 Collecting Data

To answer questions such as:

> **Which is the most popular colour of car?**
> **Is it going to rain tomorrow?**
> **Which team won the World Cup in 2010?**

we first need to collect data.

## Primary and secondary data

When data is collected by an individual or organisation to use for a particular purpose it is called **primary data**.
Primary data is obtained from experiments, investigations, surveys and by using questionnaires.

Data which is already available or has been collected by someone else for a different purpose is called **secondary data**.
Sources of secondary data include the Annual Abstract of Statistics, Social Trends and the Internet.

## Data

Data is made up of a collection of **variables**.
Each variable can be described, numbered or measured.

Data which can only be **described** in words is **qualitative**.
Such data is often organised into categories, such as make of car, colour of hair, etc.

Data which is given **numerical** values, such as shoe size or height, is **quantitative**.
Quantitative data is either **discrete** or **continuous**.

> **Discrete** data can only take certain values, usually whole numbers, but may include fractions (e.g. shoe sizes).
> **Continuous** data can take any value within a range and is measurable (e.g. height, weight, temperature, etc.).

### Example 1

State whether the following data is qualitative or quantitative.
If the data is quantitative, state whether it is discrete or continuous.

(a)   The taste of an orange.
(b)   The number of pips in an orange.
(c)   The surface area of an orange.

(a)   The taste of an orange is a qualitative variable.
(b)   The number of pips in an orange is a discrete quantitative variable.
(c)   The surface area of an orange is a continuous quantitative variable.

## Practice Exercise 7.1

State whether the following data is qualitative or quantitative.
If the data is quantitative state whether it is discrete or continuous.

1. The colours of cars in a car park.

2. The weights of eggs in a carton.

3. The numbers of desks in classrooms.

4. The names of students in a class.

5. The sizes of spanners in a toolbox.

6. The depths that fish swim in the sea.

7. The numbers of goals scored by football teams on a Saturday.

8. The brands of toothpaste on sale in supermarkets.

9. The sizes of ladies' dresses in a store.

10. The heights of trees in a wood.

## Collection of data

Data can be collected in a variety of ways: by observation, by interviewing people and by using questionnaires. The method of collection will often depend on the type of data to be collected.

### Data collection sheets

**Data collection sheets** are used to record data.
To answer the question, "Which is the most popular colour of car?" we could draw up a simple data collection sheet and record the colours of passing cars by observation.

### Example 2

A **data collection sheet** for colour of car is shown, with some cars recorded.

| Colour of car | Tally | Frequency |
|---|---|---|
| Black | \|\| | 2 |
| Blue | ┼┼┼ ┼┼┼ \|\|\| | 13 |
| Green | \|\|\|\| | 4 |
| Red | ┼┼┼ ┼┼┼ \| | |
| Silver | ┼┼┼ \|\| | |
| White | ┼┼┼ ┼┼┼ \|\|\|\| | |
| | Total | |

> The colour of each car is recorded in the **tally** column by a single stroke.
> To make counting easier, groups of 5 are recorded as ┼┼┼.

*How many red cars are recorded? How many cars are recorded altogether?*

The total number of times each colour appears is called its **frequency**.
A table for data with the totals included is called a **frequency distribution**.

## Grouped data

For large amounts of discrete data, or for continuous data, we organise the data into **groups** or **classes**. When data is collected in groups it is called a **grouped frequency distribution** and the groups you put the data into are called **class intervals**.

**Example 3**

The weights of 20 boys are recorded in the grouped frequency table shown below.

| Weight ($w$ kg) | Tally | Frequency |
|---|---|---|
| $50 \leqslant x < 55$ | \| | 1 |
| $55 \leqslant x < 60$ | \|\|\| | 3 |
| $60 \leqslant x < 65$ | ЖЖ \|\|\|\| | 9 |
| $65 \leqslant x < 70$ | ЖЖ \| | 6 |
| $70 \leqslant x < 75$ | \| | 1 |
| | Total | 20 |

> Weights are grouped into class intervals of equal width.
> $55 \leqslant w < 60$
> means 55 kg, or more, but less than 60 kg.

John weighs 54.9 kg.                           David weighs 55.0 kg.
*In which class interval is he recorded?*     *In which class interval is he recorded?*

*What is the width of each class interval?*

## Practice Exercise 7.2

**1.** The tally chart shows the number of glass bottles put into a bottle bank one day.

| Colour of glass | Tally |
|---|---|
| Clear | ЖЖ ЖЖ ЖЖ \|\| |
| Brown | ЖЖ ЖЖ ЖЖ ЖЖ \| |
| Green | ЖЖ ЖЖ ЖЖ |

(a) How many green bottles were put into the bottle bank?
(b) How many brown bottles were put into the bottle bank?
(c) How many **more** brown bottles than clear bottles were put into the bottle bank?

**2.** Helen throws a dice 50 times.
The result of each throw is shown.
(a) Copy and complete this table to record her results.

| 1 | 4 | 3 | 6 | 5 |
|---|---|---|---|---|
| 4 | 3 | 2 | 1 | 6 |
| 4 | 5 | 2 | 3 | 4 |
| 5 | 6 | 4 | 5 | 3 |
| 1 | 2 | 3 | 4 | 2 |
| 3 | 5 | 1 | 1 | 4 |
| 5 | 6 | 4 | 3 | 2 |
| 5 | 4 | 6 | 5 | 6 |
| 2 | 3 | 1 | 3 | 4 |
| 1 | 6 | 5 | 2 | 2 |

| Number on dice | Tally |
|---|---|
| 1 | |
| 2 | |
| 3 | |
| 4 | |
| 5 | |
| 6 | |

(b) Which number occurred most frequently?

**3.** The marks obtained by 40 students in a test were recorded.

(a) Copy and complete this table to show the grouped frequency distribution.

| 57 | 81 | 41 | 68 | 58 |
|----|----|----|----|----|
| 63 | 47 | 32 | 55 | 54 |
| 53 | 38 | 72 | 78 | 61 |
| 37 | 52 | 44 | 74 | 77 |
| 68 | 73 | 52 | 51 | 68 |
| 80 | 79 | 46 | 60 | 69 |
| 32 | 74 | 92 | 87 | 74 |
| 42 | 37 | 88 | 98 | 56 |

| Mark | Tally | Frequency |
|------|-------|-----------|
| 30 - 39 | | |
| 40 - 49 | | |
| 50 - 59 | | |
| 60 - 69 | | |
| 70 - 79 | | |
| 80 - 89 | | |
| 90 - 99 | | |
| | Total | |

(b) In which group was the greatest number of marks recorded?

**4.** The times taken by 30 students to travel to school were recorded.
Times were recorded in minutes, to the nearest minute.

    9,   13,   21,   22,   14,   27,   17,   13,   23,   19,   19,   20,   13,   19,   24
   10,   15,   12,   14,    8,   20,   23,   15,   17,   15,    8,   18,   24,   27,   12

(a) Make a grouped frequency table for the data using the groups:
        1 - 5,   6 - 10,   11 - 15,   16 - 20,   and so on.

(b) In which group was the most data recorded?

## Bar charts

**Bar charts** are a simple but effective way of displaying data.
Bars can be drawn either horizontally or vertically.

**Example 4**

The table shows how a group of boys travelled
to school one day.

(a) Draw a bar chart to show this information.
(b) Which method of travel is the mode?

| Method of travel | Number of boys |
|------------------|----------------|
| Bus | 2 |
| Cycle | 7 |
| Car | 1 |
| Walk | 5 |

(a)

**How boys travel to school**

Number of boys vs Method of travel (Bus, Cycle, Car, Walk)

**Notice that:** Bars are the same width. There are gaps between the bars because data that can be counted is discrete.
The height of each bar gives the **frequency**.
The tallest bar represents the most frequent variable (category).

(b) The most frequently occurring variable is called the **mode** or **modal category**.
Cycle is the modal category for the boys.

## Frequency diagrams

We use **bar charts** when data can be counted and there are only a few different items of data. If there is a lot of data, or the data is continuous, we draw a **histogram** or **frequency polygon**.

## Histograms

Histograms are used to present information contained in **grouped frequency distributions**. In this section we will only be drawing histograms for grouped frequency distributions that have equal class width intervals.

> Histograms with equal class width intervals look like bar charts with no gaps.

### Example 5

A supermarket opens at 0800.
The frequency diagram shows the distribution of the times employees arrive for work.
(a)  How many employees arrive before 0730?
(b)  How many employees arrive between 0730 and 0800?
(c)  How many employees arrive after 0800?
(d)  What is the modal category?

> Individual bars are not labelled because the horizontal axis represents a **continuous** scale.

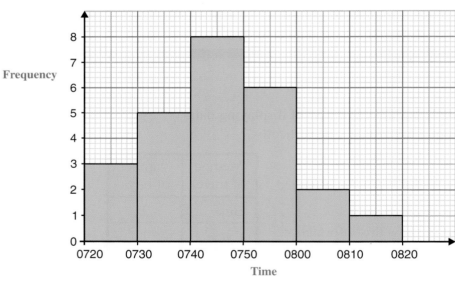

(a)  3 employees arrive before 0730.
(b)  Between 0730 and 0740, 5 employees arrive.
   Between 0740 and 0750, 8 employees arrive.
   Between 0750 and 0800, 6 employees arrive.
   Employees arriving between 0730 and 0800 = 5 + 8 + 6 = 19.
(c)  3 employees arrive after 0800.
(d)  The modal category is the time interval with the highest frequency.
   The class interval 0740 to 0750 has the highest frequency.
   The modal category is, therefore, "0740 and less than 0750".

## Frequency polygons

**Frequency polygons** are often used instead of histograms.

> To draw a frequency polygon:
> - plot the frequencies at the midpoint of each class interval,
> - join successive points with straight lines.

### Example 6

The frequency polygon shows the distribution of the distances travelled to work by the employees at a supermarket.

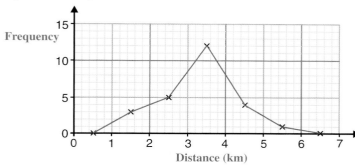

When drawing frequency polygons, frequencies are plotted at the midpoints of the class intervals.

(a) How many employees travel between 2 km and 3 km to work?

(b) How many employees travel more than 4 km to work?

(a) The frequency for the midpoint of the class interval 2 km to 3 km is 5.
So, 5 employees travel between 2 km and 3 km to work.

(b) The frequency for the midpoint of the class interval 4 km to 5 km is 4.
The frequency for the midpoint of the class interval 5 km to 6 km is 1.
So, a total of 5 employees travel more than 4 km to work.

*Can you work out how many people are employed at the supermarket?*

## Practice Exercise 7.3

1. The result of throwing a dice 30 times is shown.
   (a) Copy and complete the frequency table for these scores.

   | 1 | 3 | 5 | 1 | 5 |
   |---|---|---|---|---|
   | 2 | 5 | 2 | 1 | 2 |
   | 6 | 6 | 3 | 3 | 6 |
   | 2 | 3 | 2 | 6 | 4 |
   | 4 | 3 | 3 | 4 | 6 |
   | 3 | 5 | 1 | 4 | 5 |

   | Score | Tally | Frequency |
   |-------|-------|-----------|
   | 1 |  |  |
   | 2 |  |  |
   | 3 |  |  |

   (b) Draw a bar chart to show the data.
   (c) Which score is the mode?

**2.** A group of senior citizens were asked how many children were in their families. The table shows the results.

| Number of children | 1 | 2 | 3 | 4 | 5 | 6 | 7 |
|---|---|---|---|---|---|---|---|
| Number of families | 3 | 6 | 11 | 8 | 4 | 1 | 2 |

(a) Draw a bar chart of this information.
(b) How many families had **more than** 4 children per family?
(c) What is the modal number of children per family?

**3.** The bar chart shows the day of birth for a group of boys and girls.

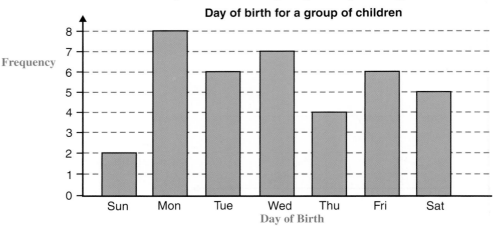

(a) How many children are in the group?
(b) How many **more** children were born on a Monday than on a Sunday?
(c) Which day of birth is the mode?

The table shows the day of birth for the girls in the group.

| Day of birth | Sun | Mon | Tue | Wed | Thu | Fri | Sat |
|---|---|---|---|---|---|---|---|
| Number of girls | 1 | 5 | 2 | 3 | 3 | 1 | 4 |

(d) Draw up a table to show the day of birth for the boys in the group.

**4.** The distances, in metres, recorded in a long jump competition are shown.

5.46, 5.80, 5.97, 5.43, 6.72, 5.93, 6.26, 6.64
5.13, 6.05, 6.36, 6.88, 6.11, 5.50, 6.38, 5.71
6.55, 6.10, 5.84, 5.49, 6.20, 5.67, 6.34, 6.00

(a) Copy and complete the following frequency distribution table.

| Distance ($m$ metres) | Frequency |
|---|---|
| $5.00 \leqslant m < 5.50$ | |
| $5.50 \leqslant m < 6.00$ | |
| $6.00 \leqslant m < 6.50$ | |
| $6.50 \leqslant m < 7.00$ | |

(b) Draw a histogram to illustrate the data.
(c) Which is the modal class?

**5.** The frequency diagram shows information about the weights of 100 people.

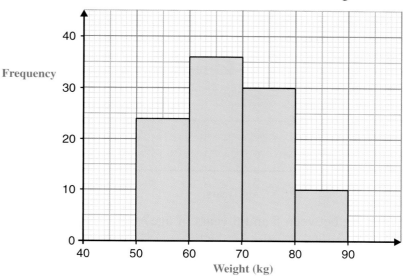

10 people weigh 80 kg or more.

(a) How many people weigh between 60 kg and 70 kg?

(b) How many people weigh less than 60 kg?

(c) How many people weigh 70 kg or more?

(d) Harry is included in the survey.

He weighs 80 kg.

In which class interval has his weight been recorded?

**6.** Here are the mileages of cars in a roadside survey.

| | | | | |
|---|---|---|---|---|
| 5442 | 2345 | 18561 | 16080 | 12500 |
| 10000 | 35001 | 34056 | 5156 | 37584 |
| 21243 | 36573 | 25057 | 18656 | 15209 |
| 29067 | 39893 | 6368 | 15987 | 24891 |
| 9999 | 3089 | 16724 | 25598 | 37151 |
| 436 | 4080 | 39949 | 27950 | 6543 |

(a) Copy and complete the frequency distribution table for these results.

| Distance ($m$ miles) | Tally | Frequency |
|---|---|---|
| $0 \leqslant m < 10\,000$ | | |
| $10\,000 \leqslant m < 20\,000$ | | |
| $20\,000 \leqslant m < 30\,000$ | | |
| $30\,000 \leqslant m < 40\,000$ | | |

(b) How many cars are included in the survey?

(c) Draw a histogram to illustrate the data.

(d) Which is the modal class?

7. The frequency polygon shows the distribution of the ages of pupils who attend a village school.

(a) How many pupils are between 5 and 6 years of age?
(b) How many pupils are under 4 years of age?
(c) How many pupils are over 7 years of age?
(d) How many pupils attend the school?

8. Here are the marks of pupils for a test in French.

| 44 | 23 | 36 | 60 | 50 | 45 | 35 | 56 | 41 | 37 |
| 31 | 57 | 43 | 29 | 67 | 45 | 34 | 54 | 29 | 25 |
| 46 | 52 | 27 | 36 | 39 | 45 | 41 | 54 | 49 | 37 |

(a) Copy and complete the frequency distribution table for these results.

| Mark | Tally | Frequency |
|---|---|---|
| 20 and less than 30 | | |
| 30 and less than 40 | | |
| 40 and less than 50 | | |
| 50 and less than 60 | | |
| 60 and less than 70 | | |

(b) Which is the modal class?
(c) How many pupils scored less than 50?
(d) Draw a frequency polygon to illustrate the data.

## Key Points

▶ **Primary data** is data collected by an individual or organisation to use for a particular purpose. Primary data is obtained from experiments, investigations, surveys and by using questionnaires.

▶ **Secondary data** is data which is already available or has been collected by someone else for a different purpose. Sources of secondary data include the Annual Abstract of Statistics, Social Trends and the Internet.

▶ **Qualitative** data – Data which can only be described in words.

▶ **Quantitative** data – Data that has a numerical value.
Quantitative data is either **discrete** or **continuous**.
**Discrete** data can only take certain values.
**Continuous** data has no exact value and is measurable.

▶ **Data Collection Sheets** – Used to record data during a survey.

▶ **Tally** – A way of recording each item of data on a data collection sheet.
A group of five is recorded as ɻ⊞.

▶ **Frequency Table** – A way of collating the information recorded on a data collection sheet.

▶ **Grouped Frequency Table** – Used for continuous data or for discrete data when a lot of data has to be recorded.

▶ **Bar chart**. Used for data which can be counted.
Often used to compare quantities of data in a distribution.
Bars can be drawn horizontally or vertically.
Bars are the same width and there are gaps between bars.
The length of each bar represents frequency.
The longest bar represents the **mode**.

▶ **Histogram**. Used to illustrate **grouped frequency distributions.**
The horizontal axis is a continuous scale.

▶ **Frequency polygon**. Used to illustrate grouped frequency distributions.
Frequencies are plotted at the midpoints of the class intervals and joined with straight lines.
The horizontal axis is a continuous scale.

## Review Exercise 7

1. The times, in seconds, taken by 20 students to complete a task are shown.

| | | | | |
|---|---|---|---|---|
| 4.3 | 12.9 | 10.0 | 5.7 | 18.2 |
| 14.0 | 11.6 | 14.9 | 8.5 | 16.0 |
| 15.0 | 13.4 | 3.7 | 6.0 | 10.5 |
| 11.6 | 15.4 | 3.7 | 8.0 | 9.3 |

(a) Copy and complete the frequency table shown, using intervals of 5 seconds.

| Time ($t$ seconds) | Tally | Frequency |
|---|---|---|
| $0 \leqslant t < 5$ | | |

(b) Which is the modal class?

**2.**

**"Do students carry too many books in their bags?"**

To investigate this, Emma carried out a survey.

She asked 30 students how many books they had in their bags as they entered school in the morning. The answers were as follows.

**3, 2, 3, 3, 4, 0, 3, 5, 3, 1, 5, 2, 3, 2, 3**
**4, 1, 3, 2, 3, 3, 2, 1, 3, 4, 3, 2, 4, 2, 2**

(a) Copy and complete this frequency distribution table.

| Number of books | Tally | Frequency |
|---|---|---|
| 0 | | |
| 1 | | |
| 2 | | |
| 3 | | |
| 4 | | |
| 5 | | |
| | Total | |

(b) What was the mode number of books carried?

**3.** Andrew measured the height of each student in his tutorial group.

He recorded heights, in centimetres, to the nearest centimetre.

**164, 180, 165, 175, 171, 170, 171, 162, 175, 174**
**169, 161, 166, 173, 182, 163, 168, 172, 178, 175**

(a) Copy and complete this frequency table for his results.

| Height ($h$ cm) | Tally | Frequency |
|---|---|---|
| 160 - 164 | | |
| 165 - 169 | | |
| 170 - 174 | | |
| 175 - 179 | | |
| 180 - 184 | | |
| | Total | |

(b) Draw a histogram to show Andrew's results.

(c) What is the modal class of the frequency distribution?

**4.**

Lyn asked 30 adults how many hours they spent using social network sites during a week.

She recorded their replies, in hours, to the nearest hour.

**10, 28, 18, 5, 11, 10, 20, 23, 1, 2, 4, 22, 4, 18, 18**
**7, 16, 10, 1, 3, 22, 4, 6, 8, 12, 11, 20, 23, 14, 9**

(a) Make a tally chart using the groups  1 - 5,  6 - 10,  11 - 15,  and so on.

(b) Draw a frequency polygon to display Lyn's data.

(c) What is the modal class?

# 8  Averages *and* Range

## Activity

Some friends went on a school trip.
They each brought different amounts of spending money, as follows:

| | | | | | |
|---|---|---|---|---|---|
| Penny £25 | Keith £35 | Nishpal £40 | Jayne £20 | Stephen £50 | Ben £60 |
| Charlotte £35 | Suzie £50 | Dan £55 | Vicki £35 | Jack £55 | |

Ben brought the most and Jayne the least.
What was the difference in the amounts of spending money Ben and Jayne brought?
Which was the most common amount of money?
Who brought the middle amount of money? How much was this?
If the friends shared out their money equally, how much would each person get?

## Range

The difference between the highest and lowest amounts is called the **range**.
Range = highest amount − lowest amount

## Types of average

The most common amount is called the **mode**.
When the amounts are arranged in order of size, the middle one is called the **median**.
If the money is shared out equally, the amount each person gets is called the **mean**.

### Example 1

The price, in pence, of a can of cola in eight different shops is shown.
$$45, \quad 49, \quad 49, \quad 42, \quad 47, \quad 45, \quad 45, \quad 50.$$
Find   (a)   the mode,          (b)   the median,          (c)   the mean price.

(a)   The **mode** is the most common value.
       The most common price is 45.
       The mode is 45 pence.   We sometimes say the modal price is 45p.

(b)   The **median** is found by arranging the values in order of size and taking the middle value.
       Arrange the prices in order of size.
       42,   45,   45,   45,   47,   49,   49,   50.

> Where there are an even number of values the median is the average of the middle two.

       The middle price is $\frac{45 + 47}{2} = 46$.
       The median is 46 pence.

(c)   The **mean** is found by finding the total of all the values and
       dividing the total by the number of values.
       Add the prices.   $45 + 49 + 49 + 42 + 47 + 45 + 45 + 50 = 372$
       The mean $= \frac{372}{8} = 46.5$.
       The mean is 46.5 pence.

**Expressions *and* Formulae**

## Practice Exercise 8.1

**Questions 1 to 6.**

Do not use a calculator. Show your working clearly.

1. Tony recorded the number of birthday cards sold each day.

   3   4   8   1   4

   (a) Work out the range of the number of cards sold each day.
   (b) Write down the mode.
   (c) Find the median number of cards sold each day.

2. Four students had the following number of books in their bags.

   3   4   1   4

   (a) What is the range of the number of books?
   (b) What is the mean number of books?

3. Claire recorded the number of e-mail messages she received each day.

   2   1   7   4   1

   (a) Write down the mode.
   (b) Find the median number of messages received each day.
   (c) Calculate the mean number of messages received each day.

4. A postman delivers letters to a block of flats.
   There are 8 flats in the block.
   The number of letters he delivers to each flat is shown below.

   1   3   4   4   2   2   6   2

   (a) What is the range of the number of letters delivered?
   (b) Write down the mode.
   (c) Calculate the mean number of letters delivered to each flat.

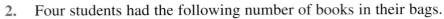

5. The price, in pence, of a bar of chocolate in four different shops is shown.

   40   37   42   45

   Find the median of these prices.

6. Gail noted the number of stamps on 6 parcels delivered to her office.

   3   2   4   5   7   3

   (a) Write down the mode.
   (b) Find the range of the number of stamps on a parcel.
   (c) Find the median number of stamps on a parcel.
   (d) Calculate the mean number of stamps on a parcel.

**Questions 7 to 9.**

You may use a calculator.

7. Here is a list of the weights of some people, in kilograms.

   68   74   63   81   76

   (a) What is the range of the weights of the five people?
   (b) Find the median weight.
   (c) Calculate the mean weight.

8. Sanjay played a computer game 8 times and recorded his scores.

   140　　135　　125　　125　　130　　135　　140　　135

   (a) Which score is the mode?
   (b) Calculate the median of his scores.
   (c) Find the mean score. Give your answer to the nearest whole number.

9. Frank counted the number of books on different shelves in a library.
   He recorded the following numbers.

   38　　40　　26　　49　　37　　43

   (a) Find the median number of books on a shelf.
   (b) What is the range of the number of books on a shelf?
   (c) Calculate the mean number of books on a shelf.
   　　Give your answer correct to one decimal place.

## Using the range and mean to compare data

In statistics we frequently need to compare two sets of data.
A simple comparison can be made by using the range to compare **spread** and the mean to compare **average**.

### Example 2

The weights of a sample of Cherry tomatoes have a range of 30 g and a mean of 45 g.
The weights of a sample of Moneymaker tomatoes have a range of 90 g and a mean of 105 g.
Compare and comment on the weights of Cherry and Moneymaker tomatoes.

**Range:**
Cherry tomatoes 30 g,　Moneymaker tomatoes 90 g.
The smaller range for Cherry tomatoes shows they are more consistent in weight.

**Mean:**
Cherry tomatoes 45 g,　Moneymaker tomatoes 105 g.
The smaller mean for Cherry tomatoes shows they have a lower average weight.

**Comment:**
The average weight of Cherry tomatoes is lower but they are more consistent in weight.

## Practice Exercise 8.2

1. The weights, in grams, of a sample of 10 economy potatoes are shown.

   70　　76　　83　　86　　95　　98　　113　　117　　122　　130

   (a) (i)　What is the range of these weights?
   　　(ii)　Calculate the mean of these weights.

   For a sample of 10 premium potatoes the range of their weights is 240 grams and the mean of their weights is 250 grams.
   (b) Compare and comment on the weights of economy and premium potatoes.

2. The lateness of 12 buses is recorded.
   The results, in minutes, are shown.

        5    6    7    8    8    10    10    10    11    12    13    14

   (a)  (i)   What is the range of lateness for these buses?
         (ii)  Calculate the mean lateness for these buses.

   The lateness of 12 trains is also recorded.
   The range in lateness for these trains is 14 minutes and the mean lateness is 5 minutes.

   (b)  Compare and comment on the lateness for these buses and trains.

3. The numbers of words typed per minute by a group of students are shown.

        45    51    58    59    63    87    64    59    58    63    53

   (a)  (i)   What is the range of their typing speeds?
         (ii)  Calculate the mean typing speed for these students.

   For another group of students the mean of their typing speeds is 42 words per minute and the range is 67.

   (b)  Comment on the typing speeds of these two groups of students.

4. The times, in minutes, taken by 8 boys to swim 50 metres are shown.

        1.8    2.0    1.7    2.2    2.1    1.9    1.8    2.1

   (a)  (i)   What is the range of these times?
         (ii)  Calculate the mean time.

   The times, in minutes, taken by 8 girls to swim 50 m are shown.

        2.1    1.9    1.8    2.3    1.6    2.0    2.6    1.9

   (b)  Comment on the times taken by these boys and girls to swim 50 m.

5. The numbers of goals scored in matches played by some first and third division football teams are shown.

   First Division:   1    5    0    2    2    3    0    4    2    0    1
   Third Division:   3    2    4    1    1    3    2    1    7

   Use the range and mean to compare the numbers of goals scored by these first and third division football teams.

6. The table shows the percentage silver content of twenty ancient coins.

   | | Percentage silver content | | | | |
   |---|---|---|---|---|---|
   | Roman coins | 5.6 | 6.7 | 6.6 | 7.2 | 6.3 |
   | Chinese coins | 6.8 | 6.7 | 6.2 | 5.4 | 7.3 |
   | Egyptian coins | 5.1 | 7.0 | 5.8 | 6.9 | 7.6 |
   | Greek coins | 5.6 | 7.2 | 6.6 | 6.8 | 5.7 |

   (a)  For each type of coin:
        (i)   calculate the range of the percentage silver content,
        (ii)  calculate the mean of the percentage silver content.
   (b)  Comment on your answers to (a).

## Frequency distributions

After data is collected it is often presented using a **frequency distribution table**.
Johti measured the lengths of some twigs. He recorded the following results.

**2, 3, 2, 6, 3, 6, 2, 3, 5, 4, 3, 2, 2, 3, 5, 6, 2, 6, 5, 6, 2**

Johti then presented his results, as shown in this frequency distribution table.

| Length (cm) | 2 | 3 | 4 | 5 | 6 |
|---|---|---|---|---|---|
| Number of twigs (frequency) | 7 | 5 | 1 | 3 | 5 |

Using the frequency distribution table we can find the mode, median, mean and range of the lengths of the twigs that Johti measured.

**To find the mode:**

The mode is the length with the greatest frequency.
There were 7 twigs of length 2 cm.
This is more than any other length of twigs.
The mode of the lengths is 2 cm.

**To find the median:**

The median is the middle length when all the lengths are arranged in order of size.
We could list the 21 twigs in order of length and split them up like this:

| 10 shortest twigs | middle twig | 10 longest twigs |
|---|---|---|

This shows that the median length is the length of the 11th twig.
From the table we can see that:

**the first 7 twigs are each 2 cm long, and the next 5 twigs are each 3 cm long.**

So, the 11th twig is 3 cm long.
The median length is 3 cm.

**To find the mean:**

$$\text{Mean} = \frac{\text{Total of all lengths}}{\text{Number of lengths}}$$

The best way to do this is to extend the frequency distribution table.

| Length (cm) $x$ | 2 | 3 | 4 | 5 | 6 | Totals |
|---|---|---|---|---|---|---|
| Number of twigs (frequency) $f$ | 7 | 5 | 1 | 3 | 5 | $\Sigma f = 21$ |
| Number of twigs × Length $f \times x$ | 14 | 15 | 4 | 15 | 30 | $\Sigma fx = 78$ |

$$\text{Mean} = \frac{\text{Total of all lengths}}{\text{Number of lengths}} = \frac{\Sigma fx}{\Sigma f}$$

$\text{Mean} = \frac{78}{21} = 3.714\ldots$

Mean length = 3.7 cm, correct to 1 decimal place.

> $\Sigma$    is the Greek letter 'sigma'.
> $\Sigma f$   means the sum of frequencies.
> $\Sigma fx$ means the sum of the values of $fx$.
> $\text{Mean} = \frac{\Sigma fx}{\Sigma f}$

**To find the range:**

Range = longest length − shortest length
      = 6 − 2 = 4 cm

The range of the lengths is 4 cm.

1. A milkman delivers bottles of milk to 30 houses in a street.
   The number of bottles of milk he delivers to each house is shown below.

   | 1 | 4 | 2 | 1 | 2 | 1 | 2 | 1 | 1 | 2 |
   |---|---|---|---|---|---|---|---|---|---|
   | 2 | 2 | 1 | 3 | 1 | 2 | 1 | 2 | 2 | 1 |
   | 3 | 2 | 3 | 1 | 3 | 1 | 4 | 3 | 1 | 4 |

   (a) Copy and complete this frequency distribution table.

   | Number of bottles | 1 | 2 | 3 | 4 |
   |---|---|---|---|---|
   | Number of houses | | | | |

   (b) What is the mode of the number of bottles delivered?
   (c) What is the median number of bottles delivered?
   (d) Calculate the mean number of bottles of milk delivered to each house.

2. Mark asked some students,
   **"How many keys do you have on your key ring?"**
   The data collection sheet shows the responses he recorded.

   | Number of keys | Tally |
   |---|---|
   | 2 | \|\| |
   | 3 | \|\|\| |
   | 4 | 卌 \|\|\| |
   | 5 | 卌 |
   | 6 | \|\| |

   (a) Use Mark's data to make a frequency distribution table.
   (b) How many students did Mark ask?
   (c) Write down the mode of the number of keys on a key ring.
   (d) Find the median number of keys.
   (e) Calculate the mean number of keys on a key ring.

3. Pat recorded the weekly earnings of a group of students.
   Her results were as follows:
   £25    £40    £30    £45    £25    £25    £30    £35    £45    £25
      £35    £30    £35    £25    £35    £30    £35    £25    £45
   (a) Show the data in a frequency distribution table.
   (b) Find the range of the weekly earnings.
   (c) What is the modal weekly earnings?
   (d) How many people were in the group?
   (e) What is the median weekly earnings?
   (f) Calculate the total weekly earnings of the group.
   (g) Calculate the mean weekly earnings.
      Give your answer to the nearest penny.

**4.** Find the mode, median and mean for the following data.

(a)

| Number of letters delivered | 1 | 2 | 3 | 4 | 5 | 6 |
|---|---|---|---|---|---|---|
| Number of days | 6 | 9 | 6 | 6 | 2 | 1 |

(b)

| Number of books read last month | 0 | 1 | 2 | 3 | 4 | 5 |
|---|---|---|---|---|---|---|
| Number of students | | 1 | 4 | 10 | 4 | 1 | 1 |

(c)

| Number of days absent in a year | 0 | 1 | 2 | 3 | 4 | 5 | 6 | 7 | 8 | 9 | 10 | 11 |
|---|---|---|---|---|---|---|---|---|---|---|---|---|
| Number of students | 56 | 0 | 0 | 4 | 14 | 10 | 24 | 11 | 21 | 15 | 8 | 2 |

## Comparing distributions

The table shows the marks gained in a test.
Compare the marks obtained by the boys and the girls.

| Mark (out of 10) | 7 | 8 | 9 | 10 |
|---|---|---|---|---|
| Number of boys | 2 | 5 | 3 | 0 |
| Number of girls | 4 | 0 | 2 | 1 |

To compare the marks we can use the range and the mean.

   Boys:   Range $= 9 - 7 = 2$
   Girls:   Range $= 10 - 7 = 3$

The girls had the higher range of marks.

   Boys:   Mean $= \dfrac{2 \times 7 + 5 \times 8 + 3 \times 9 + 0 \times 10}{10} = \dfrac{81}{10} = 8.1$

   Girls:   Mean $= \dfrac{4 \times 7 + 0 \times 8 + 2 \times 9 + 1 \times 10}{7} = \dfrac{56}{7} = 8$

The boys had the higher mean mark.

Overall the boys did better as:
   the girls' marks were more spread out with a lower average mark,
   the boys' marks were closer together with a higher average mark.

To compare the overall standard, the median could be used instead of the mean.

## Practice Exercise 8.4

**1.** Use the mean and the range to compare the number of goals scored by these teams.

**JAYS**

| Number of goals scored per hockey match | 0 | 1 | 2 | 3 | 4 | 5 |
|---|---|---|---|---|---|---|
| Number of matches | 3 | 5 | 2 | 2 | 1 | 2 |

**WASPS**

| Number of goals scored per hockey match | 0 | 1 | 2 | 3 | 4 | 5 |
|---|---|---|---|---|---|---|
| Number of matches | 0 | 2 | 3 | 1 | 2 | 0 |

2. Use the mean and the range to compare the number of visits to the cinema by these women and men.

| Number of visits to the cinema last month | 0 | 1 | 2 | 3 | 4 | 5 | 6 | More than 6 |
|---|---|---|---|---|---|---|---|---|
| Number of women | 8 | 9 | 7 | 3 | 2 | 1 | 1 | 0 |
| Number of men | 0 | 12 | 7 | 1 | 0 | 0 | 0 | 0 |

3. Use the mean and the range to compare the number of Valentine cards received by these boys and girls.

| Number of Valentine cards | 0 | 1 | 2 | 3 | 4 | 5 | 6 |
|---|---|---|---|---|---|---|---|
| Number of boys | 3 | 4 | 2 | 2 | 1 | 2 | 1 |
| Number of girls | 0 | 3 | 7 | 3 | 2 | 0 | 0 |

4. Deepak thought that the girls in his class wore smaller shoes than the boys on average, but that the boys' shoe sizes were less varied than the girls'.
He did a survey to test his ideas.
The table shows his results.
Was he correct?

| Shoe size | $4\frac{1}{2}$ | 5 | $5\frac{1}{2}$ | 6 | $6\frac{1}{2}$ | 7 | $7\frac{1}{2}$ | 8 | $8\frac{1}{2}$ | 9 | $9\frac{1}{2}$ |
|---|---|---|---|---|---|---|---|---|---|---|---|
| Number of boys | 1 | 0 | 5 | 4 | 4 | 2 | 1 | 0 | 1 | 0 | 0 |
| Number of girls | 0 | 2 | 0 | 2 | 3 | 0 | 2 | 0 | 3 | 1 | 1 |

5. (a) Find the modal class for the ages of customers in each of these two restaurants.
   (b) Which restaurant attracts more younger people?
   (c) Why is it only possible to find an approximate value for the age range of customers?

| Age (years) | MacQuick | Pizza Pit |
|---|---|---|
| 0 - 9 | 8 | 2 |
| 10 - 19 | 9 | 4 |
| 20 - 29 | 10 | 12 |
| 30 - 39 | 7 | 15 |
| 40 - 49 | 1 | 5 |
| 50 - 59 | 1 | 3 |
| 60 - 69 | 3 | 3 |
| 70 - 79 | 1 | 2 |
| 80 - 89 | 0 | 1 |

6. The graphs show the monthly sales of bicycles before and after a marketing campaign.
   Calculate the medians and the ranges.
   Use your results to compare 'Before' with 'After'.

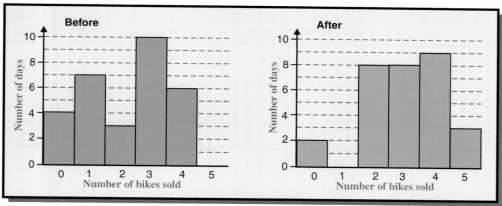

## Which is the best average to use?

Many questions in mathematics have definite answers. This one does not.
Sometimes the mean is best, sometimes the median and sometimes the mode.
It all depends on the situation and what you want to use the average for.

### Example 3

A youth club leader gets a discount on cans of drinks if she buys all one size.
She took a vote on which size people wanted. The results were as follows:

| Size of can (ml) | 100 | 200 | 330 | 500 |
|---|---|---|---|---|
| Number of votes | 9 | 12 | 19 | 1 |

Mode = 330 ml
Median = 200 ml
Mean = 245.6 ml, correct to one decimal place.

Which size should she buy?

The mean is no use at all because she can't buy cans of size 245.6 ml.
Even if the answer is rounded to the nearest whole number (246 ml), it's still no use.
The median is possible because there is an actual 200 ml can.
However, only 12 out of 41 people want this size.
In this case the **mode** is the best average to use, as it is the most popular size.

## Practice Exercise 8.5

In questions 1 to 3 find all the averages possible. State which is the most sensible and why.

1. On a bus:  23 people are wearing trainers,
             10 people are wearing boots,
              8 people are wearing lace-up shoes.

2. 20 people complete a simple jigsaw. Their times, in seconds, are recorded.
   5,   6,   8,   8,   9,   10,   11,   11,   12,   12
   12,   15,   15,   15,   15,   18,   19,   20,   22,   200

3. Here are the marks obtained by a group of 11 students in a mock exam.
   The exam was marked out of 100.

   5, 6, 81, 81, 82, 83, 84, 85, 86, 87, 88

4. The times for two swimmers to complete each of ten 25 m lengths are shown below.

| Swimmer A | 30.1 | 30.1 | 30.1 | 30.6 | 30.7 | 31.1 | 31.1 | 31.5 | 31.7 | 31.8 |
|---|---|---|---|---|---|---|---|---|---|---|
| Swimmer B | 29.6 | 29.7 | 29.7 | 29.9 | 30.0 | 30.0 | 30.1 | 30.1 | 30.1 | 44.6 |

   Which is the better swimmer? Explain why.

5. The table shows the number of runs scored by two batsmen in several innings.

| Batsman A | 0 | 0 | 10 | 12 | 20 | 22 | 50 | 51 | 81 | 104 | | |
|---|---|---|---|---|---|---|---|---|---|---|---|---|
| Batsman B | 0 | 24 | 25 | 27 | 28 | 30 | 33 | 34 | 44 | 45 | 46 | 96 |

   Which is the better batsman? Explain why.

6. A teacher sets a test. He wants to choose a minimum mark for a
   distinction so that 50% of his students get this result.
   Should he use the modal mark, the median mark or the mean mark?
   Give a reason for your answer.

7. The cost of Bed and Breakfast at 10 different hotels is given.

   £49.50, £65, £70, £60, £59, £52, £105, £69, £49.50, £55

   (a) Wyn says, **"The average cost of Bed and Breakfast is £49.50."**
       Which average is he using?
       Give a reason why this is not a sensible average to use for this data.
   (b) Which of the mode, median and mean best describes the average cost of
       Bed and Breakfast? Give a reason for your answer.

## Key Points

▶ There are three types of **average**: the **mode**, the **median** and the **mean**.
   The **mode** is the most common value.
   The **median** is the middle value (or the mean of the two middle values)
   when the values are arranged in order of size.

   $$\textbf{Mean} = \frac{\text{Total of all values}}{\text{Number of values}}$$

▶ The **range** is a measure of **spread**.
   Range = highest value − lowest value

▶ To find the mean of a **frequency distribution** use:   $\text{Mean} = \dfrac{\text{Total of all values}}{\text{Number of values}} = \dfrac{\Sigma fx}{\Sigma f}$

▶ Choosing the best average to use:
   When the most **popular** value is wanted use the **mode**.
   When **half** of the values have to be above the average use the **median**.
   When a **typical** value is wanted use either the **mode** or the **median**.
   When all the **actual** values have to be taken into account use the **mean**.
   When the average should not be distorted by a few very small or very large values
   do **not** use the mean.

**Review** Exercise **8**     Do not use a calculator for questions 1 and 2.

1.  Marcus asks 5 of his friends how many pets they have.
    The replies are:

    1   2   0   3   1

    Find the mean of these numbers.

2.  The cost of a DVD player at 11 different stores is given.

    **£35,  £26,  £45,  £20,  £29,  £28**
    **£22,  £27,  £25,  £22,  £40**

    (a)  Which cost is the mode?
    (b)  Work out the median cost.
    (c)  Give a reason why the mode would not be a sensible average for these data.

3.  The number of goals scored by the 20 teams in a hockey league in the first game of
    the season was recorded.

    | Goals | 0 | 1 | 2 | 3 | 4 | 5 |
    |---|---|---|---|---|---|---|
    | Number of teams (frequency) | 4 | 7 | 3 | 3 | 2 | 1 |

    (a)  Calculate the mean number of goals scored.
    (b)  What is the mode number of goals scored?
    (c)  Find the median number of goals scored.
    (d)  What is the range of the distribution?

4.  A group of students were each asked how many books they read last month.
    The frequency diagram shows the results.

    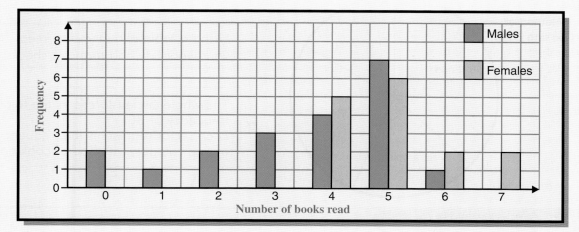

    (a)  How many students were included?
    (b)  What is the range in the number of books read by females?
    (c)  Calculate the mean number of books read by females.
    (d)  Compare and comment on the number of books read by males and the number of
         books read by females.

# 9 Pie Charts

Bar charts are useful for comparing the various types of data (categories) with each other.
To compare each category with **all** the data collected we use a **pie chart**.
A pie chart is a circle which is divided up into sectors.
The whole circle represents the total frequency.
Each sector represents the frequency of one part (category) of the data.

## Drawing pie charts

The table shows the ways in which some children like to eat eggs.

| Method of cooking | Poached | Boiled | Scrambled | Fried |
|---|---|---|---|---|
| Number of children | 5 | 8 | 6 | 11 |

To show this information in a pie chart we must find the angles of the sectors which represent each category. First calculate the angle which represents each child.

30 children are represented by 360°.
1 child is represented by 360° ÷ 30 = 12°.
Sector angle = Number of children in category × 12°

Sector angle for poached = 5 × 12° = 60°

| Method of cooking | Poached | Boiled | Scrambled | Fried | **Total** |
|---|---|---|---|---|---|
| Number of children | 5 | 8 | 6 | 11 | **30** |
| Sector angle | 60° | 96° | 72° | 132° | **360°** |

**Method of Cooking Eggs**

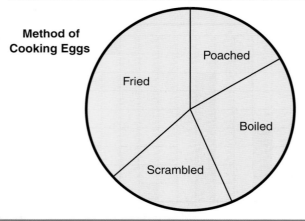

Using a table allows you to keep your work tidy and to make checks.

The whole circle represents the total frequency of 30.
Each sector represents the frequency of one category (method of cooking).

## Practice Exercise 9.1

1. The table shows information about the trees in a wood.

| Type of tree | Ash | Beech | Maple |
|---|---|---|---|
| Number of trees | 20 | 25 | 15 |

Draw a pie chart for this data.

**2.** The colour of eyes of 90 people were recorded. The table shows the results.

| Colour of eyes | Brown | Blue | Green | Other |
|---|---|---|---|---|
| Number of people | 40 | 25 | 15 | 10 |

Draw a pie chart for this data.

**3.** The table shows information about the cars owned by a company.

| Make of car | Ford | Saab | Vauxhall | BMW |
|---|---|---|---|---|
| Frequency | 10 | 9 | 15 | 6 |

Draw a pie chart for this data.

**4.** The breakfast cereal preferred by some adults is shown.

| Breakfast cereal | Corn flakes | Muesli | Porridge | Bran flakes |
|---|---|---|---|---|
| Number of adults | 25 | 20 | 12 | 15 |

Show the information in a pie chart.

**5.** The table shows the sales of ice-cream cornets at a kiosk one day.

| Ice-cream cornet | Vanilla | Strawberry | 99 |
|---|---|---|---|
| Frequency | 94 | 37 | 49 |

Draw a pie chart for this data.

**6.** The table shows the results of a survey to find the most popular takeaway food.

| Type of takeaway | Number of people |
|---|---|
| Fish & chips | 165 |
| Chicken & chips | 204 |
| Chinese meal | 78 |
| Pizza | 93 |

Draw a pie chart for this data.

## Interpreting pie charts

Pie charts are useful for showing and comparing proportions of data.
However, they do not show frequencies.
Such information can be found by interpreting the pie chart.

To interpret a pie chart we need to know:
- the sector angles (which can be measured from an accurately drawn pie chart), **and**
- the total frequency represented by the pie chart, **or**
  the frequency represented by one of the sectors.

**Example 1**

The pie chart shows the makes of 120 cars.

(a) Which make of car is the mode?

(b) How many of the cars are Ford?

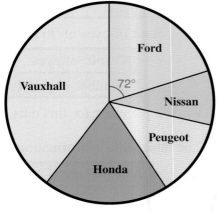

(a) The sector representing Vauxhall is the largest.
Therefore, Vauxhall is the mode.

(b) The angle of the sector representing Ford is 72°.

The number of Ford cars = $\frac{72}{360} \times 120 = 24$.

This can be worked out using a calculator
and this key sequence:

[7] [2] [÷] [3] [6] [0] [×] [1] [2] [0] [=]

*Work out the numbers of the different makes of cars.*

## Practice Exercise 9.2

1. The pie chart shows the type of holiday chosen by 36 people.

   (a) How many people chose a camping holiday?

   (b) How many people chose a self-catering holiday?

   (c) What type of holiday is the mode?

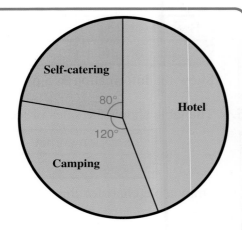

2. 

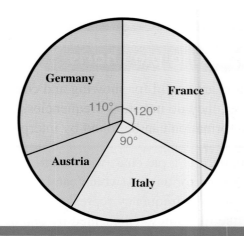

   The pie chart shows the resorts chosen in Italy by 60 skiers.

   (a) How many skiers chose Sauze d'Oulx?

   (b) How many skiers chose Foppollo?

   (c) Which resort is the mode?

3. The pie chart shows the holiday destinations of 180 people.

   (a) Which holiday destination is the mode?

   (b) How many people went to Italy?

   (c) How many people went to Germany?

   (d) How many people went to Austria?

**4.** The pie chart shows the membership of an international committee.
The USA has 7 committee members.

(a) How many committee members has the EU?

(b) How many committee members has Canada?

(c) How many committee members are there altogether?

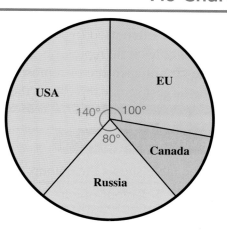

**5.**

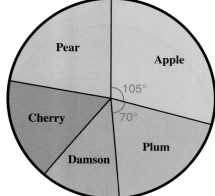

The pie chart shows the five types of fruit tree sold by a garden centre.
21 apple trees were sold.

(a) How many plum trees were sold?

(b) How many fruit trees were sold altogether?

**6.** The pie chart shows the departure airports of some travellers.

(a) Which airport is the mode?

(b) 360 travellers departed from Gatwick.
How many travellers departed from Heathrow?

(c) How many travellers are there altogether?

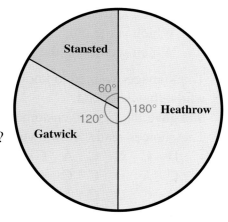

**7.**

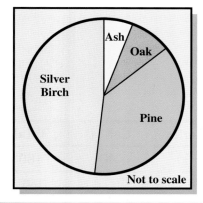

Not to scale

The pie chart shows the different types of tree in a forest.
There are 54 oak trees and these are represented by a sector with an angle of 27°.

(a) The pine trees are represented by an angle of 144°. How many pine trees are there?

(b) There are 348 silver birch trees.
Calculate the angle of the sector representing silver birch trees.

► **Pie charts** are used for data which can be counted.
They are often used to compare proportions of data, usually with the total.
► The whole circle represents all the data.
The size of each sector represents the frequency of data in that sector.
► The largest sector represents the **mode**.

## Review Exercise 9

1. The table shows the colours of cars in a car park.

| Colour of car | Blue | Green | Red | Silver | White |
|---|---|---|---|---|---|
| Number of cars | 10 | 3 | 8 | 6 | 9 |

Draw a pie chart for this data.

2. This pie chart shows which subjects a class liked best.
The bar chart shows the same information.

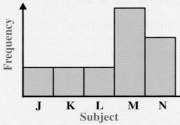
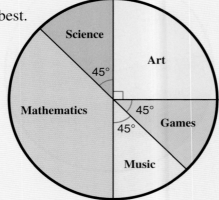

(a) Which letter on the bar chart represents Art?
(b) Which is the model category?
(c) Which sectors on the pie chart could be represented by letter **K** on the bar chart?

3. The manager wanted to know what type of music the customers preferred to hear whilst they shopped.
She gave the first 60 customers entering the shop four choices of music, **A, B, C, D**.
The choices made are shown below.

**D C C C A C C C B B A D A B B C A A C**
**C A D C C A C B D C C C A D A A A C C C**
**D C D C A C A C D A A D D B D C A A D C**

(a) Make a frequency distribution table to show the number of choices for each type of music.
(b) Draw a pie chart to represent the data.

4. A farm grows potatoes, wheat, barley and carrots.
The crops are planted over a total area of 180 hectares.
(a) What angle on a pie chart will represent 1 hectare?
(b) Copy and complete this table.

| Crop | Potatoes | Wheat | Barley | Carrots | **Total** |
|---|---|---|---|---|---|
| Number of hectares | 45 | 35 | 60 | 40 | **180** |
| Sector angle | | | | | **360°** |

 **Probability**

## What is probability?

**Probability**, or **chance**,
involves describing how likely something is to happen.

For example: ***How likely is it to rain tomorrow?***

We often make forecasts, or judgements,
about how likely things are to happen.
When trying to forecast tomorrow's weather the
following **outcomes** are possible:

> In any situation, the possible things
> that can happen are called **outcomes**.
> An outcome of particular interest is
> called an **event**.

> sun,  cloud,  wind,  rain,  snow,  …

We are interested in the particular **event**, rain tomorrow.

> The chance of an event happening can be described using these words:
> **Impossible    Unlikely    Evens    Likely    Certain**

*Use one of the words in the box to describe the chance of rain tomorrow.*

### Example 1

Describe the chance of each of the following events happening as:

> **Impossible    Unlikely    Evens    Likely    Certain**

(a)   The next person who enters the classroom is male.

(b)   A number less than 5 is scored when a normal dice is rolled.

(a)   Nearly impossible in an all-girls school.
       Nearly certain in an all-boys school.
       The probability is close to **evens** in a mixed school.

(b)   The outcomes in the event 'less than 5' are 1, 2, 3 and 4.
       The outcomes **not** in the event 'less than 5' are 5 and 6.
       There are more outcomes in the event than not in the event.
       So, the chance of the event happening is **likely**.

## Probability and the probability scale

Estimates of probabilities can be shown on a **probability scale**.
The scale goes from 0 to 1.
A **probability of 0** means that an event is **impossible**.
A **probability of 1** means that an event is **certain**.
Probabilities are written as a fraction, a decimal or a percentage.

*Describe the likelihood that an event will occur if it has a probability of $\frac{1}{2}$.*

**Example 2**

Estimate the probability that the next person to enter a shop will be left-handed.

There are a lot less left-handed people than right-handed people.

The probability is between 0 and $\frac{1}{4}$.

## Practice Exercise 10.1

1. Describe each of the following events as:

   **Impossible    Evens    Certain**

   (a) Christmas Day will be on 25th December next year.
   (b) You will be 5 centimetres shorter on your next birthday.
   (c) The next coin you drop will land 'tails' up.
   (d) A fairy lives at the bottom of your garden.
   (e) The next baby to be born will be a girl.

2. Describe each of the following events as:

   **Impossible    Unlikely    Evens    Likely    Certain**

   (a) Somewhere in the world it is raining today.
   (b) You roll a normal dice and get a 7.
   (c) You roll a normal dice and get an odd number.
   (d) A coin is tossed and it lands heads.
   (e) An apple will grow on a banana tree.
   (f) You win the next time you enter the lottery.

3. Look at the events **A**, **B**, **C**, **D** and **E** listed below.

   **A** The next person you see will be less than 10 cm tall.
   **B** 1, 2 or 3 is scored when an ordinary dice is rolled.
   **C** A day of the week ends with the letter Y.
   **D** It will snow on Christmas Day in Glasgow.
   **E** The school bus will be late tomorrow.

   (a) Which event has a probability of 0?
   (b) Which event has a probability of 1?
   (c) Which event has a probability of $\frac{1}{2}$?

4. The probability scale shows the probabilities of events **P**, **Q**, **R**, **S** and **T**.

   Which of the five events:
   (a) is certain to happen,
   (b) is impossible,
   (c) has an evens chance of happening,
   (d) is more likely to happen than to not happen, but is not certain to happen?

**5.** The probabilities of five events have been marked on a probability scale.

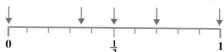

0    $\frac{1}{2}$    1

Copy the probability scale.

Event V    A coin lands 'heads' up.
Event W    A person is over 3 metres tall.
Event X    Picking a yellow sweet from a bag containing 7 yellow and 3 red sweets.
Event Y    Rolling an ordinary dice and getting a score less than 7.
Event Z    There is a 35% chance that it will rain tomorrow.

Label the arrows on your diagram to show which events they represent.

## Calculating probabilities using equally likely outcomes

Probabilities can be **calculated** where all outcomes are **equally likely**.

The probability of an event X happening is given by:

$$\text{Probability (X)} = \frac{\text{Number of outcomes in the event}}{\text{Total number of possible outcomes}}$$

**Remember**
Probabilities have values which lie between 0 and 1.
You must write probabilities as a fraction, a decimal or a percentage.

### Random and fair

In many probability questions words such as '**random**' and '**fair**' are used.
These are ways of saying that all outcomes are equally likely.
For example:
A card is taken at **random** from a pack of cards.
This means that each card has an equal chance of being taken.
A **fair** dice is rolled.
This means that the outcomes 1, 2, 3, 4, 5 and 6 are equally likely.

### Example 3

A fair dice is rolled.
What is the probability of getting:
(a)  a 6,
(b)  an odd number,
(c)  a 2 or a 3?

Total number of possible outcomes is 6.   (1, 2, 3, 4, 5 and 6)
The dice is fair, so each of these outcomes is equally likely.

(a)  1 of the possible outcomes is a 6.         $P(6) = \frac{1}{6}$

(b)  3 of the possible outcomes are odd numbers.   $P(\text{an odd number}) = \frac{3}{6} = \frac{1}{2}$

(c)  2 of the possible outcomes are 2 or 3.      $P(2 \text{ or } 3) = \frac{2}{6} = \frac{1}{3}$

**Example 4**

This table shows how 100 counters are coloured red or blue and numbered 1 or 2.

|   | Red | Blue |
|---|-----|------|
| 1 | 23  | 19   |
| 2 | 32  | 26   |

The 100 counters are put in a bag and a counter is taken from the bag at random.

(a) Calculate the probability that the counter is red.

(b) Calculate the probability that the counter is blue and numbered 1.

Total number of possible outcomes = 100.

(a) Number of red counters = 23 + 32 = 55 $\qquad$ P(red) $= \frac{55}{100} = \frac{11}{20}$

This could be written as 0.55 or 55%.

(b) There are 19 counters that are blue and numbered 1. $\quad$ P(blue and 1) $= \frac{19}{100}$

This could be written as 0.19 or 19%.

## Practice Exercise 10.2

1. A fair dice is rolled. What is the probability of getting:
   (a) a 2, $\qquad\qquad\qquad$ (b) an even number,
   (c) a number less than five, $\quad$ (d) a 3 or a 6?

2. A bag contains a red counter, a blue counter and a green counter.
   A counter is taken from the bag at random. What is the probability of taking:
   (a) a red counter, $\qquad\qquad$ (b) a red or a green counter,
   (c) a counter that is not blue?

3. A bag contains 3 red sweets and 7 black sweets.
   A sweet is taken from the bag at random. What is the probability of taking:
   (a) a red sweet, $\qquad\qquad$ (b) a black sweet?

4. You toss a fair coin. What is the probability of getting:
   (a) a head, $\qquad\qquad\qquad$ (b) a tail?

5. The letters of the word $\;$ T R I G O N O M E T R Y $\;$ are written on separate cards.
   The cards are shuffled and dealt, face down, onto a table.
   A card is selected at random. What is the probability that the card shows:
   (a) the letter Y, $\qquad\qquad$ (b) the letter R?
   Write your answers in their simplest form.

6. This fair spinner is used in a game.
   In the game a player spins the arrow.
   What is the probability that the player:
   (a) loses a turn,
   (b) has an extra go,
   (c) wins 5 points or loses 5 points?

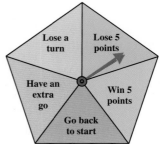

7. A card is taken at random from a full pack of 52 playing cards with no jokers.
   What is the probability that the card:
   (a) is red, $\qquad\qquad$ (b) is a heart, $\qquad\qquad$ (c) is the ace of hearts?

8. A bag contains 4 red counters, 3 white counters and 3 blue counters.
   A counter is taken from the bag at random.
   What is the probability that the counter is:
   (a) red,                    (b) white or blue,
   (c) red, white or blue,     (d) green?

9. In a hat there are twelve numbered discs. Nina takes a disc from the hat at random.
   What is the probability that Nina takes a disc:
   (a) with at least one 4 on it,
   (b) that does not have a 4 on it,
   (c) that has a 3 or a 4 on it?

10. This table shows how 50 counters are numbered either 1 or 2 and coloured red or blue.
    One of the counters is chosen at random.
    What is the probability that the counter is:
    (a) a 1,          (b) blue,          (c) blue and a 1?

    |   | Red | Blue |
    |---|-----|------|
    | 1 | 12  | 8    |
    | 2 | 8   | 22   |

    A blue counter is chosen at random.
    (d) What is the probability that it is a 1?

    A counter numbered 1 is chosen at random.
    (e) What is the probability that it is blue?

11. Tim plays a friend at Noughts and Crosses.
    He says: "I can win, draw or lose, so the probability that I will win must be $\frac{1}{3}$."
    Explain why Tim is wrong.

12. The table shows the number of boys and girls in a class of 30 pupils who wear glasses.
    A pupil from the class is picked at random.
    (a) What is the probability that it is a boy?
    (b) What is the probability that it is a girl
        who does not wear glasses?

    |                      | Boy | Girl |
    |----------------------|-----|------|
    | Wears glasses        | 3   | 1    |
    | Does not wear glasses| 11  | 15   |

    A girl from the class is picked at random.
    (c) What is the probability that she wears glasses?

    A pupil who wears glasses is picked at random.
    (d) What is the probability that it is a boy?

## Estimating probabilities using relative frequency

In real-life situations, such as insurance and investment, people make use of probability.
**Estimates** are made about the probability of events happening in the future based on events that
have happened in the past.

In question 11 in Exercise 10.2, probabilities **cannot** be calculated using equally likely outcomes.
In such situations, probabilities can be estimated using the idea of **relative frequency**.
It is not always necessary to perform an experiment or make observations.
Sometimes the information required can be found in past records.

The relative frequency of an event is given by:

$$\text{Relative frequency} = \frac{\text{Number of times the event happens in an experiment (or in a survey)}}{\text{Total number of trials in the experiment (or observations in the survey)}}$$

**Example 5**

In an experiment, a drawing pin is dropped for 100 trials.
The drawing pin lands "point up" 37 times.
What is the relative frequency of the drawing pin landing "point up"?

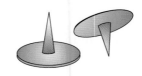

Relative frequency $= \frac{37}{100} = 0.37$

Relative frequency gives a better estimate of probability the larger the number of trials.

## Practice Exercise **10.3**

1.  50 cars are observed passing the school gate. 14 red cars are observed.
    What is the relative frequency of a red car passing the school gate?

2.  In an experiment, a gardener planted 40 daffodil bulbs, of which 36 grew to produce flowers. Use these results to find the relative frequency that a daffodil bulb will produce a flower.

3.  The results from 40 spins of a numbered spinner are:
    2, 1, 4, 3, 2, 1, 3, 4, 5, 2, 1, 2, 2, 3, 2, 1, 2, 4, 5, 2
    1, 5, 3, 4, 2, 3, 3, 3, 2, 4, 2, 3, 4, 2, 1, 5, 3, 3, 5, 3
    Use these results to estimate the probability of getting a 2 with the next spin.

4.  Gemma keeps a record of her chess games with Helen.
    Out of the first 10 games, Gemma wins 6. Out of the first 30 games, Gemma wins 21.
    Based on these results, estimate the probability that Gemma will win her next game of chess with Helen.

5.  500 tickets are sold for a prize draw. Greg buys some tickets.
    The probability that Greg wins first prize is $\frac{1}{20}$.
    How many tickets did he buy?

6.  A bypass is to be built to avoid a town.
    There are three possible routes that the road can take.
    A survey was carried out in the town.
    30 people opted for Route C.

    | Route | A | B | C |
    | --- | --- | --- | --- |
    | Relative frequency | 0.4 | 0.5 | 0.1 |

    (a) How many people were surveyed altogether?
    (b) How many people opted for Route A?
    (c) How many people opted for Route B?

## The probability of an event not happening

The events A and not A cannot happen at the same time.
Because the events A and not A are certain to happen:   P(not A) = 1 − P(A)

**Example 6**

A bag contains 3 red (R) counters, 2 blue (B) counters and 5 green (G) counters.
A counter is taken from the bag at random.

What is the probability that the counter is:
(a) red,      (b) green,      (c) red or green?

Find the total number of counters in the bag.
$3 + 2 + 5 = 10$
Total number of possible outcomes = 10.

(a)  There are 3 red counters.     $P(R) = \frac{3}{10}$

(b)  There are 5 green counters.   $P(G) = \frac{5}{10} = \frac{1}{2}$

(c)  There are 3 red counters and 5 green counters.
     There is a total of  $3 + 5 = 8$  possible outcomes.
$$P(R \text{ or } G) = \frac{8}{10} = \frac{4}{5}$$

**Example 7**

A bag contains 10 counters.
3 of the counters are red (R).
A counter is taken from the bag at random.

What is the probability that the counter is:
(a) red,      (b) not red?

Total number of possible outcomes = 10.

(a)  There are 3 red counters.   $P(R) = \frac{3}{10}$

(b)  $P(\text{not } R) = 1 - P(R) = 1 - \frac{3}{10} = \frac{7}{10}$

**Example 8**

Seven plastic balls are placed in a bag.
2 of the balls are red, 3 are yellow and 2 are white.

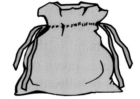

(a)  A ball is taken from the bag at random.
     What is the probability that it is yellow?
(b)  The ball taken from the bag was yellow and was not put back.
     It was replaced by 2 red balls and 2 white balls.
     What is the probability that the next ball drawn from the bag is not yellow?

(a)  Total number of possible outcomes = 2(Red) + 3(Yellow) + 2(White) = 7.
     There are 3 yellow counters.   $P(\text{Yellow}) = \frac{3}{7}$

(b)  Total number of possible outcomes = 4(Red) + 2(Yellow) + 4(White) = 10.
     $P(\text{not Yellow}) = 1 - P(\text{Yellow})$

        $P(\text{Yellow}) = \frac{2}{10} = \frac{1}{5}$

     $P(\text{not Yellow}) = 1 - \frac{1}{5} = \frac{4}{5}$

If a question involves:
- something being selected and not replaced, or
- something being selected and then extra items added,

it is a good idea to list the total number of possible outcomes before trying to answer the second part of the question.

## Practice Exercise 10.4

1. **"The risk of rain in Fife tomorrow is $\frac{2}{5}$."**
   What is the probability that it will not rain in Fife tomorrow?

2. Tina has a bag of beads.
   She takes a bead from the bag at random.
   The probability that the bead is white is 0.6.
   What is the probability that the bead is not white?

3. The probability of a switch working is 0.96.
   What is the probability of a switch not working?

4. Six out of every 100 men are taller than 1.85 m.
   A man is picked at random.
   What is the probability that he is not taller than 1.85 m?

5. A tin contains 4 red, 5 yellow and 5 green sweets.
   (a) A sweet is taken out of the tin and eaten.
       What is the probability that the sweet is red?
   (b) A second sweet is taken out of the tin.
       What is the probability that the second sweet is not yellow?

6. A machine is being developed to make electronic components.
   15% of the components produced by the machine are faulty.
   (a) A component is selected at random.
       What is the risk of the component not being faulty?
   (b) A batch of 1000 components are tested.
       How many of the components tested are at risk of being faulty?

7. A box contains 10 batteries.
   3 of the batteries are worn out and of no use.
   2 batteries are selected at random from the box.
   (a) What is the probability that the first battery selected is a good one?
   (b) The first battery was tested and found to be good.
       A second battery is taken from the remaining batteries.
       What is the probability that it is a good battery?

8. A bag contains red, white and blue balls.
   A ball is taken from the bag at random.
   The probability of taking a red ball is 0.4.
   The probability of taking a white ball is 0.35.
   What is the probability of taking a white ball or a blue ball?

9. Tom and Sam buy some tickets in a raffle.
   The probability that Tom wins 1st prize is $\frac{3}{100}$.

   The probability that Sam wins 1st prize is $\frac{1}{100}$.
   (a) What is the probability that Tom or Sam win 1st prize?
   (b) What is the probability that Tom does not win 1st prize?

10. A spinner can land on red, white or blue.
    The probability of the spinner landing on red is 0.2.
    The probability of the spinner landing on red or on blue is 0.7.
    The spinner is spun once.
    What is the probability that the spinner lands: (a) on blue, (b) on white?

11. A bag contains red, green, blue, yellow and white counters.
    The table shows the probabilities of obtaining each colour when a counter is taken
    from the bag at random.

    | Red | Green | Blue | Yellow | White |
    |-----|-------|------|--------|-------|
    | $\frac{4}{10}$ | $\frac{2}{10}$ | $\frac{1}{10}$ | $\frac{2}{10}$ | $\frac{2}{10}$ |

    (a) (i) How can you tell that there is a mistake in the table?
        (ii) The probability of getting a white counter is wrong.
             What should it be?

    A counter is taken from the bag at random.
    (b) (i) What is the probability that it is either green or blue?
        (ii) What is the probability that it is red, green or blue?
        (iii) What is the probability that it is not yellow?

12. Some red, white and blue cubes are numbered 1 or 2.
    The table shows the probabilities of obtaining each colour and number when a cube is
    taken at random. One cube is taken at random.

    |   | Red | White | Blue |
    |---|-----|-------|------|
    | 1 | $\frac{1}{10}$ | $\frac{3}{10}$ | 0 |
    | 2 | $\frac{3}{10}$ | $\frac{1}{10}$ | $\frac{2}{10}$ |

    (a) What is the probability of taking a red cube?
    (b) What is the probability of taking a cube numbered 2?
    (c) State whether or not the following pairs of events are mutually exclusive
        (cannot happen at the same time).
        Give a reason for each answer.
        (i) Taking a cube numbered 1 and taking a blue cube.
        (ii) Taking a cube numbered 2 and taking a blue cube.
    (d) (i) What is the probability of taking a cube which is blue or numbered 1?
        (ii) What is the probability of taking a cube which is blue or numbered 2?
        (iii) What is the probability of taking a cube which is numbered 2 or red?

**13.** A class of 20 students is split into two groups.

(a) A student is selected at random from **Group A**.
What is the probability that a girl is selected?

(b) The groups are combined.
A student is selected at random.
Marie says that a boy is more likely to be selected.
Is Marie correct? You must show your working.

|  | Boys | Girls |
|---|---|---|
| **Group A** | 6 | 4 |
| **Group B** | 3 | 7 |

## Key Points

▶ **Probability** describes how likely or unlikely it is that an event will occur.

▶ Probabilities can be shown on a probability scale.

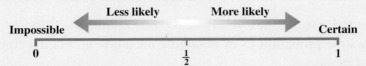

Probabilities are written as **fractions**, **decimals** or **percentages**.

▶ Probabilities can be calculated where all the outcomes are **equally likely**.

> The probability of an event X happening is given by:
>
> $$\text{Probability (X)} = \frac{\text{Number of outcomes in the event}}{\text{Total number of possible outcomes}}$$

▶ Probabilities can be estimated using **relative frequency**.

> The relative frequency of an event is given by:
>
> $$\text{Relative frequency} = \frac{\text{Number of times the event happens in an experiment (or in a survey)}}{\text{Total number of trials in the experiment (or observations in the survey)}}$$

▶ The probability of an event, A, **not happening** is given by: $\boxed{\text{P(not A)} = 1 - \text{P(A)}}$

## Review Exercise 10

**1.** These cards are shuffled and placed face down on a table.

A card is selected at random.
What is the probability that the card selected is:
(a) a red card,    (b) a heart,    (c) not a 6,    (d) a spade or a diamond?

**2.** Rachel selects 40 holiday brochures at random.
The probability of a brochure being for a holiday in Italy is found to be $\frac{1}{5}$.
How many brochures did Rachel select for holidays in Italy?

3. **"There is a 0.5% risk of catching malaria when visiting a country for a month."**
    (a) Write this risk as a fraction in its simplest form.
    (b) 2000 people visit the country for a month.
        How many are at risk of catching malaria?

4. A bag contains 2 blue, 3 yellow and 5 green cubes.
    (a) A cube is taken from the bag.
        What is the probability that it is yellow?

    The cube is replaced and 2 more yellow cubes are added.
    (b) A cube is taken from the bag.
        What is the probability that it is **not** blue?

5. The table shows the way that 120 pupils from Year S1 travel to Fairpark School.
    A pupil from Year S1 is chosen at random.
    What is the probability that the pupil:
    (a) walks to school,
    (b) is a girl who travels by car,
    (c) is a boy who does not travel by bus?

|       | Walk | Bus | Car | Bike |
|-------|------|-----|-----|------|
| Boys  | 23   | 15  | 12  | 20   |
| Girls | 17   | 20  | 8   | 5    |

    A girl from Year S1 is chosen at random.
    What is the probability that:
    (d) she walks to school,
    (e) she does not travel by car?

    A Year S1 pupil who travels by bike is chosen at random.
    (f) What is the probability that the pupil is a boy?

6. A game is played with two fair spinners.
    In each turn of the game both spinners are spun
    and the numbers are added to get a score.

    (a) Copy and complete the table to show each possible score.
    (b) What is the probability of:
        (i) scoring 6,
        (ii) not scoring 6?
    (c) To start the game a player needs to score either 2 or 5.
        What is the probability that the game starts on the
        first spin?

|   | 1 | 2 | 3 | 4 |
|---|---|---|---|---|
| 1 |   |   |   |   |
| 2 |   |   |   |   |
| 3 |   |   |   |   |

7. Between 5% and 20% of a population get the flu each year.
    (a) Write these risks as fractions in their simplest form.

    A village has a population of 360.
    (b) What is the least number of cases of flu expected each year?
    (c) What is the greatest number of cases of flu expected each year?

# Section Review: Expressions *and* Formulae

**Try to do questions 1 to 25 without using a calculator.**

1.  (a) Find the missing numbers in these sequences.
       (i)  11, 18, 25, 32, ...     (ii) ..., 3, 7, 11, 15
    (b) Draw the next pattern in this sequence.

2.  Simplify  $2(x - 3) + 5$.

3.  (a) Pens cost $x$ pence each. Write an expression for the cost of 3 pens.
    (b) A ruler costs 7 pence more than a pen. Write an expression for the cost of a ruler.

4.  (a) How many vertices has a cuboid?
    (b) How many faces has a square-based pyramid?
    (c) Here are the nets of some 3-D shapes.
        Write down the mathematical name of each 3-D shape.
        (i)                          (ii)                         (iii)

    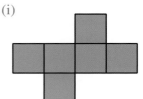 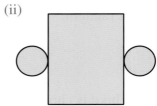 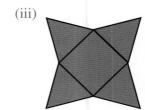

5.  Simplify  $3m + 5n + m - 3n + 2m$.

6.  The number of fish caught by 30 anglers is shown in the table below.

    | Fish caught       | 0 | 1 | 2 | 3 | 4 | 5 |
    |-------------------|---|---|---|---|---|---|
    | Number of anglers | 8 | 9 | 5 | 4 | 2 | 2 |

    (a) Find the range of the number of fish caught.
    (b) Write down the mode number of fish caught.
    (c) Find the median number of fish caught.
    (d) Calculate the mean number of fish caught.

7.  Edwina does a part-time job. Her pay is calculated using this rule:

    | **Pay = Hourly rate × Number of hours** |
    |---|

    Calculate her pay when she works 7 hours at an hourly rate of £8.50.

8.  (a) What are the coordinates of $P$?
    (b) $Q$ is the point (3, 8).
        Find the gradient of the line joining $P$ and $Q$.

    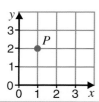

9. These patterns show the first three terms in a sequence.

   **Pattern 1**          **Pattern 2**                **Pattern 3**

   (a) Draw the next pattern in the sequence.
   (b) Copy and complete the table.

| Pattern number | 1 | 2 | 3 | 4 |
|---|---|---|---|---|
| Number of squares | 1 | 3 | 5 | |

   (c) How many squares will be in Pattern 5?
   (d) Explain why a pattern in this sequence cannot have 20 squares.

10. $x = 15$ and $y = 6$.
    Find the value of  (a) $x + 2y$   (b) $x - 3y$   (c) $\frac{x}{y}$   (d) $xy$   (e) $6(x - y)$

11. Multiply out and simplify where possible.   (a) $3(x - 5)$       (b) $5(3p + 2) + 5p$

12. For each shape write down its order of rotational symmetry.
    (a)                              (b)                        (c)

13. Factorise   (a) $4a + 2b$,      (b) $6n + 9$.

14. (a)     This shape is made using 1 cm cubes.
            What is the volume of the shape?

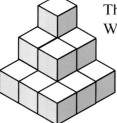

    (b) Calculate the volume of this cuboid.

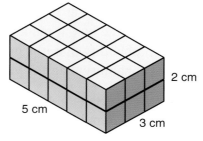

2 cm

5 cm

3 cm

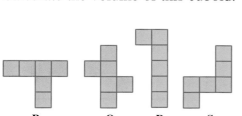

    P          Q       R       S

    (c) Which of these diagrams is a net of a cube?

15. (a) On graph paper, plot the points $A(1, 3)$ and $B(-3, -1)$.
    (b) $M$ is the midpoint of the line $AB$.
        What are the coordinates of $M$?
    (c) Calculate the gradient of the line $AB$.

**16.** A fair six-sided dice and a fair coin are thrown together.
    (a) List all the possible outcomes.
    (b) What is the probability of getting a tail and a six?

**17.** Grant buys $a$ apples costing 15 pence each and $b$ bananas costing 18 pence each.
Write an expression for the total cost of the apples and bananas.

**18.** This box holds screws for computer cabinets.
    (a) Draw a net that could be used to make the box.
    (b) Calculate the total surface area of the box.
    (c) Calculate the volume of the box.

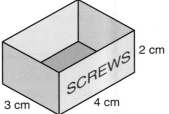

**19.** The diagram shows a parallelogram and a rectangle.
Both shapes have the same area.
Calculate the length of the rectangle.

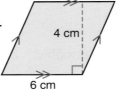
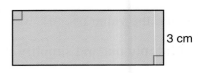

**20.** Starting with the numbers 4 and 5,
Alan writes down the following number pattern: **4, 5, 9, 14, 23**
The number pattern is continued.
What is the next number in the pattern?
Explain how you found your answer.

**21.** Expand and simplify. $2(4x + 3) - 5x$

**22.** (a) Crayons cost 12p each.
       Write an expression in pence for the cost of $t$ crayons.
    (b) Find the value of $\dfrac{2a + 3b}{5}$ when $a = 7$ and $b = -3$.

**23.** A box contains 20 plastic ducks.
3 of the ducks are green, 10 are blue and the rest are yellow.
A duck is taken from the box at random.
    (a) What is the probability that it is green?
    (b) What is the probability that it is yellow?

**24.** The diagram shows a rectangle $ABCD$.
The coordinates of $A$, $B$ and $C$ are given.
    (a) What are the coordinates of $D$?
    (b) What is the order of rotational symmetry
        of a rectangle?

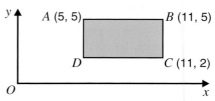

    (c) Find the coordinates of the centre of rotational symmetry of rectangle $ABCD$.

**25.** What is the area of the triangle?

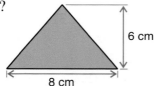

**You may use a calculator for questions 26 to 34.**

26. This shape is made up of a right-angled triangle and a semicircle. Calculate the total area of the shape.
    Give your answer to a suitable degree of accuracy.

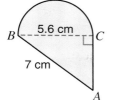

27. The total cost of a camping holiday was £180.
    (a) What angle on a pie chart represents £1?
    (b) Copy and complete this table.

| Expense | Transport | Site fee | Food | Spending money | Total |
|---|---|---|---|---|---|
| Cost (£) | 35 | 45 | 65 | 35 | 180 |
| Sector angle | | | | | 360° |

    (c) Draw a pie chart to represent the data.

28. (a) What is the value of $2xy$ when $x = 3$ and $y = 4$?
    (b) Work out the value of $ab + c$ when $a = 3$, $b = -2$ and $c = 5$.
    (c) What is the value of $3p - q$ when $p = -1$ and $q = 2$?

29. Here are the first five terms of a sequence: 50  49  47  44  40  …
    Write down the next term. Explain how you worked out the answer.

30. Find the area of these shapes.
    (a)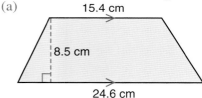
    (b)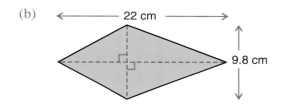

31. Mrs Anchram recorded the time taken to complete six journeys to visit her mother.

> 1 hour 20 minutes,  2 hours 30 minutes,  1 hour 45 minutes
> 3 hours 10 minutes,  1 hour 13 minutes,  2 hours 8 minutes

    (a) What is the range of the times taken for this journey?
    (b) Calculate the mean time to complete the journey.
        Give your answer in hours and minutes.

32. A circular dinner plate has a diameter of 25 cm.
    (a) Find the circumference of the plate. Give your answer correct to 1 decimal place.
    (b) Find the area of the plate. Give your answer correct to the nearest whole number.

33. (a) Write down a formula for the perimeter, $P$ cm, of this shape.
    (b) Find $P$ when $a = 3.2$ and $b = 3.8$.

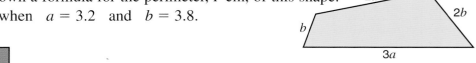

34. Carpet tiles measure 45 cm by 45 cm.
    How many tiles are needed to cover a
    floor which measures 4.05 m by 5.4 m?

# 11 Straight Line Graphs

## Linear functions

Look at these coordinates: (0, 1), (1, 2), (2, 3), (3, 4).
*Can you see any number patterns?*

The same coordinates can be shown in a **table**.

| $x$ | 0 | 1 | 2 | 3 |
|---|---|---|---|---|
| $y$ | 1 | 2 | 3 | 4 |

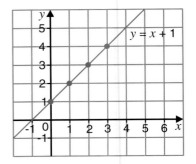

The diagram shows the coordinates plotted on a **graph**.
The points all lie on a **straight line**.

A **rule** connects the $x$ coordinate with the $y$ coordinate.
**All** points on the line obey the rule   $y = x + 1$.

$y = x + 1$   is an example of a **linear function**.
The graph of a linear function is a **straight line**.

## Drawing a graph of a linear function

**To draw a linear graph:**
- Find at least two pairs of corresponding values of $x$ and $y$.
- Plot the points.
- Join the points with a straight line.

### Example 1

(a)  Complete the table of values for   $y = 2x - 3$.

| $x$ | 0 | 1 | 2 | 3 |
|---|---|---|---|---|
| $y$ | | | 1 | |

(b)  Draw the graph of the equation   $y = 2x - 3$.

(c)  Use your graph to find the value of $y$ when   $x = 2.5$.

(a)  Substitute values of $x$ into   $y = 2x - 3$.

| $x$ | 0 | 1 | 2 | 3 |
|---|---|---|---|---|
| $y$ | $-3$ | $-1$ | 1 | 3 |

When   $x = 0$,   $y = 2 \times 0 - 3 = -3$.
When   $x = 1$,   $y = 2 \times 1 - 3 = -1$.
When   $x = 2$,   $y = 2 \times 2 - 3 = 1$.
When   $x = 3$,   $y = 2 \times 3 - 3 = 3$.

(b)

Plot the points $(0, -3)$, $(1, -1)$, $(2, 1)$ and $(3, 3)$.
The straight line which passes through these points is the graph of
the equation   $y = 2x - 3$.

(c)  When   $x = 2.5$,   $y = 2$.
Reading from the graph along the dotted line.

## Special graphs

This diagram shows the graphs:   $x = 4$   $y = 1$
$x = -2$   $y = -5$

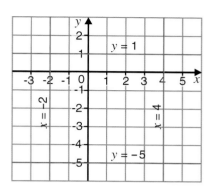

The graph of   $x = 4$   is a **vertical** line.
All points on the line have $x$ coordinate 4.
The gradient of a vertical line is **undefined**.

The graph of   $y = 1$   is a **horizontal** line.
All points on the line have $y$ coordinate 1.
The gradient of a horizontal line is **zero**.

$x = 0$ is the $y$ axis.
$y = 0$ is the $x$ axis.

## Practice Exercise 11.1

1.  Write down the equations of the labelled lines drawn on these diagrams.

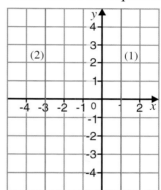  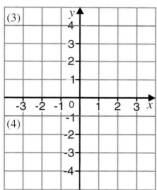  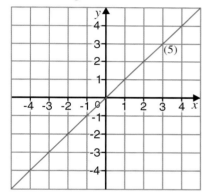

2.  Draw $x$ and $y$ axes from $-4$ to 4.
    On your diagram, draw and label the graphs of these equations.
    (a)  $x = 3$          (b)  $y = 2$          (c)  $x = -2$          (d)  $y = -1$

3.  (a)  Copy and complete a table of values, like the one shown, for each of
        these equations.

| $x$ | 0 | 1 | 2 | 3 |
|---|---|---|---|---|
| $y$ | | | | |

(i)  $y = x + 2$          (ii)  $y = 2x$          (iii)  $y = -x$          (iv)  $y = 2 - x$
    (b)  Draw graphs for each of the equations in part (a).

4.  (a)  Copy and complete the table of values for the equation   $y = 3 - 2x$.

| $x$ | $-1$ | 1 | 3 |
|---|---|---|---|
| $y$ | | | |

(b)  Draw the graph of   $y = 3 - 2x$   for values of $x$ from $-1$ to 3.
    (c)  What are the coordinates of the point where the graph crosses the $x$ axis?

5.  (a) Draw the graph of $y = 3x - 2$ for values of $x$ from $-1$ to 2.
    (b) What are the coordinates of the point where the graph crosses the $y$ axis?

6.  (a) Copy and complete this table and use it to draw the straight line
        graph of $y = 4 - x$.

    | $x$ | $-2$ | $-1$ | 0 | 1 | 2 |
    |-----|------|------|---|---|---|
    | $y$ |      | 5    |   |   | 2 |

    Draw and label the $x$ axis from $-3$ to 3 and the $y$ axis from $-1$ to 6.
    (b) Use your graph to find the value of:
        (i) $y$ when $x = 1.5$,   (ii) $y$ when $x = -0.5$.

7.  (a) Draw the graph of $y = 4x + 1$ for values of $x$ from $-2$ to 2.
    (b) Use your graph to find the value of:
        (i) $y$ when $x = -1.5$,   (ii) $x$ when $y = 3$.

8.  (a) Draw the graph of $y = 2x - 1$ for values of $x$ from $-2$ to 3.
    (b) Use your graph to find the value of $x$ when $y = 0$.

9.  (a) Draw the graph of $y = 5 - 2x$ for values of $x$ from $-2$ to 3.
    (b) Use your graph to find:
        (i) the value of $y$ when $x = 0$,
        (ii) the value of $x$ when $y = 0$,
        (iii) the value of $x$ when $y = 8$.

## Gradient and intercept

We found the gradient of a straight line in Chapter 3.
The gradient of a straight line graph is found by
drawing a right-angled triangle.

$$\text{Gradient} = \frac{\text{vertical height}}{\text{horizontal distance}}$$

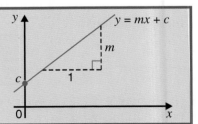

Positive gradient        Negative gradient

The gradient of a line can be positive, negative, zero or undefined.

In general, the equation of any straight line
can be written in the form
$$y = mx + c$$
where $m$ is the **gradient** of the line and
$c$ is the **$y$-intercept**.

### Example 2

Write down the gradient and $y$-intercept for each of the following graphs.

(a) $y = 3x + 5$          (b) $y = 4x - 1$          (c) $y = 6 - x$

(a) $y = 3x + 5$          (b) $y = 4x - 1$          (c) $y = 6 - x$
    Gradient $= 3$,           Gradient $= 4$,           Gradient $= -1$,
    $y$-intercept $= 5$.       $y$-intercept $= -1$.     $y$-intercept $= 6$.

**Practice** Exercise **11.2**

1. (a) Draw these graphs **on the same diagram**:
   (i) $y = x + 2$
   (ii) $y = x + 1$
   (iii) $y = x$
   (iv) $y = x - 1$
   Draw and label the $x$ axis from 0 to 3 and the $y$ axis from $-1$ to 5.
   (b) What do the lines all have in common? What is different?

2. (a) Write down the gradient and $y$-intercept of $y = 3x - 1$.
   (b) Draw the graph of $y = 3x - 1$ to check your answer.

3. Which of the following graphs are parallel?

   | $y = 3x$ | $y = x + 2$ | $y = 2x + 3$ | $y = 3x + 2$ |

4. Copy and complete this table.

| graph | gradient | $y$-intercept |
|---|---|---|
| $y = 3x + 5$ | 3 | |
| $y = 2x - 3$ | | |
| $y = 4 - 2x$ | | 4 |
| $y = \frac{1}{2}x + 3$ | | |
| $y = 2x$ | | |
| $y = 3$ | | |

5. Match the following equations to their sketch graphs.

   (1) $y = x - 6$

   (2) $y = 6 - x$

   (3) $y = 2x + 1$

   (4) $y = 2x - 1$

    A

    B

   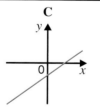 C

   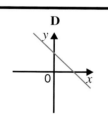 D

6. A plumber charges a fixed call-out charge and an hourly rate. The graph shows the charges made for jobs up to 4 hours.

   (a) What is the fixed call-out charge?
   (b) What is the hourly rate?
   (c) Calculate the total charge for a job which takes 8 hours.

   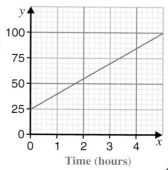

7. The graph shows the taxi fare for journeys up to 3 km.
   (a) What is the fixed charge?
   (b) What is the charge per kilometre?
   (c) Calculate the taxi fare for a journey of 5 km.

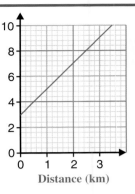

8. The graph represents the journey of a car.
   What is the speed of the car in kilometres per hour?

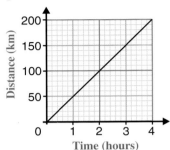

## Key Points

▶ The graph of a **linear function** is a **straight line**.

▶ A **rule** connects the $x$ coordinate with the $y$ coordinate.

▶
> **To draw a linear graph:**
> ● Find at least two pairs of corresponding values of $x$ and $y$.
> ● Plot the points.
> ● Join the points with a straight line.

▶ The **gradient** of a line can be found by drawing a right-angled triangle.

$$\text{Gradient} = \frac{\text{vertical height}}{\text{horizontal distance}}$$

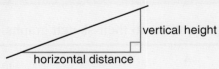

▶ The general equation of a linear function is $y = mx + c$,
   where $m$ is the **gradient** of the line and $c$ is the **y-intercept**.

## Review Exercise 11

1. (a) Write down the equations of the lines labelled on the graph below.
   (b) What are the coordinates of the point where lines (1) and (2) cross?

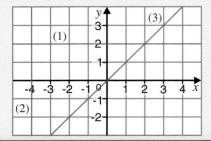

2. Match the equations to the graphs.

   **A:** $y = 2$    **B:** $y = x + 2$    **C:** $x = 2$

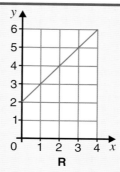

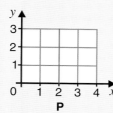

P

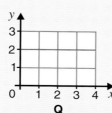

Q

R

3. (a) On the same diagram, draw and label the lines:  $x = 3$ and $y = 4$.
   (b) Write down the coordinates of the point where the lines cross.

4. (a) Copy and complete the table of values
      for the equation  $y = x + 3$.
   (b) Draw the graph of the line  $y = x + 3$.
      Label the $x$ axis from $-3$ to $2$ and the $y$ axis from $0$ to $5$.

   | $x$ | $-3$ | $0$ | $2$ |
   |-----|------|-----|-----|
   | $y$ |      |     |     |

   (c) Use your graph to find the value of $y$ when  $x = 1.5$.

5. (a) Write down the gradient and $y$-intercept of the graph  $y = 4x + 3$.
   (b) Write down the coordinates of the point where the graph of  $y = 5x - 2$
      crosses the $y$ axis.

6. The graph represents the journey of a train.
   What is the speed of the train in metres per second?

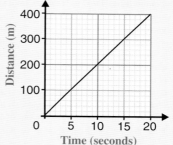

7. Two firms hire out scaffolding.
   The charges made by each firm are shown.
   **Scaffold Plus: £50 plus £10 per day.**
   **Scaffold Ltd: £100 plus £5 per day.**
   Alison draws two graphs, using the same axes, to compare the charges.

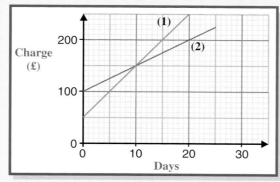

   (a) The graphs are labelled (**1**) and (**2**).
      Which graph represents the charges made by **Scaffold Plus**?
   (b) For how many days do both firms make the same charge?
   (c) A builder needs to hire scaffolding for 20 days.
      Which firm would be cheaper and by how much?

# 12 Equations *and* Formulae

Can you solve these puzzles?

- **Nueve** is a Spanish number.
  If you add 1 to **nueve** you get 10.
  What is **nueve**?

- What number must be put in each shape to make the statements correct?

  $\square + 3 = 8$ $\qquad$ $\bigcirc \times 3 = 30$ $\qquad$ $2 \times \bigcirc - 3 = 7$

These are all examples of **equations.**
Equations like these can be solved using a method known as **inspection**.
Instead of words or boxes, equations are usually written using letters for the unknown numbers.
**Solving** an equation means finding the numerical value of the letter which fits the equation.

### Example 1

Solve these equations by inspection.

(a) $\quad x - 2 = 6$
$\quad\quad x = 8$
$\quad$ Reason: $\mathbf{8} - 2 = 6$

(b) $\quad 2y = 10$
$\quad\quad y = 5$
$\quad$ Reason: $2 \times \mathbf{5} = 10$

> **Remember:**
> A letter or a symbol stands for an unknown number.
> $2y$ means $2 \times y$.

## Practice Exercise 12.1

1. What number must be put in the box to make each of these statements true?
   (a) $\square + 4 = 7$ $\quad$ (b) $15 - \square = 11$ $\quad$ (c) $13 = \square + 4$ $\quad$ (d) $11 = \square - 5$

2. Solve these equations by inspection.
   (a) $x + 2 = 6$ $\quad$ (b) $a + 7 = 10$ $\quad$ (c) $y - 4 = 4$ $\quad$ (d) $6 + t = 12$
   (e) $h - 15 = 7$ $\quad$ (f) $d + 4 = 5$ $\quad$ (g) $z - 5 = 25$ $\quad$ (h) $p + 7 = 7$
   (i) $c + 1 = 100$ $\quad$ (j) $5 - x = 3$ $\quad$ (k) $12 = y + 4$ $\quad$ (l) $7 = q - 3$

3. What number must be put in the box to make each of these statements true?
   (a) $3 \times \square = 15$ $\quad$ (b) $\square \times 4 = 20$ $\quad$ (c) $\square \div 2 = 9$ $\quad$ (d) $7 = \square \div 3$

4. Solve these equations by inspection.
   (a) $3a = 12$ $\quad$ (b) $5e = 30$ $\quad$ (c) $8 = 2p$ $\quad$ (d) $4 = 8y$
   (e) $\frac{d}{2} = 5$ $\quad$ (f) $\frac{t}{3} = 3$ $\quad$ (g) $\frac{m}{7} = 4$ $\quad$ (h) $\frac{x}{5} = 20$

5. What number must be put in the box to make each of these statements true?
   (a) $2 \times \square + 3 = 5$ $\quad$ (b) $\square \times 3 + 5 = 17$ $\quad$ (c) $3 + \square \times 2 = 11$

   (d) $5 \times \square - 1 = 9$ $\quad$ (e) $4 \times \square - 5 = 7$ $\quad$ (f) $\square \times 3 - 6 = 9$

## Solving equations by working backwards

I think of a number and then subtract 3.
The answer is 5.
What is the number I thought of?

Imagine that $x$ is the number I thought of.
The steps of the problem can be shown in a diagram.

$x$ ⟶ | subtract 3 | ⟶ **Answer 5**

Now work backwards, doing the opposite calculation.

**8** ⟵ | add 3 | ⟵ **5**

The number I thought of is 8.

| Remember: | |
|-----------|-----------|
| Forwards | Backwards |
| add | subtract |
| subtract | add |
| multiply | divide |
| divide | multiply |

### Example 2

I think of a number, multiply it by 3 and add 4.
The answer is 19.
What is my number?

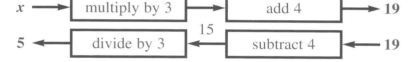

The number I thought of is 5.

## Practice Exercise 12.2    Solve these equations by working backwards.

1. I think of a number and then multiply it by 2.   The answer is 10.
   What is my number?

2. Jan thinks of a number and then subtracts 5.   Her answer is 9.
   What is her number?

3. Lou thinks of a number.   He multiplies it by 2 and then subtracts 5.   The answer is 7.
   What is his number?

4. I think of a number, subtract 5 and then multiply by 2.   The answer is 12.
   What is my number?

5. I think of a number, add 4 then multiply by 3.   The answer is 24.
   What is my number?

6. Steve thinks of a number.   He multiplies it by 5 and then adds 2.   The answer is 17.
   What is his number?

7. I think of a number, multiply it by 3 and then subtract 5.   The answer is 7.
   What is my number?

8. Solve this puzzle.

   | | |
   |---|---|
   | 1. Begin with $x$. | 3. The result is equal to 17. |
   | 2. Double it and then add 3. | 4. What is the value of $x$? |

**9.** Kathryn thinks of a number. She adds 3 and then doubles the result.
    (a) What number does Kathryn start with to get an answer of 10?
    (b) Kathryn starts with $x$. What is her answer in terms of $x$?

**10.** Sarah thinks of a number. She subtracts 2 and multiplies by 3.
    (a) What number does Sarah start with to get an answer of 21?
    (b) Sarah starts with $x$. What is her answer in terms of $x$?

## The balance method

Mathematicians always try to find efficient methods of working.
Here is a method used to solve equations that works a bit like a balance.

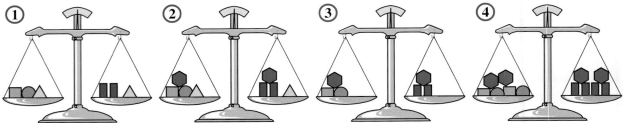

| ① These scales are balanced. | ② You can add the same amount to both sides and they still balance. | ③ You can subtract the same amount from both sides and they still balance. | ④ You can double (or halve) the amount on both sides and they still balance. |

**Equations** work in the same way.
If you do the same to both sides of an equation, it is still true.

**Example 3**

Solve $d - 13 = 5$.

$d - 13 = 5$
Add 13 to both sides.
$d = 18$

**Example 4**

Solve $x + 7 = 16$.

$x + 7 = 16$
Subtract 7 from both sides.
$x = 9$

> The aim is to find out what number the letter stands for, by ending up with **one letter** on one side of the equation and a **number** on the other side.

**Example 5**

Solve $4a = 20$.

$4a = 20$
Divide both sides by 4.
$a = 5$

**Example 6**

Solve $4n + 5 = 17$.

$4n + 5 = 17$
Subtract 5 from both sides.
$4n = 12$
Divide both sides by 4.
$n = 3$

Look at the examples carefully.
The steps taken to solve the equations are explained.

> Doing the same to both sides of an equation means:
> **Adding** the **same number** to both sides.
> **Subtracting** the **same number** from both sides.
> **Dividing** both sides by the **same number**.
> **Multiplying** both sides by the **same number**.

## Practice Exercise **12.3**

1. Use the balance method to solve these equations.
   Write down the steps that you use to solve each equation.
   - (a) $y + 4 = 7$
   - (b) $x + 5 = 11$
   - (c) $a + 10 = 20$
   - (d) $e + 9 = 24$
   - (e) $d + 6 = 17$
   - (f) $c + 15 = 35$
   - (g) $9 + x = 11$
   - (h) $2 + y = 21$
   - (i) $8 + m = 15$

2. Use the balance method to solve these equations.
   Explain each step of your working.
   - (a) $q - 5 = 2$
   - (b) $m - 2 = 8$
   - (c) $n - 7 = 9$
   - (d) $p - 6 = 12$
   - (e) $x - 11 = 20$
   - (f) $y - 3 = 14$
   - (g) $a - 1 = 1$
   - (h) $g - 3 = 1$
   - (i) $h - 5 = 7$

3. Use the balance method to solve these equations.
   - (a) $28 + x = 42$
   - (b) $t - 15 = 13$
   - (c) $f + 16 = 34$
   - (d) $y - 12 = 7$
   - (e) $14 + b = 21$
   - (f) $x - 9 = 20$
   - (g) $7 + m = 11$
   - (h) $k - 2 = 3$
   - (i) $5 + y = 12$

4. Use the balance method to solve these equations.
   Write down the steps that you use.
   - (a) $3c = 12$
   - (b) $5a = 20$
   - (c) $4f = 12$
   - (d) $8p = 24$
   - (e) $6h = 30$
   - (f) $10u = 20$

5. Use the balance method to solve these equations.
   Show each step of your working.
   - (a) $2p + 1 = 9$
   - (b) $4t - 1 = 11$
   - (c) $3h - 7 = 14$
   - (d) $3 + 4b = 11$
   - (e) $5d - 8 = 42$
   - (f) $2x + 3 = 15$
   - (g) $2 + 3c = 17$
   - (h) $3n - 1 = 8$
   - (i) $4x + 3 = 11$

6. Solve these equations.
   There is no need to explain your working if you are confident of what you are doing.
   - (a) $a - 5 = 7$
   - (b) $7x = 28$
   - (c) $3a = 27$
   - (d) $3x + 5 = 11$
   - (e) $4b + 8 = 32$
   - (f) $6x - 9 = 15$
   - (g) $6k - 7 = 5$
   - (h) $7b + 4 = 25$
   - (i) $9c - 12 = 6$
   - (j) $5c + 7 = 42$
   - (k) $8y - 5 = 27$
   - (l) $2x + 5 = 17$

7. Solve these equations.
   - (a) $x - 1 = -3$
   - (b) $3 + 2n = 2$
   - (c) $2 - x = 3$
   - (d) $4 - 3y = 13$
   - (e) $2x - 1 = -3$
   - (f) $3 - 5x = 18$
   - (g) $4x + 1 = -5$
   - (h) $-2 - 3x = 10$
   - (i) $2 - 4x = 8$

8. Use the balance method to solve these equations.
   Show each step of your working.
   **Remember:** The opposite of dividing is multiplying.
   - (a) $\frac{d}{3} = 10$
   - (b) $\frac{e}{2} = 7$
   - (c) $\frac{f}{4} = 5$

## Equations with letters on both sides

In some questions letters appear on both sides of the equation.

### Example 7

Solve $3x + 1 = x + 7$.

$3x + 1 = x + 7$
Subtract 1 from both sides.
$3x = x + 6$
Subtract $x$ from both sides.
$2x = 6$
Divide both sides by 2.
$x = 3$

### Example 8

Solve $2a - 3 = 9 - a$.

$2a - 3 = 9 - a$
Add 3 to both sides.
$2a = 12 - a$
Add $a$ to both sides.
$3a = 12$
Divide both sides by 3.
$a = 4$

## Practice Exercise 12.4

1. Solve the following equations. Write down the steps that you use.
   - (a) $3x = 20 - x$
   - (b) $5q = 12 - q$
   - (c) $2t = 15 - 3t$
   - (d) $5e - 9 = 2e$
   - (e) $3g - 8 = g$
   - (f) $y + 3 = 5 - y$
   - (g) $4x + 1 = x + 7$
   - (h) $7k + 3 = 3k + 7$
   - (i) $3a - 1 = a + 7$
   - (j) $3p - 1 = 2p + 5$
   - (k) $6m - 1 = m + 9$
   - (l) $3d - 5 = 5 + d$
   - (m) $2y + 1 = y + 6$
   - (n) $3 + 5u = 2u + 12$
   - (o) $4q + 3 = q + 3$

2. Solve.
   - (a) $3d = 32 - d$
   - (b) $3q = 12 - q$
   - (c) $3c + 2 = 10 - c$
   - (d) $4t + 2 = 17 - t$
   - (e) $4w + 1 = 13 - 2w$
   - (f) $2e - 3 = 12 - 3e$
   - (g) $2g + 5 = 25 - 2g$
   - (h) $2z - 6 = 14 - 3z$
   - (i) $3m + 9 = m + 1$
   - (j) $5a - 4 = 3a + 6$
   - (k) $2 - 4t = 12 + t$
   - (l) $17 - 3p = 3 - 5p$

## Using equations to solve problems

So far, you have been given equations and asked to solve them.
The next step is to **form an equation** first using the information given in a problem.
The equation can then be solved in the usual way.

### Example 9

The triangle has sides of length: $x$ cm, $2x$ cm and $7$ cm.

(a) Write an expression, in terms of $x$, for the perimeter of the triangle.
Give your answer in its simplest form.

(b) The triangle has a perimeter of $19$ cm.
By forming an equation find the value of $x$.

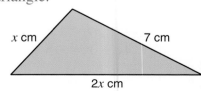

(a) The perimeter of the triangle is: $x + 2x + 7$ cm
In its simplest form, the perimeter is: $(3x + 7)$ cm

(b) The perimeter of the triangle is $19$ cm, so, $3x + 7 = 19$
$$3x = 12$$
$$x = 4$$

**Practice** Exercise **12.5**

1.  (a)  Write an expression, in terms of $x$,
        for the sum of the angles of the triangle.
        Give your answer in its simplest form.
    (b)  The sum of the angles is 180°.
        By forming an equation, find the value of $x$.

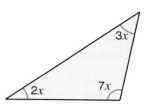

2.  The weights of three boxes are shown.

    $k$ kilograms          $2k$ kilograms          $3k$ kilograms

    (a)  Write an expression, in terms of $k$, for the total weight of the boxes.
    (b)  The boxes weigh 15 kilograms altogether.
        By forming an equation, find the weight of the lightest box.

3.  (a)  Write an expression, in terms of $y$,
        for the perimeter of this shape.
        Give your answer in its simplest form.
    (b)  The shape has a perimeter of 39 cm.
        By forming an equation, find the value of $y$.

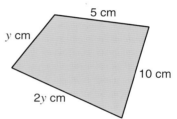

5 cm
$y$ cm
10 cm
$2y$ cm

4.  A bag contains the following balls.

        $a$      yellow balls
    $2a + 1$    red balls
    $3a + 2$    blue balls

    (a)  Write an expression, in terms of $a$, for the total number of balls in the bag.
    (b)  The bag contains 45 balls.
        How many yellow balls are in the bag?

5.  Dominic is 7 years older than Marcie.
    (a)  Dominic is $n$ years old.
        Write an expression, in terms of $n$, for Marcie's age.
    (b)  The sum of their ages is 43 years.
        By forming an equation, find the ages of Dominic and Marcie.

6.  The diagram shows the lengths of three rods.

    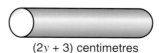

    $(y - 5)$ centimetres          $y$ centimetres          $(2y + 3)$ centimetres

    (a)  Write an expression, in terms of $y$, for the total length of the rods.
    (b)  The total length of the rods is 30 centimetres.
        What is the length of the longest rod?

# Formulae

A **formula** represents a **rule** written using numbers, letters and mathematical signs.
Formulae were first covered in Chapter 2.

## Rearranging formulae

Sometimes it is easier to use a formula if you **rearrange** it first.

The formula $k = \frac{8m}{5}$ can be used to change distances in miles to distances in kilometres.

Rearrange this to give a formula which can be used to change distances in kilometres into distances in miles.

$k = \frac{8m}{5}$

Multiply both sides by 5.

$5k = 8m$

Divide both sides by 8.

$\frac{5k}{8} = m$

Here is a reminder of some operations and their inverses.

| Operation | Inverse operation |
|-----------|-------------------|
| Addition $+a$ | Subtraction $-a$ |
| Subtraction $-a$ | Addition $+a$ |
| Multiplication $\times a$ | Division $\div a$ |
| Division $\div a$ | Multiplication $\times a$ |

We say we have
**rearranged the formula** $k = \frac{8m}{5}$ as $m = \frac{5k}{8}$ to make $m$ the **subject** of the formula.

### Example 10

Make $w$ the subject of the formula $E = 3w - k$.

$E = 3w - k$

Add $k$ to both sides.

$E + k = 3w$

Divide both sides by 3.

$w = \frac{E + k}{3}$

### Example 11

Make $n$ the subject of the formula $h = \frac{v}{n}$.

$h = \frac{v}{n}$

Multiply both sides by $n$.

$hn = v$

Divide both sides by $h$.

$n = \frac{v}{h}$

## Practice Exercise 12.6

1. Make $m$ the subject of these formulae.
   (a) $a = m + 5$     (b) $a = x + m$     (c) $a = m - 2$     (d) $a = m - b$

2. Make $x$ the subject of these formulae.
   (a) $y = 4x$     (b) $y = ax$     (c) $y = \frac{x}{2}$     (d) $y = \frac{x}{a}$     (e) $y = \frac{3x}{5}$

3. Make $p$ the subject of these formulae.
   (a) $y = 2p + 6$     (b) $t = 5p + q$     (c) $m = 3p - 2$     (d) $r = 4p - q$

4. The cost, £$C$, of hiring a car for $n$ days is given by $C = 35 + 24n$.
   Make $n$ the subject of the formula.

5. $V = IR$. Rearrange the formula to give $R$ in terms of $V$ and $I$.

6. The perimeter of a square is $P = 4d$.
   (a) Rearrange the formula to give $d$ in terms of $P$.
   (b) Find $d$ when $P = 28\,\text{cm}$.

7. The area of a rectangle is $A = lb$.
   (a) Rearrange the formula to give $l$ in terms of $A$ and $b$.
   (b) Find $l$ when $A = 27 \, cm^2$ and $b = 3 \, cm$.

8. The speed of a car is $S = \dfrac{D}{T}$.
   (a) (i) Change the subject to $D$.
       (ii) Find $D$ when $S = 48 \, km/h$ and $T = 2$ hours.
   (b) (i) Change the subject to $T$.
       (ii) Find $T$ when $S = 36 \, km/h$ and $D = 90 \, km$.

9. A straight line has equation $y = mx + c$.
   (a) Rearrange the formula to give $x$ in terms of $y$, $m$ and $c$.
   (b) Calculate $x$ when $y = 5$, $m = 4$ and $c = 3$.

10. You are given the formula $v = u + at$.
    (a) Rearrange the formula to give $t$ in terms of $v$, $u$ and $a$.
    (b) Work out the value of $t$ when $v = 8$, $u = 20$ and $a = -6$.

11. The area of a triangle is given by $A = \dfrac{bh}{2}$.
    (a) Rearrange the formula to give $b$ in terms of $A$ and $h$.
    (b) Calculate $b$ when $A = 9.6$ and $h = 3$.

## Key Points

▶ The solution of an equation is the value of the unknown letter that fits the equation.

▶ You should be able to use the **balance method** to solve equations.
   If you do the same to both sides of an equation, it is still true.
   Doing the same to both sides means:

> **Adding** the **same number** to both sides.
> **Subtracting** the **same number** from both sides.
> **Dividing** both sides by the **same number**.
> **Multiplying** both sides by the **same number**.

▶ You should be able to **rearrange** a formula to make another letter (variable) the subject.

## Review Exercise 12

1. What number must be put in the box to make each of these statements correct?
   (a) $\square + 5 = 9$    (b) $7 - \square = 4$    (c) $3 \times \square = 18$    (d) $\dfrac{\square}{3} = 6$

2. Petra thinks of a number, then doubles it. Her answer is 16.
   What number did she think of?

3. Solve these equations.
   (a) $5y = 20$    (b) $3y + 2 = 11$    (c) $2y - 5 = 2 + y$

4. Solve.
   (a) $5m - 7 = 28$   (b) $3t + 3 = 5t - 7$

5. (a) Hilda is twice as old as Evie. Their ages add up to 51 years.
       How old is Hilda?
   (b) Colin is 2 years older than John. Their ages add up to 36 years.
       How old is Colin?

6. The diagram shows two cans of oil.
   The cans hold a total of 9 litres of oil.
   By forming an equation, find the amount
   of oil in the larger can.

   $n$ litres    $(3n + 1)$ litres

7. The perimeter of a rectangle is given by the formula $P = 2x - 5$.
   Rearrange the formula to make $x$ the subject.

8. The cost, $C$ pence, of printing $n$ business cards is given by the
   formula $C = 15n + 500$.
   (a) What is the cost of printing 80 cards?
       Give your answer in pounds.
   (b) Rearrange the formula $C = 15n + 500$ to make $n$ the subject.
   (c) Fred pays £50 for some business cards to be printed.
       How many cards did he have printed?

9. Bernadette pays £2.97 for a newspaper and a magazine.
   The magazine costs twice as much as the newspaper.
   (a) The newspaper costs $x$ pence.
       Write an expression, in terms of $x$, for the price of the magazine.
   (b) By forming an equation find the price of the magazine.

10. Grace is given a weekly allowance of £$p$.
    Aimee is given £4 a week **more** than Grace.
    Lydia is given £3 a week **less** than Grace.
    (a) Write an expression, in terms of $p$, for the amount given to
        (i) Aimee,   (ii) Lydia,   (iii) all three girls.
    (b) The three girls are given a total of £25 a week altogether.
        By forming an equation find the weekly allowance given to each girl.

11. If $ax - b = c$, make $x$ the subject of the formula.

12. Solve the equation $6x + 27 = 99$.

13. The quantity of wallpaper required to decorate a room is given by the formula $R = \dfrac{hp}{5}$.
    $R$ is the number of rolls of wallpaper, $h$ is the height of the room to be decorated
    and $p$ is the perimeter of the room.
    (a) A room is 2.4 m high and has a perimeter of 15 m.
        How many rolls of wallpaper should Graham buy to decorate the room?
    (b) Rearrange the formula $R = \dfrac{hp}{5}$ to make $p$ the subject.

# 13 Pythagoras' Theorem

The longest side in a right-angled triangle is called the **hypotenuse**.

In any right-angled triangle it can be proved that:

> *"The square on the hypotenuse is equal to the sum of the squares on the other two sides."*

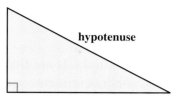

This is known as the **Theorem of Pythagoras**, or **Pythagoras' Theorem**.

## Checking the Theorem of Pythagoras

Look at this triangle.

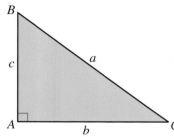

Notice that: the side opposite angle $A$ is labelled $a$,
the side opposite angle $B$ is labelled $b$,
the side opposite angle $C$ is labelled $c$.

$ABC$ is a right-angled triangle because $\angle BAC = 90°$.

$a = 5$ cm, so, $a^2 = 25$ cm$^2$.
$b = 4$ cm, so, $b^2 = 16$ cm$^2$.
$c = 3$ cm, so, $c^2 = 9$ cm$^2$.
$a^2 = b^2 + c^2$

When we know the lengths of two sides of a right-angled triangle, we can use the Theorem of Pythagoras to find the length of the third side.

## Finding the hypotenuse

### Example 1

The roof of a house is 12 m above the ground.
What length of ladder is needed to reach the roof, if the foot of the ladder has to be placed 3 m away from the wall of the house?

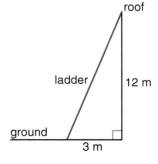

Using Pythagoras' Theorem.    Take the square root of both sides.

$l^2 = 3^2 + 12^2$              $l = \sqrt{153}$

$l^2 = 9 + 144$               $l = 12.369 \ldots$

$l^2 = 153$                The ladder needs to be 12.37 m long, correct to 2 d.p.

## Practice Exercise 13.1

1. These triangles are right-angled. Calculate the length of the hypotenuse.

   (a)
   
   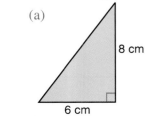

   (b)
   
   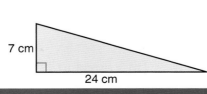

   (c)
   
   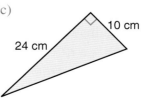

**2.** These triangles are right-angled. Calculate the length of side $a$ to one decimal place.

(a)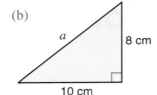

(b)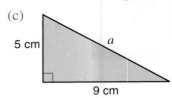

(c)

**3.** $AB$ and $CD$ are lines, drawn on a centimetre-squared grid. Calculate the exact length of
(a) $AB$,
(b) $CD$.

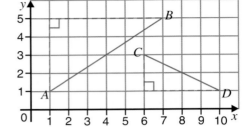

**4.** Calculate the distance between the following points.
(a) $A\,(2, 0)$ and $B\,(6, 3)$.
(b) $C\,(6, 3)$ and $D\,(0, 10)$.
(c) $E\,(2, 2)$ and $F\,(-3, -10)$.
(d) $G\,(-2, -2)$ and $H\,(-6, 5)$.
(e) $I\,(3, -1)$ and $J\,(-3, -5)$.

**5.** The coordinates of the vertices of a parallelogram are $P\,(1, 1)$, $Q\,(3, 5)$, $R\,(x, y)$ and $S\,(7, 3)$.
(a) Find the coordinates of $R$.
(b) $X$ is the midpoint of $PQ$. Find the coordinates of $X$.
(c) $Y$ is the midpoint of $PS$. Find the coordinates of $Y$.
(d) Calculate the distance $XY$.

## Finding one of the shorter sides

To find one of the shorter sides we can rearrange the Theorem of Pythagoras.

To find $b$ we use:
$$b^2 = a^2 - c^2$$
To find $c$ we use:
$$c^2 = a^2 - b^2$$

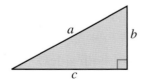

To find the length of a shorter side of a right-angled triangle:
Subtract the square of the known short side from the square on the hypotenuse.
Take the square root of the result.

**Example 2**

A wire used to keep a radio aerial steady is 9 metres long.
The wire is fixed to the ground 4.6 metres from the base of the aerial.
Find the height of the aerial, giving your answer correct to one decimal place.

Using Pythagoras' Theorem.
$$9^2 = h^2 + 4.6^2$$

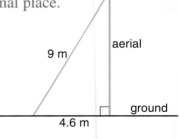

Rearranging this we get:
$$h^2 = 9^2 - 4.6^2$$
$$h^2 = 81 - 21.16$$
$$h^2 = 59.84$$

Take the square root of both sides.
$$h = \sqrt{59.84}$$
$$h = 7.735\ldots$$
$$h = 7.7\,\text{m, correct to 1 d.p.}$$

The height of the aerial is 7.7 m, correct to 1 d.p.

## Practice Exercise 13.2

1. Work out the length of side *b*.

(a)
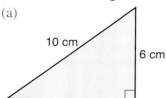

(b)
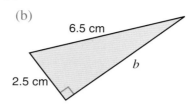

(c)
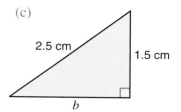

2. Work out the length of side *c*, correct to one decimal place.

(a)
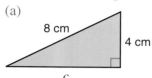

(b)
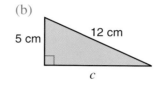

(c)
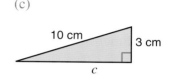

3.
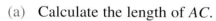

Two boats, *A* and *B*, are 360 m apart.
Boat *A* is 120 m due east of a buoy.
Boat *B* is due north of the buoy.
How far is boat *B* from the buoy?
Give your answer to the nearest metre.

4. The diagram shows a right-angled triangle, *ABC*, and a square, *ACDE*.
*AB* = 2.5 cm and *BC* = 6.5 cm.

(a) Calculate the length of *AC*.
(b) Calculate the area of the square, *ACDE*.

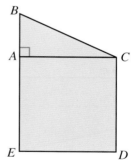

5. The diagram shows a right-angled triangle, *ABC*, and a square, *XYBA*.

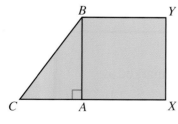

*BC* = 6 cm.
The square, *XYBA*, has an area of 23.04 cm².
Calculate the length of *AC*.

6. In triangle *ABC*:
*AB* = 13 m and *BC* = 20 m.
Angle *ADB* = 90° and *BD* = 12 m.
Calculate the length of:
(a) *AD*, (b) *CD*, (c) *AC*.
(d) Calculate the perimeter of triangle *ABC*.

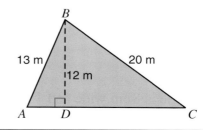

# Problems involving the use of Pythagoras' Theorem

Questions leading to the use of Pythagoras' Theorem often involve:

**Understanding the problem.**

What information is given?

What are you required to find?

**Drawing diagrams.**

In some questions a diagram is not given.

Drawing a diagram may help you to understand the problem.

**Selecting a suitable right-angled triangle.**

In more complex problems you will have to select a right-angled triangle which can be used to answer the question.

It is a good idea to draw this triangle on its own, especially if it has been taken from a three-dimensional drawing.

## Example 3

The diagram shows the side view of a swimming pool.
It slopes steadily from a depth of 1 m to 3.6 m.
The pool is 20 m long.
Find the length of the sloping floor of the pool,
giving the answer correct to one decimal place.

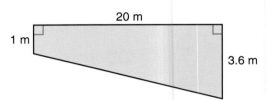

$\Delta CDE$ is a suitable right-angled triangle.

$CD = 3.6 - 1 = 2.6\,\text{m}$

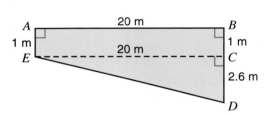

Using Pythagoras' Theorem in $\Delta CDE$.

$DE^2 = CD^2 + CE^2$

$DE^2 = 2.6^2 + 20^2$

$DE^2 = 6.76 + 400$

$DE^2 = 406.76$

$DE = \sqrt{406.76}\ \text{m}$

$DE = 20.1682\ldots\ \text{m}$

The length of the sloping floor of the pool is 20.2 m, correct to 1 d.p.

## Practice Exercise 13.3

1. In each of the following, work out the length of the side marked $x$.

   (a)

   (b)

   (c)

   (d)

   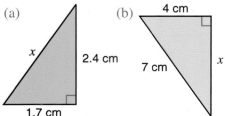
   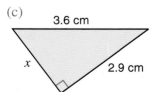
   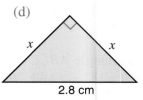

2. A rectangle is 8 cm wide and 15 cm long.
   Work out the length of its diagonals.

3. The length of a rectangle is 24 cm. The diagonals of the rectangle are 26 cm.
   Work out the width of the rectangle.

4. A square has sides of length 6 cm.
   Work out the length of its diagonals.

5. The diagonals of a square are 15 cm.
   Work out the length of its sides.

6. The height of an isosceles triangle is 12 cm. The base of the triangle is 18 cm.
   Work out the length of the equal sides.

7. An equilateral triangle has sides of length 8 cm.
   Work out the height of the triangle.

8. The diagram shows the side view of a car ramp.
   The ramp is 110 cm long and 25 cm high.
   The top part of the ramp is 40 cm long.
   Calculate the length of the
   sloping part of the ramp.

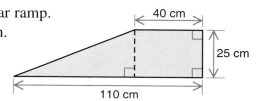

9.

   A rectangular field is 60 metres wide.
   A footpath, which crosses the field from
   one corner of the opposite corner, is
   150 metres long.
   Calculate the length of the field.
   Give your answer to the nearest metre.

10. A builder is making a rectangular concrete base for a conservatory.
    The concrete base must measure 3.3 m wide and 5.0 m long.
    Explain how the builder can check that the base is truly rectangular by measuring the
    diagonals of the rectangle.

## Key Points

▶ The longest side in a right-angled triangle is called the **hypotenuse**.

▶ The **Theorem of Pythagoras** states:

> *"In any right-angled triangle the square on the hypotenuse*
> *is equal to the sum of the squares on the other two sides."*

$$a^2 = b^2 + c^2$$

Rearranging gives:

$$b^2 = a^2 - c^2$$
$$c^2 = a^2 - b^2$$

▶ When we know the lengths of two sides of a right-angled triangle, we can use the
Theorem of Pythagoras to find the length of the third side.

1. The diagram shows a right-angled triangle, *PQR*.
   *PR* = 12 cm   and   *QR* = 9 cm
   Calculate the length of *PQ*.

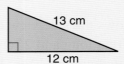

2.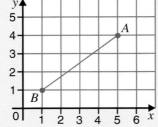
   The coordinates of the points *A* and *B* are (5, 4) and (1, 1).
   Work out the length of *AB*.

3. A sketch of a right-angled triangle is shown.
   Calculate the perimeter of the triangle.

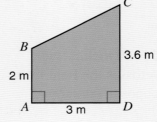

4. The diagram shows the end of a shed.
   Calculate the length of *BC*.

5. The diagram consists of two right-angled triangles.
   *AB* = 9.5 cm,   *BC* = 4.3 cm   and   *AD* = 8.7 cm.

   Calculate the length of *CD*.
   Give your answer to an appropriate degree of accuracy.

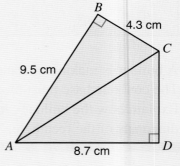

6. Mike is standing 200 m due west of a power station and 300 m due north of a pylon.
   Calculate the distance of the power station from the pylon.

7. The diagram shows how a triangular flower bed is to be made in a rectangular lawn.

   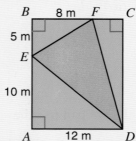

   (a) Calculate the length of *EF*.
       Give your answer to one decimal place.
   (b) Show that the perimeter of triangle *DEF* is greater
       than 40 metres.
       You must show your working.

# 14 Scale Factors *and* Similar Figures

## Enlargement

The change in position or size of a shape is called a **transformation**.
This diagram shows a transformation called an **enlargement**.

When a shape is enlarged:
> **angles** remain unchanged,
> all **lengths** are multiplied by
> a **scale factor**.

For example:
> Shape **B** is an enlargement of Shape **A**.
> The scale factor is 2.

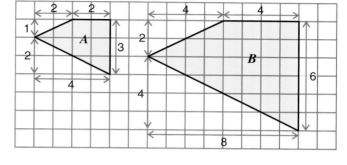

> Scale factor = $\dfrac{\text{new length}}{\text{original length}}$
>
> This can be rearranged to give:   new length = original length $\times$ scale factor

## Using a scale factor which is a fraction

When the scale factor is a value between 0 and 1, such as 0.5 or $\frac{1}{3}$, the new shape is **smaller** than the original shape. This transformation is called a **reduction**.

In the diagram above, Shape **B** is an enlargement of Shape **A**.
The scale factor of the enlargement is 2.
However, what happens if you start with Shape **B**?
Shape **A** is a reduction of Shape **B**.
The scale factor of the reduction is $\frac{1}{2}$.

> In general:   If Shape **A** is enlarged by scale factor $n$ to get Shape **B**,
>
> then Shape **B** is reduced by scale factor $\dfrac{1}{n}$ to get Shape **A**.

## Practice Exercise 14.1

1.  Copy each diagram and draw an enlargement with the given scale factor.

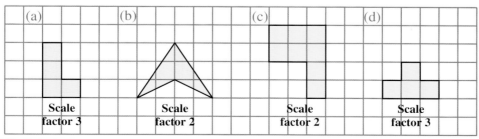

(a) Scale factor 3

(b) Scale factor 2

(c) Scale factor 2

(d) Scale factor 3

**2.** Shape **A** is enlarged to make Shape **B**. What is the scale factor of the enlargement?

(a)

(b)

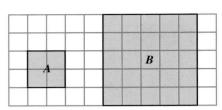 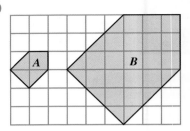

**3.** Shape **P** is enlarged to make Shape **Q**. What is the scale factor of the enlargement?

(a)

(b)

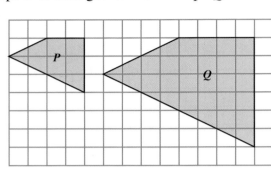 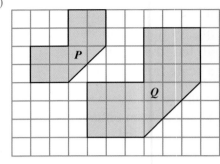

**4.** Copy each diagram and draw a reduction with the given scale factor.

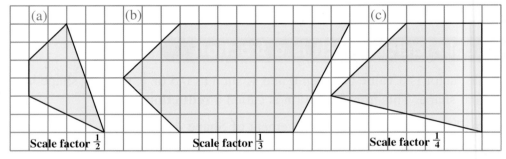

**5.** (a) Shape **Q** is an enlargement of Shape **P**.
     What is the scale factor?
   (b) Shape **P** is a reduction of Shape **Q**.
     What is the scale factor?

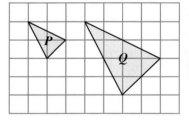

**6.** In each diagram, $A'B'C'D'$ is an enlargement or reduction of $ABCD$.
    Find the scale factor of each enlargement or reduction.

(a)

(b)

(c)

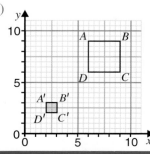 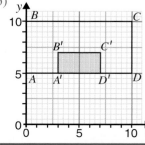 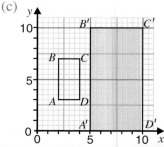

7. In each diagram, $A'B'C'$ is a reduction or enlargement of $ABC$.
   Find the scale factor of each reduction or enlargement.

(a)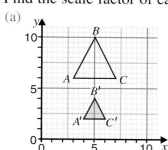

(b)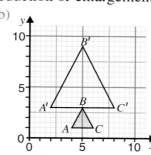

(c)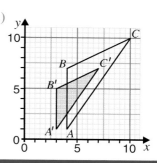

## Similar figures

When one figure is an enlargement of another, the two figures are **similar**.

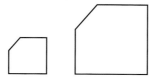

Sometimes one of the figures is rotated or reflected.

For example:
   Figures **C** and **E** are enlargements of figure **A**.
   Figures **A**, **C** and **E** are similar.

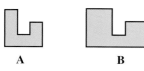   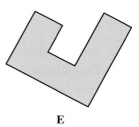

| A | B | C | D | E |

When two figures are **similar**:
   their **shapes** are the same,
   their **angles** are the same,
   corresponding **lengths** are in the same ratio, this ratio is the **scale factor** of the enlargement.

$$\text{Scale factor} = \frac{\text{new length}}{\text{original length}}$$

This can be rearranged to give:   new length = original length × scale factor

### Example 1

A photo has width 6 cm and height 9 cm.
An enlargement is made, which has width 8 cm.
Calculate the height of the enlargement.

Scale factor $= \frac{8}{6}$

$h = 9 \times \frac{8}{6}$

$h = 12$ cm

9 cm

6 cm

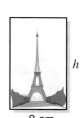

$h$

8 cm

## Example 2

These two figures are similar.
Calculate the lengths of $x$ and $y$.
Write down the size of the angle marked $a$.

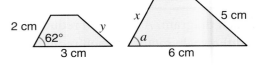

The scale factor $= \frac{6}{3} = 2$

Lengths in the large figure are given by: length in small figure $\times$ scale factor.

$$x = 2 \times 2$$
$$x = 4\,\text{cm}$$

Lengths in the small figure are given by: length in large figure $\div$ scale factor.

$$y = 5 \div 2$$
$$y = 2.5\,\text{cm}$$

The angles in similar figures are the same. So, $a = 62°$.

## Practice Exercise 14.2

1. The shapes in this question have been drawn accurately.
   Explain why these two shapes are not similar to each other.

2. Which of the following must be similar to each other?
   (a) Two circles.
   (b) Two kites.
   (c) Two parallelograms.
   (d) Two squares.
   (e) Two rectangles.

3. These rectangles are all similar. The diagrams have not been drawn accurately.
   Work out the lengths of the sides marked $a$ and $b$.

   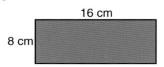

4. These two kites are similar.

   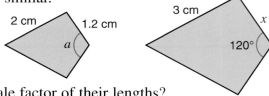

   (a) What is the scale factor of their lengths?
   (b) Find the length of the side marked $x$.
   (c) What is the size of angle $a$?

5. A shape has width 8 cm and length 24 cm.
   It is enlarged to give a new shape with width 10 cm.
   Calculate the length of the new shape.

6. In each part, the two figures are similar. Lengths are in centimetres.
   Calculate the lengths and angles marked with letters.

   (a)

   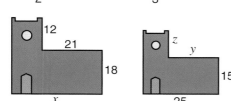

   (b)

   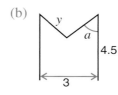

   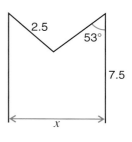

   (c)

   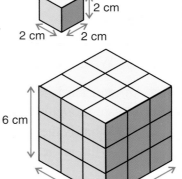

7. The smallest angle in triangle *T* is 18°. Triangle *T* is enlarged by a scale factor of 2.
   What size is the smallest angle in the enlarged triangle?

8. A castle has height 30 m. The height of the castle wall is 6 m.
   A scale model of the castle has height 25 cm.
   Calculate the height of the castle wall in the scale model.

9. The dimensions of three sizes of paper are given.
   All the sizes are similar.
   Calculate the values of *x* and *y*.

   | Length (cm) | 24 | 30 | *y* |
   |---|---|---|---|
   | Width (cm) | *x* | 20 | 32 |

## Lengths, areas and volumes of similar figures

## Activity

1. Some cubes have side 2 cm.
   They are built together to make a larger cube with side 6 cm.
   This represents an enlargement with scale factor 3.
   Copy and complete the table.

   |  | Length of side (cm) | Area of face (cm²) | Volume of cube (cm³) |
   |---|---|---|---|
   | Small cube | 2 |  | 8 |
   | Large cube | 6 | 36 |  |
   | Scale factor | $\frac{6}{2} = 3$ | $\frac{36}{\phantom{0}} =$ | $\frac{\phantom{0}}{8} =$ |

   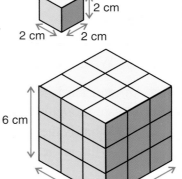

   *What do you notice about the three scale factors?*

2. A cuboid is enlarged with scale factor 2,
   as shown.
   What effect has the enlargement
   on length, area and volume?

   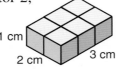

   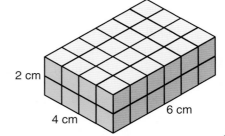

   Investigate for other cubes and cuboids.

# Scale factors for length, area and volume

When the **length** scale factor $= k$, the **area** scale factor $= k^2$, the **volume** scale factor $= k^3$

### Example 3

A prototype for a new plane is made.
The real plane will be an enlargement of the
prototype with scale factor 5.

It can be assumed that "scale factor"
refers to the length scale factor, unless
specified differently in a question.

(a) The length of the wing on the real plane is 20 m.
What is the length of the wing on the prototype?
(b) The area of the windows on the prototype is $0.18\,m^2$.
Find the area of the real windows.

(a) Length scale factor $= 5$
Prototype length $= 20 \div 5 = 4\,m$
(b) Area scale factor $= 5^2 = 25$
Real area $= 0.18 \times 25 = 4.5\,m^2$

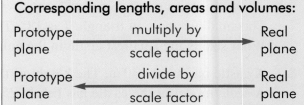

Corresponding lengths, areas and volumes:

Prototype plane ——multiply by scale factor——> Real plane

Prototype plane <——divide by scale factor—— Real plane

## Practice Exercise **14.3**

1. A model of a train is 60 cm long.
It is made on a scale of 1 to 50.
What is the length of the actual train in metres?

2. A rectangle has length 8 cm and width 6 cm.
A similar rectangle has length 12 cm.

6 cm

8 cm          12 cm

(a) What is the scale factor of their lengths?
(b) What is the width of the larger rectangle?

3. A motor car is 4.2 m long and 1.4 m high.
A scale model of the car is 8.4 cm long.
(a) What is the scale of the model?
(b) What is the height of the model?

4. The lengths of the sides of a kite are doubled.
What happens to its area?

5. A company logo is printed on all its stationery.
On small sheets of paper the logo is 1.2 cm high and covers an area of $3.5\,cm^2$.
On large sheets of paper the logo covers an area of $14\,cm^2$.
What is the height of the logo on large sheets of paper?

6. The lengths of the sides of a square are halved.
What happens to its area?

7.  A picture is 30 cm high and has an area of 360 cm².
    A print of the same picture is 15 cm high.
    What is its area?

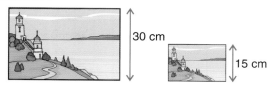

30 cm

15 cm

8.  A king-size photograph is 18 cm long and 12 cm wide.
    A standard size photograph is 12 cm long.
    (a)  What is the width of a standard size photograph?
    (b)  What is the area of a standard size photograph?

9.  The measurements of a rabbit hutch are all doubled.
    How many times bigger is its volume?

10. A teapot has a volume of 500 ml.
    A similar teapot is double the height.
    What is the volume of this teapot?

11. Joe wants to enlarge a picture so that its area is doubled.
    What length scale factor should he use?

## Key Points

▶ When a shape is **enlarged** or **reduced**:   all **lengths** are multiplied by a **scale factor**,
                                                **angles** remain unchanged.

$$\text{Scale factor} = \frac{\text{new length}}{\text{original length}}$$   New length = original length × scale factor

The size of the original shape is:
        **increased** by using a scale factor greater than 1,
        **reduced** by using a scale factor which is a fraction, i.e., between 0 and 1.

▶ When two figures are **similar**:
        their **shapes** are the same,         $\text{Scale factor} = \dfrac{\text{new length}}{\text{original length}}$
        their **angles** are the same,
        corresponding **lengths** are in the same ratio, this ratio is the **scale factor** of
        the enlargement.

▶ All circles are similar to each other.

▶ All squares are similar to each other.

▶ You should be able to find corresponding lengths and areas in **similar figures**.

For similar areas and volumes:
When the **length** scale factor $= k$
    the **area** scale factor    $= k^2$

1.  Copy each diagram and draw an enlargement, or reduction, with the given scale factor.

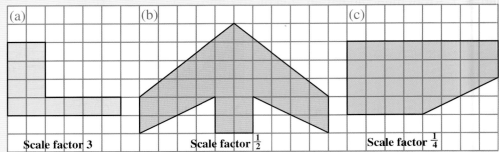

    (a) Scale factor 3      (b) Scale factor $\frac{1}{2}$      (c) Scale factor $\frac{1}{4}$

2.  (a)  Triangle *ABC* is a reduction of
        triangle *PQR*.
        What is the scale factor?
    (b)  Triangle *PQR* is an enlargement of
        triangle *ABC*.
        What is the scale factor of
        the enlargement?

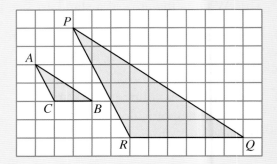

3.  In each diagram, *A'B'C'D'* is a reduction of *ABCD*.
    Find the scale factor of each reduction.

    (a)      (b)      (c)

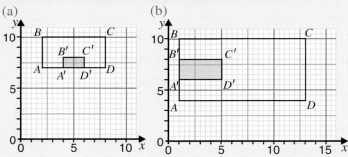 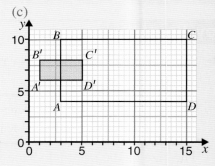

4.  These pairs of figures are similar.
    Calculate the lengths of the unknown sides
    marked with letters.

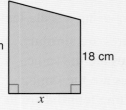 

5.  A model of a hall is made to scale of 2 cm to 1 m.
    The height of the model is 16 cm and its floor area is 800 cm².
    Find the height and floor area of the hall.

6.  A photo has width 16 cm and height 28 cm.
    A reduction is made, which has height 7 cm.
    (a)  Calculate the width of the reduction.
    (b)  How many times smaller is the reduction
        than the original photo?

    28 cm      7 cm

    16 cm

# 15 Using Angle Properties

## Angle properties

Here is a reminder of some angle properties.

| Angles at point | Complementary angles | Supplementary angles | Vertically opposite angles |
|---|---|---|---|
|  |  | 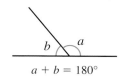 | 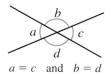 |
| $a + b + c = 360°$ | $x + y = 90°$ | $a + b = 180°$ | $a = c$ and $b = d$ |

## Parallel lines and angles

Each diagram shows two parallel lines crossed by another straight line called a **transversal**.
Arrowheads are used to show that lines are **parallel**.
**Parallel lines** are lines which never meet.

| Corresponding angles | | Alternate angles | | Allied angles | |
|---|---|---|---|---|---|
| 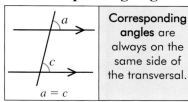 | Corresponding angles are always on the same side of the transversal. | 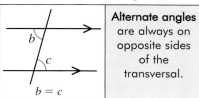 | Alternate angles are always on opposite sides of the transversal. | 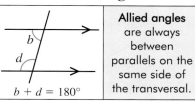 | Allied angles are always between parallels on the same side of the transversal. |
| $a = c$ | | $b = c$ | | $b + d = 180°$ | |

### Example 1

Without measuring, work out the size of the angles marked with letters.

(a)

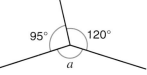

Angles at a point add up to 360°.
$a + 95° + 120° = 360°$
$a = 360° - 95° - 120°$
$a = 145°$

(b)

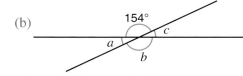

$b = 154°$  (vertically opposite angles)
$a + 154° = 180°$  (supplementary angles)
$a = 180° - 154°$
$a = 26°$
$c = 26°$
$a = 26°, \quad b = 154°, \quad c = 26°$

(c)

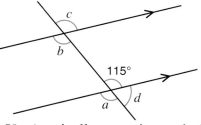

$a = 115°$  (vertically opposite angles)
$b = 115°$  (alternate angles)
$c = 115°$  (corresponding angles)
$d + 115° = 180°$  (supplementary angles)
$d = 180° - 115°$
$d = 65°$

(d)  $x + 76° = 180°$  (allied angles)
$x = 180° - 76°$
$x = 104°$

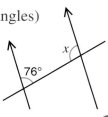

## **Practice** Exercise **15.1**

The diagrams in this exercise have **not** been drawn accurately.

**1.** These angles are complementary.
Work out the size of angle $p$ in each diagram.

(a)
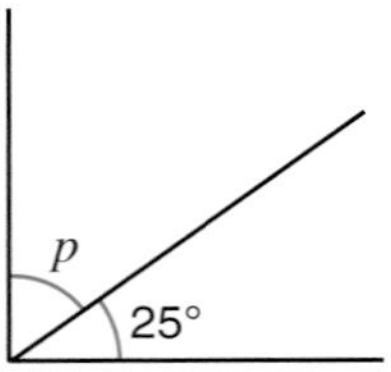


(b)
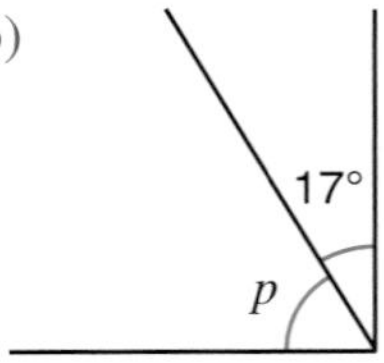


(c)
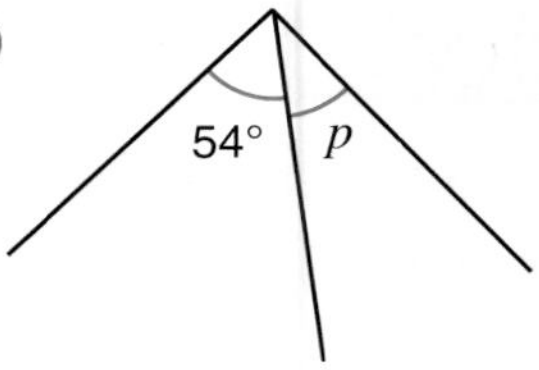


**2.** These angles are supplementary.
Work out the size of angle $q$ in each diagram.

(a)
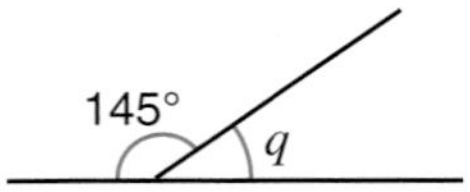


(b)
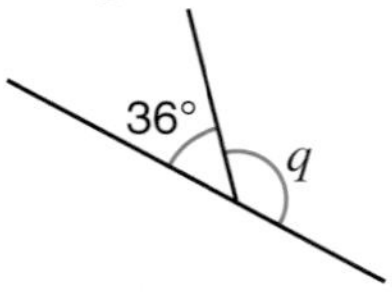


(c)
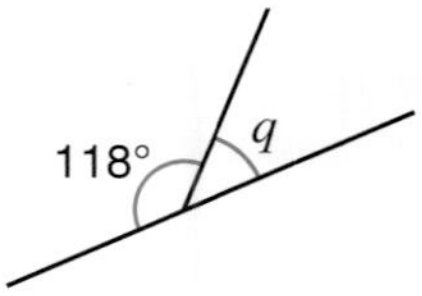


**3.** $PQ$ and $RS$ are straight lines.
Work out the size of angle $x$ in each diagram.

(a)
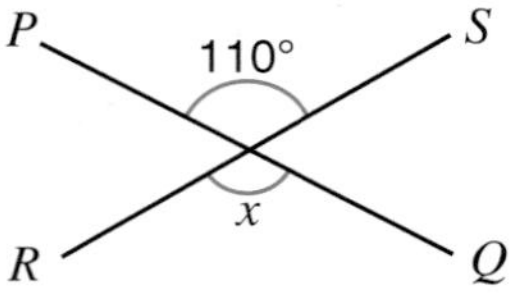


(b)
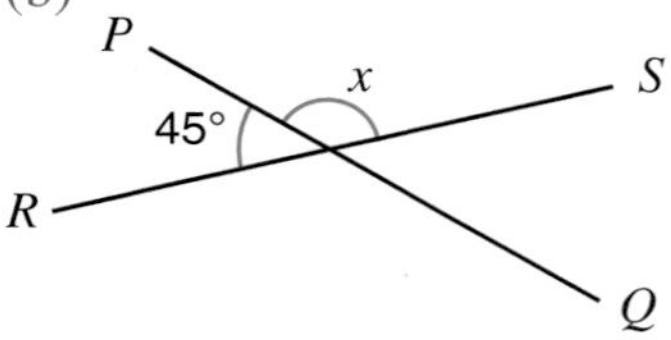


(c)
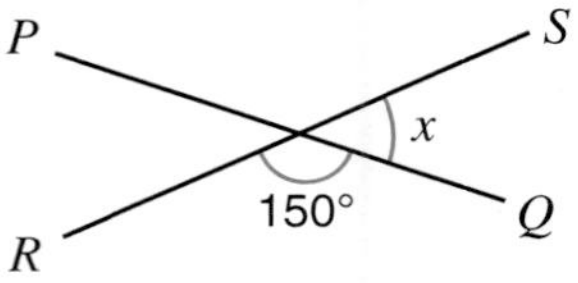


**4.** Work out the size of angle $y$ in each diagram.

(a)
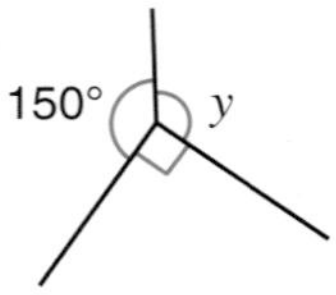


(b)
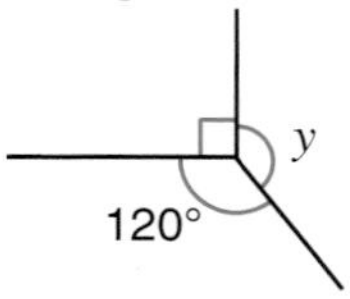


(c)
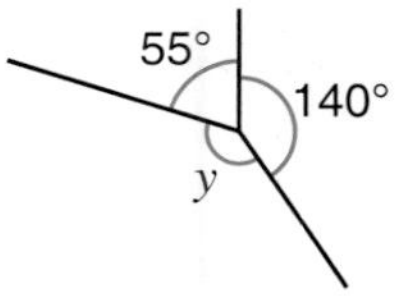


**5.** Work out the size of the angles marked with letters.

(a)
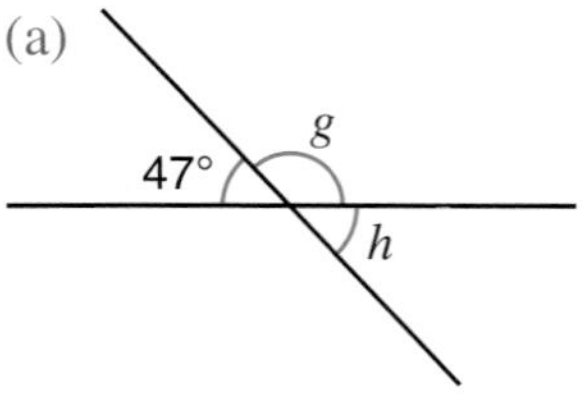


(b)
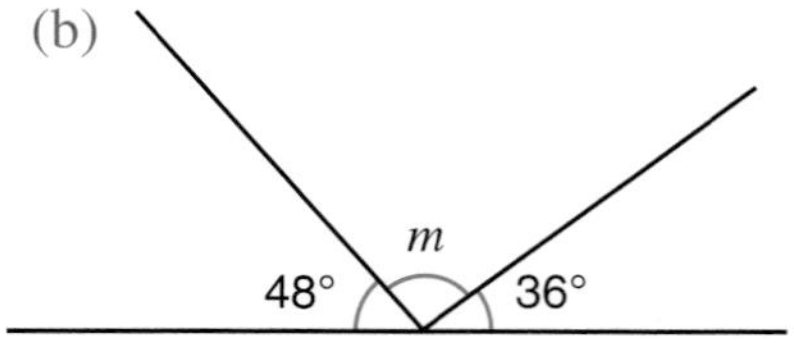


(c)
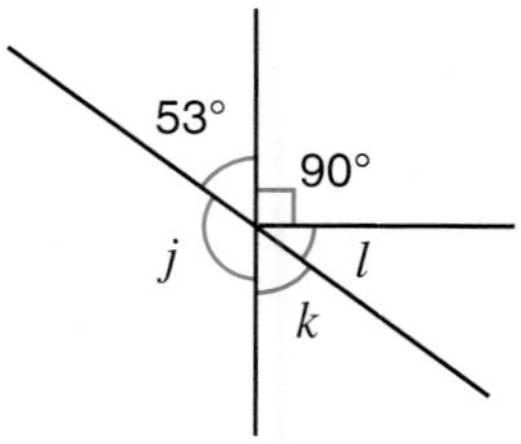


**6.** Work out the size of the angles marked with letters.
Give a reason for each answer.

(a)
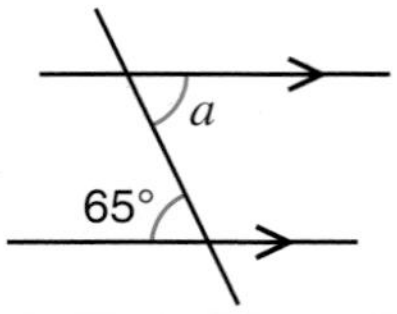


(b)
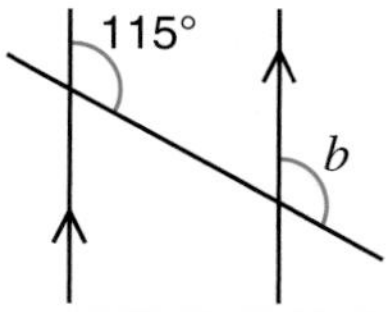


(c)
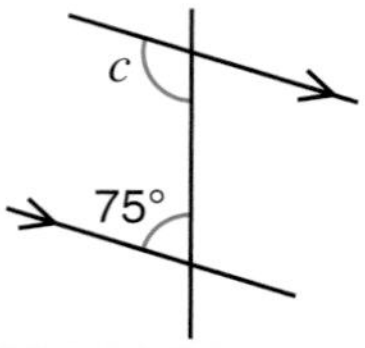


(d)
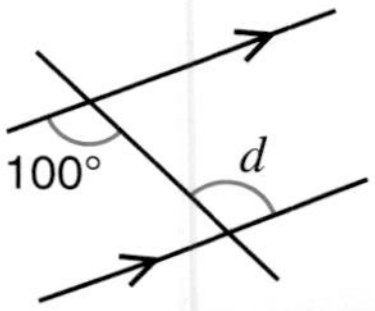

7. Work out the size of the angles marked with letters.

(a)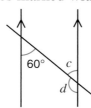

(b)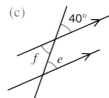

(c)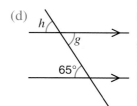

(d)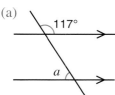

8. Calculate the size of the angles marked with letters.

(a)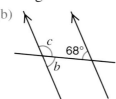

(b)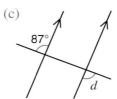

(c)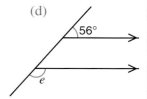

(d)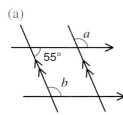

9. Calculate the size of the angles marked with letters.

(a)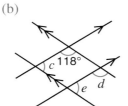

(b)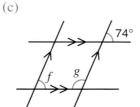

(c)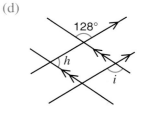

(d)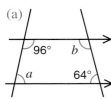

10. Calculate the size of the angles marked with letters.

(a)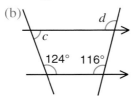

(b)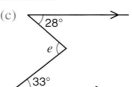

(c)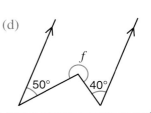

(d)

## Naming angles

Up to now we have used small letters to name angles.
This is not always convenient.
Another method is to use three capital letters.
Lines meet at a point, called a **vertex**.
Where lines meet, angles are formed.

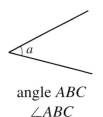

angle $ABC$
$\angle ABC$

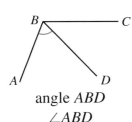

angle $ABD$
$\angle ABD$

$\angle$ means 'angle'.
$\angle CBA$ is the same as $\angle ABC$.
We usually write the letters either side of the vertex (shown by the middle letter) in alphabetical order.

Notice that the middle letter is where the angle is made.

## Practice Exercise 15.2

The diagrams in this exercise have **not** been drawn accurately.

**1.** (a) *PQ* is a
straight line.
Find ∠*QOR*.

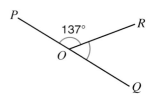

(b) *AB* and *CD* are
straight lines.
Find ∠*AOD*.

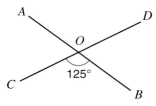

(c) *PQ* and *RT* are
parallel.
Find ∠*XOQ*.

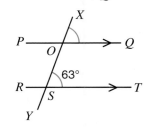

**2.** (a) Find ∠*ABC*.

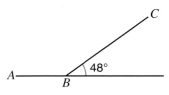

(b) Find ∠*QRS*.

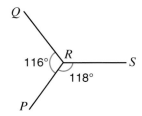

(c) Find ∠*ZYV*.

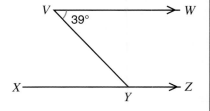

(d) Find ∠*LMN*.

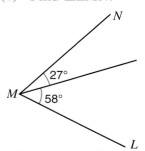

(e) Find ∠*ABC*

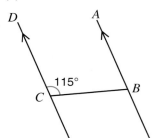

(f) Find ∠*QSP* and ∠*STU*

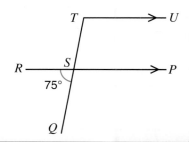

## Triangles

A **triangle** is a shape made by three straight lines.

## The sum of the angles in a triangle

The sum of the three angles in a triangle is 180°.
$$a + b + c = 180°$$
This can easily be proved.

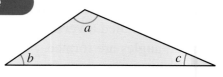

Draw a line which is parallel to one side of the triangle, as shown.

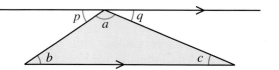

$p + a + q = 180°$ (supplementary angles)
$p = b$ (alternate angles)
$q = c$ (alternate angles)

Substitute $p = b$ and $q = c$ into $p + a + q = 180°$.
So, $b + a + c = 180°$, which can be written as $a + b + c = 180°$.

**Example 2**

Without measuring, work out the size of the angle marked $a$.

The sum of the angles in a triangle is $180°$.
$$a + 102° + 37° = 180°$$
$$a + 139° = 180°$$
$$a = 180° - 139°$$
$$a = 41°$$

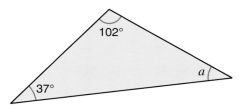

# Exterior angle of a triangle

When one side of a triangle is extended, as shown, the angle formed is called an **exterior angle**.

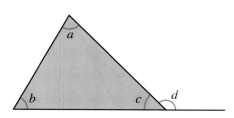

This result can easily be proved.
$a + b + c = 180°$
(sum of angles in a triangle)
$c + d = 180°$
(supplementary angles)
$a + b + c = c + d$
$a + b = d$

In any triangle the exterior angle is always equal to the sum of the two opposite interior angles.
Check this by measuring the angles $a$, $b$ and $d$ in the diagram.

**Example 3**

Find the sizes of the angles marked $a$ and $b$.

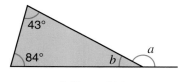

$$a = 84° + 43° \quad (\text{ext. } \angle \text{ of a } \Delta)$$
$$a = 127°$$

$$b + 127° = 180° \quad (\text{supp. } \angle \text{s})$$
$$b = 180° - 127°$$
$$b = 53°$$

**Short but accurate:**
In Geometry we often abbreviate words and use symbols to provide the reader with full details using the minimum amount of writing.

$\Delta$ is short for triangle.
ext. $\angle$ of a $\Delta$ means exterior angle of a triangle.
supp. $\angle$s means supplementary angles.

# Special triangles

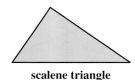

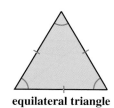

**scalene triangle**

Sides have different lengths.
Angles are all different.

**isosceles triangle**

Two equal sides.
Two angles equal.

**equilateral triangle**

Three equal sides.
All angles are $60°$.

# Naming parts of a triangle

Triangles are named by labelling each vertex with a capital letter.
Triangle *ABC* can be written as Δ*ABC*.

Triangle *ABC* is formed by the sides *AB*, *BC* and *AC*.
Triangles and lines are often named in alphabetical order.
Δ*ABC* is the same as Δ*BCA*.

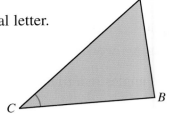

The angles of a triangle are also described in terms of the vertices.
For example, the angle marked on the diagram is angle *ACB* or ∠*ACB*.
The middle letter is the vertex where the angle is made.

## Practice Exercise 15.3

The diagrams in this exercise have **not** been drawn accurately.

1. Without measuring, work out the size of the third angle in each of these triangles.

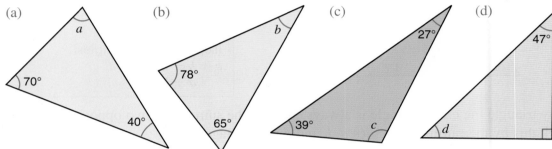

2. The diagram shows a triangle with one side extended.
   Explain why angle *x* is 35°.

3. Work out the size of the marked angles.

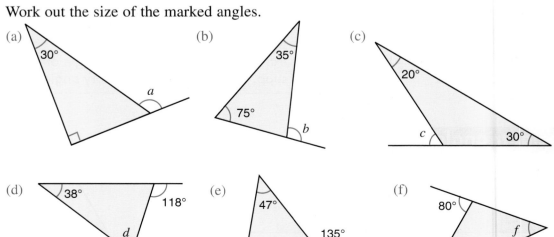

4. Work out the size of the marked angles.

(a)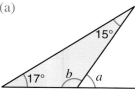

(b)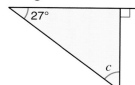

(c)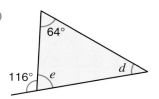

5. In the diagram, $AE = BE = BD = DE$ and $CDE$ is a straight line.

(a) What special name is given to $\triangle ABE$?

(b) What special name is given to $\triangle BDE$?

(c) Triangle $BDC$ is scalene.
Give the three-letter name of another scalene triangle in the diagram.

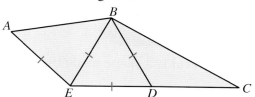

6. On squared paper, draw an isosceles triangle with coordinates:
$A(3, 3)$, $B(9, 3)$ and $C(6, 10)$.
Which two sides are equal?
Which two angles are equal?

7. Work out the size of angle $a$ in each triangle.

(a)

(b)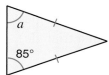

(c)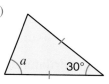

(d)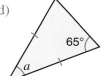

8. Work out the size of the angles marked with letters.

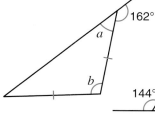

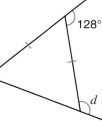

9. In the diagram $AD = DB = BC = CD$.

(a) What type of triangle is $BCD$?

(b) What is the size of angle $BDC$?

(c) Work out the size of angle $ABC$.

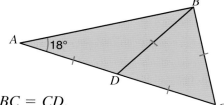

10. In the diagram $AB = BD = DA$ and $BC = CD$.
$CD$ is extended to $E$.

(a) What type of triangle is $BCD$?

(b) What is the size of angle $BDC$?

(c) Work out the size of angle $ADE$.

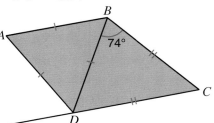

**11.** Work out the size of the required angles.

(a)
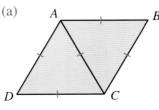

Find $\angle BCD$.

(b)
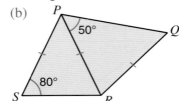

Find $\angle PRQ$ and $\angle QRS$.

(c)
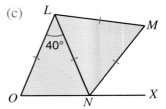

$ONX$ is a straight line.
Find $\angle MNX$.

## Quadrilaterals

A **quadrilateral** is a shape made by four straight lines.

## Sum of the angles of a quadrilateral

The sum of the four angles of a quadrilateral is $360°$.
$$a + b + c + d = 360°$$

This result can easily be proved.
Split the quadrilateral into two triangles $A$ and $B$, as shown.

In triangle $A$: $\quad p + q + r = 180°$   (sum of angles in a triangle)
In triangle $B$: $\quad w + x + y = 180°$   (sum of angles in a triangle)

The sum of the angles of the quadrilateral is given by:
$$p + q + r + w + x + y = 180° + 180°$$
$$p + q + r + w + x + y = 360°$$

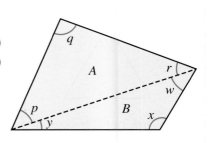

## Special quadrilaterals

### Square

Four equal sides.
Opposite sides parallel.
Angles of 90°.
Diagonals bisect each other at 90°.

### Rhombus

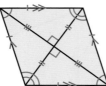

Four equal sides.
Opposite sides parallel.
Opposite angles equal.
Diagonals bisect each other at 90°.

### Parallelogram

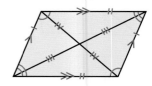

Opposite sides equal
and parallel.
Opposite angles equal.
Diagonals bisect each other.

### Kite

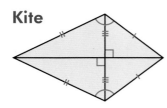

Two pairs of adjacent sides equal.
One pair of opposite angles equal.
One diagonal bisects the other at 90°.

### Rectangle

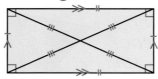

Opposite sides equal and parallel.
Angles of 90°.
Diagonals bisect each other.

### Trapezium

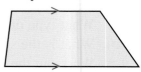

One pair of parallel sides.

**Example 4**

*PQRS* is a parallelogram.
Work out the size of the angle marked *x*.

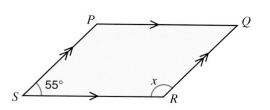

The opposite angles of a parallelogram are equal.
$$55° + 55° + x + x = 360°$$
$$110° + 2x = 360°$$
$$2x = 360° - 110°$$
$$2x = 250°$$
$$x = 125°$$

## Practice Exercise 15.4

The diagrams in this exercise have **not** been drawn accurately.

1. Work out the size of angle *a* in each of these quadrilaterals.

(a)    (b) 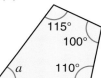   (c) 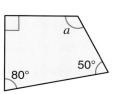   (d)

2. Work out the size of the angles marked with letters in each of these rectangles.

(a) 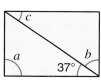   (b)    (c)    (d)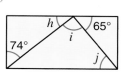

3. Work out the size of the angles marked with letters in each of these parallelograms.

(a) 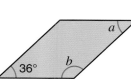   (b)    (c) 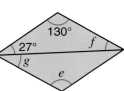   (d)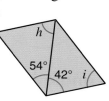

4. Work out the size of the angles marked with letters in each of these kites.

(a)    (b) 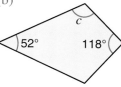   (c) 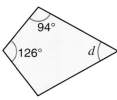   (d)

5. The diagram shows a trapezium.
   Find the size of angle *a* and angle *b*.

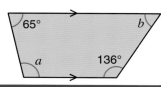

**6.** WXYZ is an isosceles trapezium.
WZ = XY.
Work out the size of angle WXY and angle XYZ.

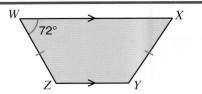

**7.** Work out the size of the angles marked with letters.

(a)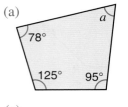

(b)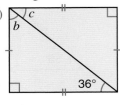

(c)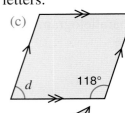

(d)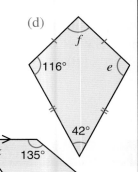

(e)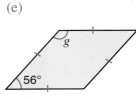

(f)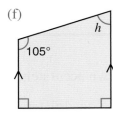

(g)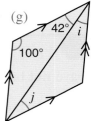

(h)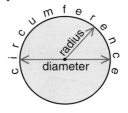

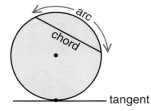

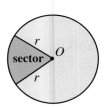

**8.** OABC is a kite. O is the point (0, 0), B (5, 5), C (3, 1).
Find the coordinates of A.

**9.** STUV is a square with S at (1, 3) and U at (5, 3).
Find the coordinates of T and V.

## Circle terms and properties

A **circle** is the shape drawn by keeping a pencil the same distance from a fixed point on a piece of paper. Here is a reminder of some of the terms that are used about circles.

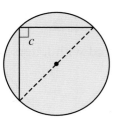

## The angle in a semicircle is a right angle

Angles which are:
   at the circumference,
    standing on a diameter,
are equal to 90°.

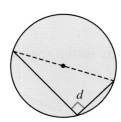

$c = 90°$
$d = 90°$

## A tangent is perpendicular to the radius of a circle

The diagram shows a tangent drawn from a point, $P$, to touch the circle, centre $O$, at $T$.
$\angle PTO = 90°$.

A **tangent** to a circle is a straight line which touches the circumference at one point only. A tangent is perpendicular to the radius at the point of contact.

**Example 5**

In the diagram, $O$ is the centre of the circle.
$AB$ is a diameter.
Work out the size of the marked angles.

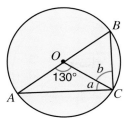

Triangle $OAC$ is isosceles.
$\angle OAC = \angle OCA$
$a = (180° - 130°) \div 2$
$a = 50° \div 2$
$a = 25°$
$\angle ACB = 90°$ (angle in a semicircle)
$b = 90° - 25°$
$b = 65°$

$OA = OC$ = radius of circle.
So, $\triangle OAC$ is isosceles.

**Example 6**

In the diagram, $O$ is the centre of the circle.
$TQ$ is a tangent to the circle at $P$.
$PR$ is a diameter of the circle.
Angle $PRS = 35°$.
Calculate the size of angle $QPS$.

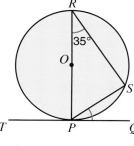

$\angle PSR = 90°$ (angle in a semicircle)
$\angle SPR = 180° - 35° - 90°$ (sum of $\angle$s in a $\triangle = 180°$)
$\angle SPR = 55°$
$\angle QPS = 90° - 55°$ (tangent perpendicular to radius)
$\angle QPS = 35°$

**Practice** Exercise **15.5**

1. The following diagrams show triangles drawn in semicircles.
   Work out the size of the marked angles.

   (a)    (b) 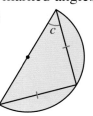  (c) 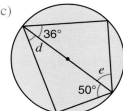  (d)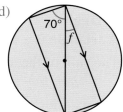

2. $O$ is the centre of the circle.
   Work out the size of the marked angles.

   (a)  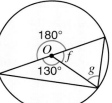  (b) 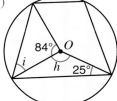  (c)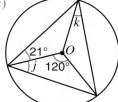

**3.** *O* is the centre of the circle. A tangent has been drawn to the circle.
Work out the size of the marked angles.

(a)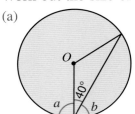

(b)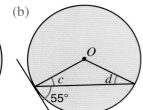

(c)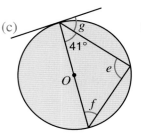

(d)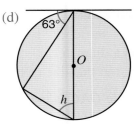

(e)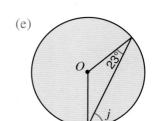

(f)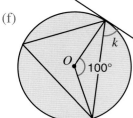

(g)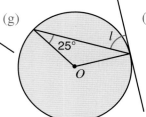

(h)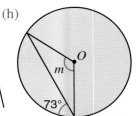

## Key Points

▶ **Angle properties**

| Angles at point | Complementary angles | Supplementary angles | Vertically opposite angles |
|---|---|---|---|
| 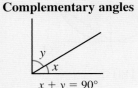 | | | 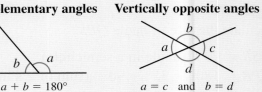 |
| $a + b + c = 360°$ | $x + y = 90°$ | $a + b = 180°$ | $a = c$ and $b = d$ |

▶ **Parallel lines and angles**

**Parallel lines** are lines which never meet.

| Corresponding angles | Alternate angles | Allied angles |
|---|---|---|
|  |  |  |
| $a = c$ | $b = c$ | $b + d = 180°$ |

> Arrowheads are used to show that lines are **parallel**.

▶ **Triangle**

A **triangle** is a shape made by three straight sides.

▶ The sum of the angles in a triangle is 180°.

$$a + b + c = 180°$$

▶ The exterior angle is equal to the sum of the two opposite interior angles.

$$a + b = d$$

▶ Types of triangle:

Scalene     Isosceles     Equilateral

> A **sketch** is used when an accurate drawing is not required. Dashes across lines show sides that are equal in length. Equal angles are marked using arcs.

▶ A **quadrilateral** is a shape made by four straight lines.
▶ The sum of the angles in a quadrilateral is 360°.
$$a + b + c + d = 360°$$
▶ Facts about these special quadrilaterals:

rectangle    square    parallelogram    rhombus    trapezium    kite

| Quadrilateral | Sides | Angles | Diagonals |
|---|---|---|---|
| Rectangle | Opposite sides equal and parallel | All 90° | Bisect each other |
| Square | 4 equal sides, opposite sides parallel | All 90° | Bisect each other at 90° |
| Parallelogram | Opposite sides equal and parallel | Opposite angles equal | Bisect each other |
| Rhombus | 4 equal sides, opposite sides parallel | Opposite angles equal | Bisect each other at 90° |
| Trapezium | 1 pair of parallel sides | | |
| Kite | 2 pairs of adjacent sides equal | 1 pair of opposite angles equal | One bisects the other at 90° |

▶ **Circle**

A **circle** is the shape drawn by keeping a pencil the same distance from a fixed point on a piece of paper.

▶ You should know the meaning of the words shown on the diagrams below.

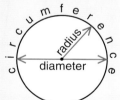 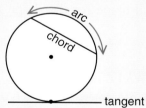 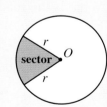

▶ You should know these **circle properties**.

The angle in a semicircle is a right angle.

A tangent is perpendicular to the radius at the point of contact.

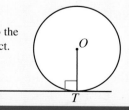

## Review Exercise 15

1. Work out the size of the angles marked with letters. Give a reason for each answer.

(a)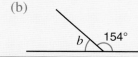

(b)

(c)

**2.** In the diagram the line *AB* is parallel to the line *CD*.

(a) Work out the size of angle *p*.

(b) Work out the size of angle *q*.

(c) Work out the size of angle *r*.

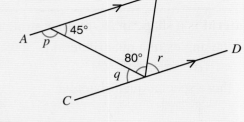

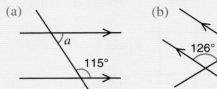

**3.** Work out the size of angle *a*.
Give a reason for your answer.

**4.** Work out the size of the angles marked with letters.

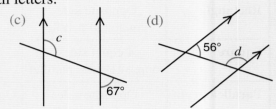

(a)  (b)  (c)  (d)

**5.** Work out the size of the angles marked with letters.

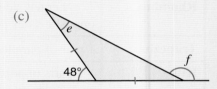

(a)  (b)  (c)

**6.** Triangle *PQR* is isosceles with angle *QPR* = angle *PRQ*.
*P* is the point (3, 5) and *R* is the point (9, 5).
Give the coordinates of the two possible positions of *Q*
so that angle *PQR* is a right angle.

**7.** (a) What is the mathematical name for the shape *PQRS*?

(b) Find the size of ∠*PSR*.

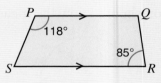

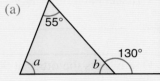

**8.** *WXYZ* is a rectangle.
Calculate angles *a*, *b*, *c* and *d*.

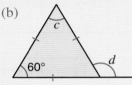

**9.** Work out the size of the marked angles.
*O* is the centre of the circle.

(a)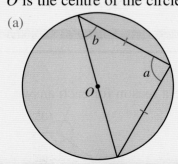

(b)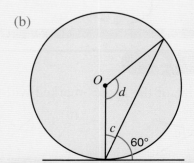

# 16 Trigonometry

We use **trigonometry** to find the lengths of sides and the sizes of angles in right-angled triangles.
We already know that the longest side of a right-angled triangle is called the **hypotenuse**.
In order to understand the relationships between sides and angles the
other sides of the triangle also need to be named.
The **opposite** side is the side directly opposite the angle being
used and the **adjacent** side is the side next to the angle.

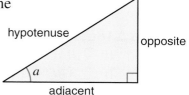

## The sine ratio

For any right-angled triangle: $\sin a = \dfrac{\text{opposite}}{\text{hypotenuse}}$

The sine ratio links three pieces of information:
    the size of an **angle**,
    the length of the side **opposite** the angle,
    the length of the **hypotenuse**.
If we are given the values for two of these we can find the value of the third.

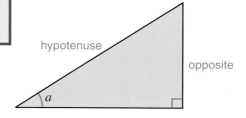

### Finding the length of the opposite side

**Example 1**

Find the height of a kite when it is flying at an angle of 40° and the kite string is 12 m long.
Give the answer correct to 2 decimal places.

$\sin a = \dfrac{\text{opp}}{\text{hyp}}$

Substitute known values.

$\sin 40° = \dfrac{h}{12}$

Multiply both sides by 12.

$h = 12 \times \sin 40°$

| Mathematical shorthand: | |
|---|---|
| Word | Abbreviation |
| sine | sin |
| opposite | opp |
| hypotenuse | hyp |

Using your calculator, press: [ 1 ] [ 2 ] [ × ] [ sin ] [ 4 ] [ 0 ] [ = ]

    $h = 7.713\ldots$
    $h = 7.71$ m, correct to 2 d.p.    The height of the kite is 7.71 m, correct to 2 d.p.

## Practice Exercise 16.1

1. Find the height, $h$, of these kites.
   Give your answers correct to 2 decimal places.

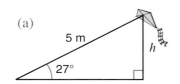

(a)   5 m   $h$   27°

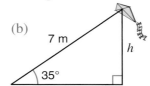

(b)   7 m   $h$   35°

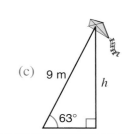

(c)   9 m   $h$   63°

**2.** Calculate the lengths marked $x$.
Give your answers correct to 1 decimal place.

(a)

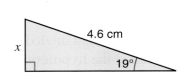

(b)

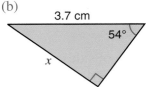

(c)

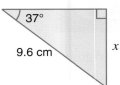

**3.** In $\triangle ABC$, angle $ACB = 90°$.
(a) If $\angle BAC = 47.5°$ and $AB = 4.6$ m, find $BC$.
(b) If $\angle ABC = 67.4°$ and $AB = 12.4$ m, find $AC$.
Give your answers correct to 1 decimal place.

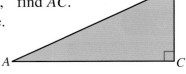

**4.** In $\triangle ABC$, angle $ACB = 90°$.
(a) If $\angle BAC = 15.8°$ and $AC = 17.4$ cm, find $BC$.
(b) If $\angle BAC = 35°$ and $AB = 8.5$ cm, find the size of $\angle ACB$ and then find $AB$.
Give your answers correct to 1 decimal place.

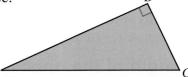

## Finding an angle

If you are given the sine of an angle and asked to find the angle, use the inverse sine function, $\sin^{-1}$, on your calculator.

Using your calculator, press:
The display should read 0.5.

Clear the display and press:
*What do you notice?*

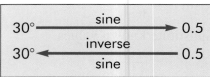

### Example 2

Find the size of angle $a$ when the kite string is 12 m long
and the kite is flying 7 m above the ground.
Give the answer correct to one decimal place.

$\sin a = \dfrac{\text{opp}}{\text{hyp}}$

Substitute known values.

$\sin a° = \dfrac{7}{12}$

$a = \sin^{-1}\dfrac{7}{12}$

Using your calculator, press:

$a = 35.685\ldots$

$a = 35.7°$, correct to 1 d.p.

## Practice Exercise 16.2

1. Find the size of angle *a* for each of these kites.
   Give your answers correct to one decimal place.

   (a)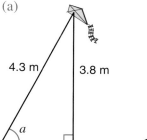
   4.3 m    3.8 m    *a*

   (b)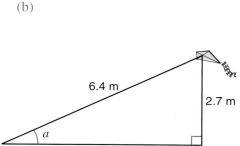
   6.4 m    2.7 m    *a*

   (c)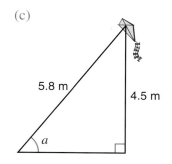
   5.8 m    4.5 m    *a*

2. Find the size of angle *x* in each of these triangles.
   Give your answers correct to one decimal place.

   (a)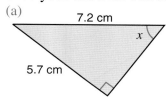
   7.2 cm    *x*    5.7 cm

   (b)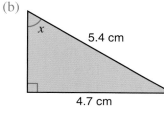
   *x*    5.4 cm    4.7 cm

   (c)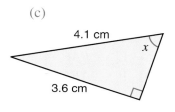
   4.1 cm    *x*    3.6 cm

3. In Δ*PQR*, angle *PQR* = 90°.
   (a) If *QR* = 4 m    and    *PR* = 10 m,    find the size of ∠*QPR*.
   (b) If *PQ* = 4.7 cm   and    *PR* = 5.2 cm,   find the size of ∠*PRQ*.
   (c) If *QR* = 7.2 m    and    *PR* = 19.4 m,   find the size of ∠*QPR*.
   (d) If *PQ* = 3.7 cm   and    *PR* = 9.1 cm,   find the size of ∠*QRP*
        and then find the size of ∠*QPR*.
   Give your answers correct to one decimal place.

## Finding the hypotenuse

### Example 3

Find the length of the string, *l*, when a kite is 6 m high
and the string makes an angle of 50° with the ground.
Give the answer correct to 2 decimal places.

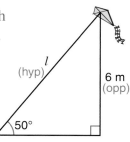

$$\sin a = \frac{\text{opp}}{\text{hyp}}$$

Substitute known values.

$$\sin 50° = \frac{6}{l}$$

Multiply both sides by *l*.

$$l \times \sin 50° = 6$$

Divide both sides by sin 50°.

$$l = \frac{6}{\sin 50°}$$

Using your calculator,

press: [6] [÷] [sin] [5] [0] [=]

$$l = 7.832\ldots$$
$$l = 7.83 \text{ m, correct to 2 d.p.}$$

The length of the string is 7.83 m, correct to 2 d.p.

1.  Find the lengths, *l*, of these kite strings.
    Give your answers correct to 1 decimal place.

    (a)

    (b)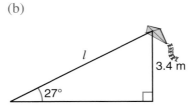

    (c)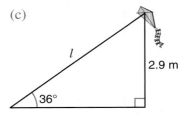

2.  Calculate the length of side *x* in each of these triangles.
    Give your answers correct to two decimal places.

    (a)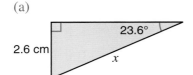

    (b)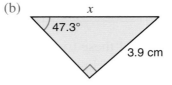

    (c)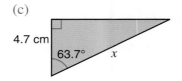

3.  In $\triangle ABC$, angle $ACB = 90°$.
    (a)  If $\angle BAC = 36.2°$ and $BC = 4.5$ m, find $AB$.
    (b)  If $\angle ABC = 64.7°$ and $AC = 15.8$ m, find $AB$.
    (c)  If $\angle BAC = 12.7°$ and $BC = 14.7$ m, find $AB$.
    (d)  If $\angle BAC = 72.8°$ and $AC = 7.6$ m,
         find the size of $\angle ABC$ and then find $AB$.
    Give your answers correct to 2 decimal places.

    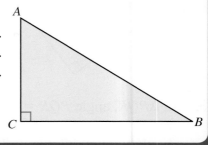

## The cosine ratio

For any right-angled triangle:
$$\cos a = \frac{\text{adjacent}}{\text{hypotenuse}}$$

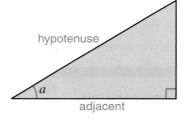

The cosine ratio links three pieces of information:
    the size of an **angle**,
    the length of the side **adjacent** to the angle,
    the length of the **hypotenuse**.

If we are given the values of two of
these we can find the value of the third.

## The tangent ratio

For any right-angled triangle:
$$\tan a = \frac{\text{opposite}}{\text{adjacent}}$$

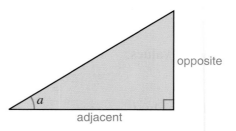

The tangent ratio links three pieces of information:
    the size of an **angle**,
    the length of the side **opposite** to the angle,
    the length of the side **adjacent** to the angle.

If we are given the values of two of
these we can find the value of the third.

## Example 4

Write down the sin, cos and tan ratios
for angle $a$ in the triangle.

$$\sin a = \frac{\text{opp}}{\text{hyp}} = \frac{8}{17}$$

$$\cos a = \frac{\text{adj}}{\text{hyp}} = \frac{15}{17}$$

$$\tan a = \frac{\text{opp}}{\text{adj}} = \frac{8}{15}$$

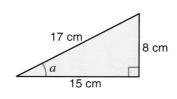

| Mathematical shorthand: | |
|---|---|
| Word | Abbreviation |
| adjacent | adj |
| opposite | opp |
| hypotenuse | hyp |
| sine | sin |
| cosine | cos |
| tangent | tan |

# How to select and use the correct ratio

There are only 3 different types of question for each of the ratios.
Selecting the correct ratio is most important.
To do this:

1. Go to the angle you know (or want to find).

2. Name sides (opp, adj, hyp).
   If you are trying to find the length of a side, name that side first together with one other side
   of known length.
   If you are trying to find the size of an angle, name two sides of known length.

3. Select the correct ratio and write it down.

   $$\sin a = \frac{\text{opp}}{\text{hyp}} \qquad \cos a = \frac{\text{adj}}{\text{hyp}} \qquad \tan a = \frac{\text{opp}}{\text{adj}}$$

   One way to remember the ratios is to use the initial letters, SOHCAHTOA.
   You may know another method.

4. Substitute known values from the question.

5. Rearrange to isolate the angle, or side, you are trying to find.

6. Use your calculator to find the size of the angle, or side, writing down more figures than
   you need for the final answer.

7. Correct to the required degree of accuracy.

8. Give the answer, stating the degree of approximation and giving the correct units.
   When giving the answer to a problem you should use a short sentence.

## Example 5

Find the length, $h$, giving the answer to
2 decimal places.

$$\tan a = \frac{\text{opp}}{\text{adj}}$$

Substitute known values.

$$\tan 28° = \frac{h}{12.4}$$

Multiply both sides by 12.4.

$$h = 12.4 \times \tan 28°$$

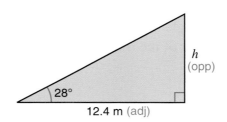

Using your calculator,

press: `1` `2` `.` `4` `×` `tan` `2` `8` `=`

$h = 6.593\ldots$

$h = 6.59\,\text{m}$, correct to 2 d.p.

## Example 6

Find the size of angle $a$, correct to one decimal place.

$$\cos a = \frac{\text{adj}}{\text{hyp}}$$

Substitute known values.

$$\cos a° = \frac{11}{16}$$

$$a = \cos^{-1} \frac{11}{16}$$

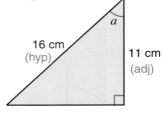

Using your calculator, press: [cos⁻¹] [(] [1] [1] [÷] [1] [6] [)] [=]

$$a = 46.56…$$
$$a = 46.6°, \text{ correct to 1 d.p.}$$

## Practice Exercise 16.4

1. Write down the sin, cos and tan ratios for angle $p$ in each of the following triangles.

(a)

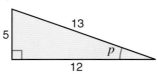

(b)

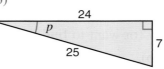

(c)

2. By choosing the correct ratio, calculate angle $p$ in each of the following triangles. Give your answers correct to one decimal place.

(a)

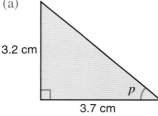

(b)

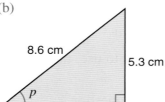

(c)

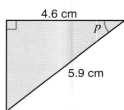

(d)

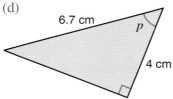

(e)

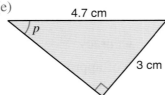

(f)

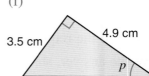

3. An equilateral triangle has sides of length 5 cm. Calculate the height of the triangle.

4. An isosceles triangle has sides of length 10 cm, 10 cm and 6 cm. Calculate the angles of the triangle.

5. By choosing the correct ratio, calculate side *a* in each of the following triangles.

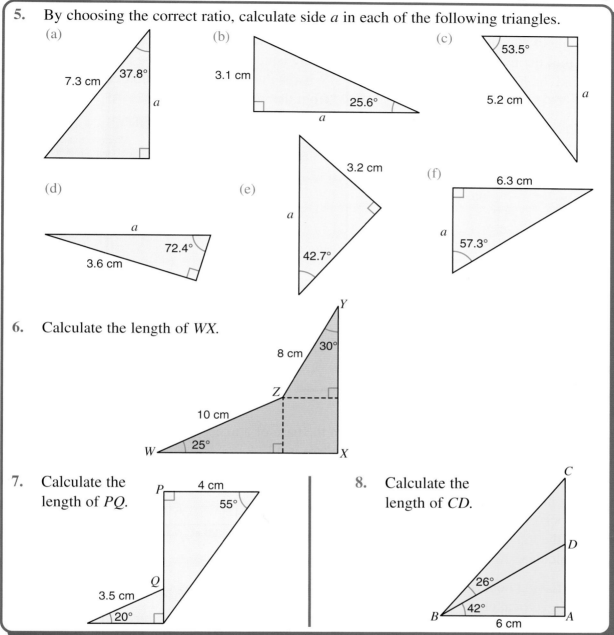

(a) 7.3 cm   37.8°   *a*

(b) 3.1 cm   25.6°   *a*

(c) 53.5°   5.2 cm   *a*

(d) *a*   72.4°   3.6 cm

(e) 3.2 cm   *a*   42.7°

(f) 6.3 cm   *a*   57.3°

6. Calculate the length of *WX*.

Y   30°   8 cm   Z   10 cm   W   25°   X

7. Calculate the length of *PQ*.

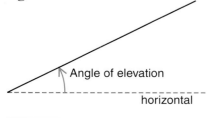

P   4 cm   55°   Q   3.5 cm   20°

8. Calculate the length of *CD*.

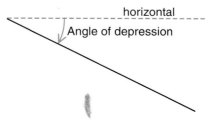

C   D   26°   42°   B   6 cm   A

## Angles of elevation and depression

When we look **up** from the horizontal the angle we turn through is called an **angle of elevation**.

Angle of elevation
horizontal

When we look **down** from the horizontal the angle we turn through is called an **angle of depression**.

horizontal
Angle of depression

## Example 7

From a point on the ground, 30 m from the base of a pylon, the angle of elevation to the top of the pylon is 50°.
Find the height of the pylon.

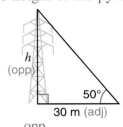

$$\tan a = \frac{\text{opp}}{\text{adj}}$$

$$\tan 50° = \frac{h}{30}$$

$$h = 30 \times \tan 50°$$
$$h = 35.75...$$
$$h = 35.8 \text{ m, correct to 1 d.p.}$$

The height of the pylon is 35.8 m, correct to 1 d.p.

## Example 8

Staten Island Ferry is 270 m away from the base of the Statue of Liberty.
The ferry can be seen from a viewing point in the lantern, 85 m above the ground.
What is the angle of depression to the ferry from the viewing point?

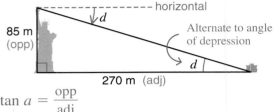

$$\tan a = \frac{\text{opp}}{\text{adj}}$$

$$\tan d° = \frac{85}{270}$$

$$d = \tan^{-1} \frac{85}{270}$$
$$d = 17.47...$$
$$d = 17.5°, \text{ correct to 1 d.p.}$$

The angle of depression to the ferry from the viewing point is 17.5°, correct to 1 d.p.

## Practice Exercise 16.5

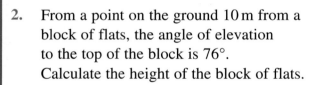

1. From a point on the ground 20 m from the base of a tree, the angle of elevation to the top of the tree is 47°.
   Calculate the height of the tree.

2. From a point on the ground 10 m from a block of flats, the angle of elevation to the top of the block is 76°.
   Calculate the height of the block of flats.

3. A fishing boat is 200 m from the bottom of a vertical cliff.
   From the top of the cliff the angle of depression to the fishing boat is 34°.
   (a) Calculate the height of the cliff.
   (b) A buoy is 100 m from the bottom of the cliff.
       Calculate the angle of depression to the buoy from the top of the cliff.

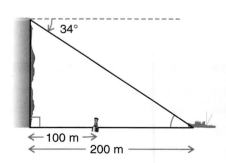

4. A tree, 6 m high, casts a shadow of 4.8 m on horizontal ground.
   Calculate the angle of elevation to the sun.

5. From a point, A, on the ground, the angle of elevation to a hot air balloon is 9°.
   The balloon is 150 m above the ground.
   Calculate the distance from A to the balloon.

## Key Points

▶ **Trigonometry** is used to find the lengths of sides and the sizes of angles in right-angled triangles.

▶ You should know the **sine**, **cosine** and **tangent** ratios.

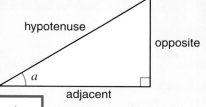

$$\sin a = \frac{\text{opposite}}{\text{hypotenuse}} \qquad \cos a = \frac{\text{adjacent}}{\text{hypotenuse}} \qquad \tan a = \frac{\text{opposite}}{\text{adjacent}}$$

Each ratio links the size of an angle with the lengths of two sides in a right-angled triangle. If we are given the values for two of these we can find the value of the third.

▶ When we look **up** from the horizontal the angle we turn through is called the **angle of elevation**.

▶ When we look **down** from the horizontal the angle we turn through is called the **angle of depression**.

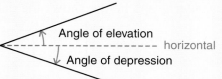

## Review Exercise 16

1. Find the lengths or angles, marked by letters, in these right-angled triangles.

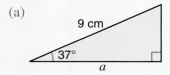

(a) 9 cm, 37°, a

(b) 8 cm, 7 cm, b

(c) 10 cm, 48°, c

2. Triangle *ABC* is isosceles. Angle *BAC* = 52°. *AB* = 12 cm.
   (a) Find the height, *BE*, of the isosceles triangle.
   (b) Find the length of *AE*.
   (c) Find the perimeter of the triangle, *ABC*.

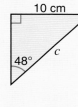

3. Calculate (a) the length of *AC*,
              (b) the length of *CE*.

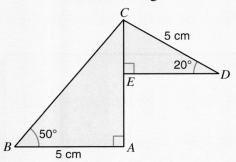

4. Calculate (a) the length of *RQ*,
              (b) angle *SPR*.

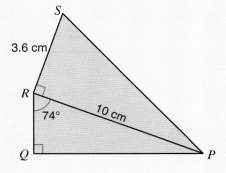

5. A cat is on the ground 25 m from the foot of a house.
   A bird is perched on the gutter of the house 15 m from the ground.
   Calculate the angle of elevation from the cat to the bird.

# 17 Scatter Graphs

When we investigate statistical information, we often find there are connections between sets of data, for example, height and weight. In general, taller people weigh more than shorter people. The table shows the weights and heights of 10 boys.

| Weight (kg) | 36.5 | 38.0 | 38.5 | 39.5 | 40.0 | 41.0 | 42.5 | 42.5 | 44.0 | 44.0 |
|-------------|------|------|------|------|------|------|------|------|------|------|
| Height (cm) | 123  | 124  | 127  | 130  | 136  | 136  | 135  | 140  | 142  | 146  |

To see if there is a connection between two sets of data we can plot a **scatter graph**.
The scatter graph below shows the data given in the table.

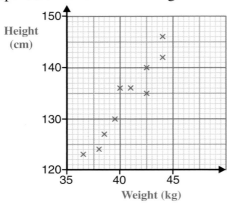

Each cross plotted on the graph represents the weight and height of one boy.

The diagram shows that taller boys generally weigh more than shorter boys.

## Correlation

The relationship between two sets of data is called **correlation**.
In general, the scatter graph of the heights and weights shows that as height increases, weight increases.
This type of relationship shows there is a **positive correlation** between height and weight.
But if as the value of one variable increases the value of the other variable decreases, then there is a **negative correlation** between the variables.
When no linear relationship exists between two variables there is **zero correlation**.
This does not necessarily imply "no relationship", but merely "no linear relationship".
The following graphs show types of correlation.

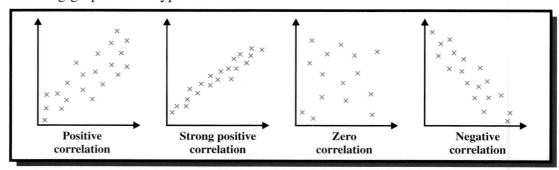

Positive correlation     Strong positive correlation     Zero correlation     Negative correlation

As points get closer to a straight line the stronger the correlation.
**Perfect correlation** is when all the points lie on a straight line.

**Practice** Exercise **17.1**

1.  The scatter graph shows the marks obtained by a group of students in a test in English and a test in French.

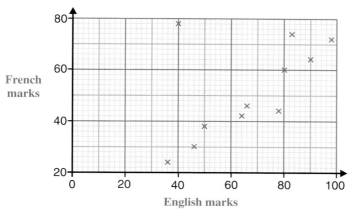

(a) Janice got the top mark in English. What mark did she get in French?
(b) The results of one student look out of place.
    (i)  What marks did the student get in English and in French?
    (ii) Give a possible reason why this student has different results from the rest of the group.

2.  The scatter graph shows the age and mileage of a number of cars.

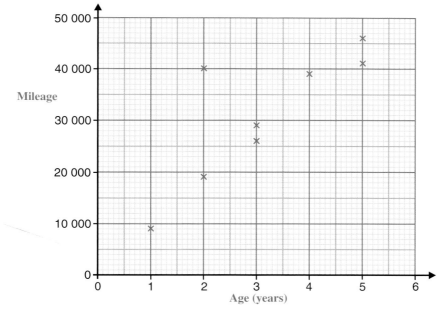

(a) One of these cars is 4 years old. What is the mileage of this car?
(b) Describe the relationship shown by the scatter graph.
(c) The age and mileage of one of these cars looks out of place.
    (i)  What is the age and mileage of this car?
    (ii) Give a possible reason why the results for this car are different from the rest of the group.

**3.** (a) Which of these graphs shows the strongest positive correlation?
(b) Which of these graphs shows perfect negative correlation?
(c) Which of these graphs shows the weakest correlation?

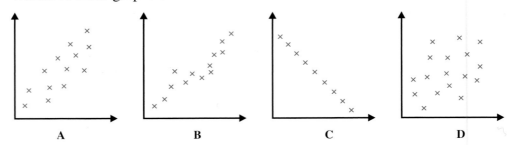

A        B        C        D

**4.** The table shows the distance travelled and time taken by motorists on different journeys.

| Distance travelled (km) | 30 | 45 | 48 | 80 | 90 | 100 | 125 |
|---|---|---|---|---|---|---|---|
| Time taken (hours) | 0.6 | 0.9 | 1.2 | 1.2 | 1.3 | 2.0 | 1.5 |

(a) Draw a scatter graph for the data.
(b) What do you notice about distance travelled and time taken?
(c) Give one reason why the distance travelled and the time taken are not perfectly correlated.

**5.** Tyres were collected from a number of different cars.
The table shows the distance travelled and depth of tread for each tyre.

| Distance travelled (1000 km) | 4 | 5 | 9 | 10 | 12 | 15 | 18 | 25 | 30 |
|---|---|---|---|---|---|---|---|---|---|
| Depth of tread (mm) | 9.2 | 8.4 | 7.6 | 8 | 6.5 | 7.4 | 7 | 6.2 | 5 |

(a) Draw a scatter graph for the data.
(b) What do you notice about the distance travelled and the depth of tread?
(c) Explain how you can tell that the relationship is quite strong.

**6.** Describe the type of correlation you would expect between:
(a) the age of a car and its secondhand selling price,
(b) the heights of children and their ages,
(c) the shoe sizes of children and the distance they travel to school,
(d) the number of cars on the road and the number of road accidents,
(e) the engine size of a car and the number of kilometres it can travel on one litre of fuel.

**7.** Some students took a mathematics test and a test in Spanish.
The table shows their results.

| Mark in mathematics test | 10 | 15 | 18 | 20 | 26 | 30 | 34 | 36 | 46 | 51 |
|---|---|---|---|---|---|---|---|---|---|---|
| Mark in Spanish test | 15 | 50 | 30 | 12 | 40 | 19 | 28 | 48 | 21 | 42 |

(a) Plot a scatter graph of this information.
(b) Describe the correlation between the marks in the mathematics test and the marks in the Spanish test.

## Line of best fit

When there is a relationship between two sets of data, a **line of best fit** can be drawn on the scatter graph.

The scatter graph of heights and weights has been redrawn below and a **line of best fit** has been drawn, by eye, to show the relationship between height and weight.

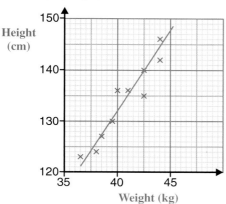

Draw the best line you can.
Place your ruler on the graph and try it in various positions.
Aim for a slope which matches the general slope of the points, where the points are balanced with some on both sides of the line.
The line of best fit does not have to go through the origin of the graph.
The **slope** of the line of best fit shows the **trend** of data.

Where there is a relationship between the two sets of data the line of best fit can be used to estimate other values.
A boy is 132 cm tall.
Using the line of best fit an estimate of his weight is 40 kg.
In a similar way we can use the line to estimate the height of a boy when we know his weight.
*A boy weighs 43 kg. Estimate his height.*

## Practice Exercise 17.2

1. The table shows the ages and weights of ten babies.

| Age (weeks) | 2 | 4 | 9 | 7 | 13 | 5 | 6 | 1 | 10 | 12 |
|---|---|---|---|---|---|---|---|---|---|---|
| Weight (kg) | 3.5 | 3.3 | 4.2 | 4.7 | 5 | 3.8 | 4 | 3 | 5 | 5.5 |

(a) Use this information to draw a scatter graph.
(b) What type of correlation is shown on the scatter graph?
(c) Draw a line of best fit.
(d) Mrs Wilson's baby is 11 weeks old.
Use the graph to estimate the weight of her baby.

2. The table shows the temperature of water as it cools in a freezer.

| Time (minutes) | 5 | 10 | 15 | 20 | 25 | 30 |
|---|---|---|---|---|---|---|
| Temperature (°C) | 36 | 29 | 25 | 20 | 15 | 8 |

(a) Use this information to draw a scatter graph.
(b) What type of correlation is shown?
(c) Draw a line of best fit.
(d) Use the graph to estimate the time when the temperature of the water reaches 0°C.

3. The table shows the weights and fitness factors for a number of women.
   The higher the fitness factor the fitter a person is.

| Weight (kg) | 45 | 48 | 50 | 54 | 56 | 60 | 64 | 72 | 99 | 112 |
|---|---|---|---|---|---|---|---|---|---|---|
| Fitness Factor | 41 | 48 | 40 | 40 | 35 | 40 | 34 | 30 | 17 | 15 |

   (a) Use this information to draw a scatter graph.
   (b) What type of correlation is shown on the scatter graph?
   (c) Draw a line of best fit.
   (d) Use the graph to estimate:
       (i)  the fitness factor for a woman whose weight is 80 kg,
       (ii) the weight of a woman whose fitness factor is 22.

4. The following table gives the marks obtained by some candidates taking examinations in French and German.

| Mark in French | 53 | 35 | 39 | 53 | 50 | 59 | 36 | 43 |
|---|---|---|---|---|---|---|---|---|
| Mark in German | 64 | 32 | 44 | 70 | 56 | 68 | 40 | 48 |

   (a) (i)  Use this information to draw a scatter graph.
       (ii) Draw the line of best fit by eye.
   (b) Use the graph to estimate:
       (i)  the mark in German for a candidate who got 68 in French,
       (ii) the mark in French for a candidate who got 58 in German.
   (c) Which of the two estimates in (b) is likely to be more reliable?
       Give a reason for your answer.

5. The table shows the times taken by some boys to run 200 metres and their inside-leg measurements.

| Time (seconds) | 31 | 33 | 34 | 38 | 38 | 38 | 42 | 43 | 45 | 47 |
|---|---|---|---|---|---|---|---|---|---|---|
| Inside-leg (cm) | 69 | 65 | 72 | 63 | 69 | 75 | 70 | 65 | 74 | 69 |

   (a) Plot a scatter graph of these data.
   (b) Explain why a line of best fit for these data would not be useful in estimating the time for a different boy to run 200 metres by taking his inside-leg measurement.

## Key Points

► A **scatter graph** can be used to show the relationship between two sets of data.
► The relationship between two sets of data is referred to as **correlation**.
► You should be able to recognise **positive** and **negative** correlation.
   The correlation is stronger as points get closer to a straight line.

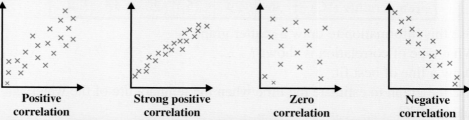

| Positive correlation | Strong positive correlation | Zero correlation | Negative correlation |

> ▶ When there is a relationship between two sets of data, a **line of best fit** can be drawn on the scatter graph. The **slope** of the line of best fit shows the **trend** of the data.
> ▶ The line of best fit can be used to **estimate** a value from one set of the data when a corresponding value from the other set is known.

## Review Exercise 17

1. The data from a survey of cars was used to plot these scatter graphs.

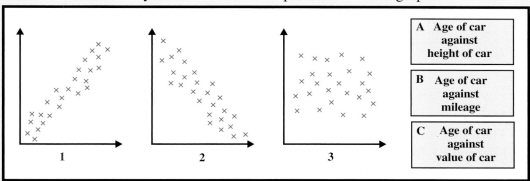

| A | Age of car against height of car |
| B | Age of car against mileage |
| C | Age of car against value of car |

Match each scatter graph to the correct description.

2. In each of the following cases, decide if the possible correlation is positive, zero or negative.
   (a) The outside temperature and the amount of electricity used in a house.
   (b) The distances students live from school and their journey times to school.
   (c) The marks obtained by pupils in a test and the house numbers where they live.

3. The heights of 10 boys and their fathers are given in this table.

| Height of father (cm) | 167 | 168 | 169 | 171 | 172 | 172 | 174 | 175 | 176 | 182 |
|---|---|---|---|---|---|---|---|---|---|---|
| Height of son (cm) | 164 | 166 | 166 | 168 | 169 | 170 | 170 | 171 | 173 | 177 |

   (a) Use this information to draw a scatter graph.
   (b) Draw a line of best fit by eye.
   (c) Use your graph to estimate the height of a boy whose father is 1.7 m tall.

4. The table gives information about the age and value of a number of cars of the same type.

| Age (years) | 1 | $4\frac{1}{2}$ | 6 | 3 | 5 | 2 | 4 |
|---|---|---|---|---|---|---|---|
| Value (£) | 8200 | 4900 | 3800 | 6200 | 4500 | 7600 | 5200 |

   (a) Use the information to draw a scatter graph.
   (b) What type of correlation is there between the age and value of these cars?
   (c) Draw a line of best fit.
   (d) Jo has a car of this type which is 7 years old and is in average condition. Use the graph to estimate its value.

**Try to do questions 1 to 18 without using a calculator.**

1.  (a)  Simplify  $3m + 4m + 5m$ .
    (b)  Solve the equations.  (i)  $y + 3 = 11$   (ii)  $4a = 32$

2.  Solve the equations  (a)  $2g = 9$ ,   (b)  $2g + 1 = 9$ ,   (c)  $2(g + 1) = 9$ .

3.  (a) 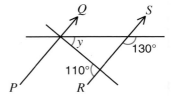   (i)  Find the size of the angle marked $x$ .
        Give a reason for your answer.
     (ii)  Which word describes angle $x$ ?
        acute   obtuse   reflex   right-angled

    (b)  In the diagram, lines $PQ$ and $RS$ are parallel.
        They are crossed by two other straight lines.
        Find the size of the angle marked $y$ .

4.  The table shows the ages and weights of chickens.

| Age (days)  | 10  | 20  | 40   | 50   | 70   | 80   | 100  |
|-------------|-----|-----|------|------|------|------|------|
| Weight (g)  | 100 | 300 | 1000 | 1300 | 2000 | 2000 | 2400 |

    (a)  Use this information to draw a scatter graph.
    (b)  Describe the correlation between the age and weight of these chickens.
    (c)  Draw a line of best fit.
    (d)  Explain how you know the relationship is quite strong.

5.  Solve.   (a)  $7x = 35$   (b)  $3 = x + 5$   (c)  $5x + 3 = 18$

6.  If  $4(x + a) = 22 + x$ ,  make $x$ the subject of the formula.

7.  (a)  Which of these shapes are similar to each other?

**P**

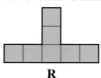
**Q**

**R**

**S**

    This shape is drawn on centimetre-squared paper
    (b)  The shape is reduced with scale factor $\frac{1}{2}$ .
        (i)  What is the perimeter of the reduced shape?
        (ii)  What is the area of the reduced shape?

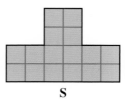
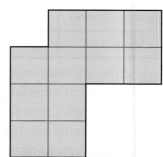

8. (a) Simplify $3t - t - 3$.
   (b) Solve (i) $2(x - 3) = 8$, (ii) $3t + 1 = 7 - t$.

9. The diagram shows a rectangle.
   Work out the size of angles $x$ and $y$.

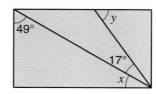

10. Solve (a) $8x + 4 = 20$, (b) $3x - 2 = 10$.

11. (a) (i) Complete this table of values for $y = 2x + 3$.

| $x$ | $-2$ | $-1$ | 0 | 1 | 2 | 3 |
|---|---|---|---|---|---|---|
| $y$ | $-1$ | | 3 | | | |

   (ii) Draw the graph of $y = 2x + 3$.
   (b) On the same grid, draw the graph of $y = 1$.
   (c) Write down the coordinates of the point where the lines cross.

12. In the diagram, $PQR$ is an isosceles triangle.
    The lines $PQ$ and $RS$ are parallel.
    (a) Work out the size of angle $x$.
    (b) (i) What is the size of angle $y$?
        (ii) Give a reason for your answer.

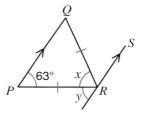

13. A candle weighs $x$ grams.
    (a) Write an expression, in terms of $x$, for the weight of 20 candles.
    (b) A box of 20 candles weighs 3800 g. The box weighs 200 g.
        By forming an equation, find the value of $x$.

14. The diagram shows a sketch of the line $2y + x = 10$.
    Find the coordinates of points $G$ and $H$.

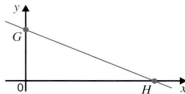

15. (a) Rearrange the formula $y = 5x + 10$ to make $x$ the subject.
    (b) Solve. (i) $\frac{t}{3} = 7$ (ii) $5(x - 3) = 3x + 1$

16. A triangle with one side extended is shown.
    Explain why the angle marked $a$ is 105°.

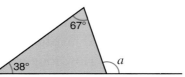

17. (a) Buns cost $x$ pence each.
        How much will 2 buns cost?
    (b) A doughnut costs 5 pence more than a bun.
        How much will 3 doughnuts cost?
    (c) The cost of buying 2 buns and 3 doughnuts is 95 pence.
        By forming an equation find the cost of a bun.

18. $O$ is the centre of the circle.
    $RS$ is a diameter of the circle.
    $PQ$ is a tangent to the circle at $T$.
    Angle $OST = 35°$.
    Calculate the size of:
    (a) angle $ROT$,
    (b) angle $OTR$,
    (c) angle $QTS$.

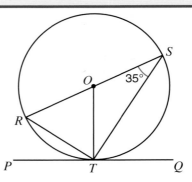

**You may use a calculator for questions 19 to 35.**

19. Solve. (a) $\frac{x}{4} = 25$ (b) $3x + 5 = x - 2$

20. Rearrange the formula $v = u + 10t$ to make $t$ the subject.

21. (a) Write, as simply as possible, an expression for the total length of these rods.
    (b) The total length of the rods is 23 cm.
        By forming an equation find the value of $a$.

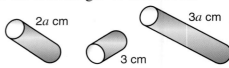

22.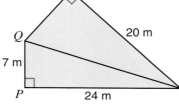

    The diagram shows the dimensions of a lawn.
    (a) Find the length of $QS$.
    (b) Find the length of $QR$.
    (c) Find the perimeter of the lawn.

23. Calculate angle $a$ in each of these triangles.
    (a)          (b)

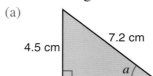

24. Rachel is standing 150 m from the base of a tower.
    The angle of elevation of the top of the tower is 28°.
    Find the height of the tower.
    Give your answer in metres, to one decimal place.

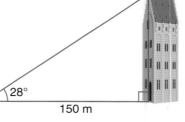

25. Colin and Dexter are standing next to each other in the sunshine.
    Colin is 150 cm tall and his shadow is 240 cm long.
    Dexter is 165 cm tall. How long is his shadow?

26. Find the size of the angles $a$, $b$ and $c$.

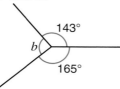
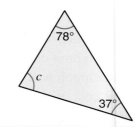

**27.** A motor car is 4.2 m long and 1.4 m high. A scale model of the car is 8.4 cm long. What is the height of the model?

**28.** Write down the gradient and *y*-intercept of the graph $y = 5 - 2x$.

**29.** Calculate the length of the side marked *x* in each of these triangles.

(a)

(b)

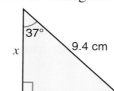

**30.** A yacht is 40 m from the bottom of a lighthouse.
From the top of the lighthouse the angle of depression to the yacht is 48°.
Calculate the height of the lighthouse.

**31.** These two tubes are similar.
The width of the small size is 2.4 cm and the height of the small size is 10 cm.
The width of the large size is 3.6 cm.
Calculate the height of the large size.

**32.**

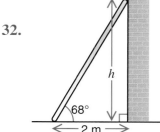

A ladder is put against a wall.
The bottom of the ladder is 2 metres away from the wall.
The ladder makes an angle of 68° with the ground.
How far up the wall does the ladder reach?

**33.** Triangle *PQR* is isosceles. $PQ = QR$.
Work out the size of angles *a* and *b*.

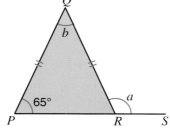

**34.** Kim thinks of a number.
She doubles it and adds 3.
The answer is 17.
What is her number?

**35.** (a) Work out the size of the angle marked *x*.
Give a reason for your answer.

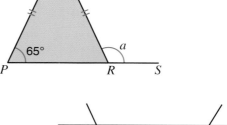

(b)

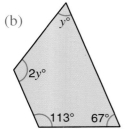
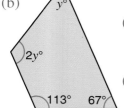

(i) What special name is given to this shape?
Give a reason for your answer.
(ii) Find the value of *y*.

# 18 Whole Numbers

The numbers 0, 1, 2, 3, 4, 5, ... can be used to count objects.

"I have 3 pound coins in my pocket."
"There are 8 tables in the room."
"There are 0 students absent today."

Such numbers are called **whole numbers**.

> Numbers that end in 0, 2, 4, 6 or 8 are called **even numbers**.
> Numbers that end in 1, 3, 5, 7 or 9 are called **odd numbers**.

## Place value

Our number system is made up of the digits 0, 1, 2, 3, 4, 5, 6, 7, 8 and 9.
The position a digit has in a number is called its **place value**.
In the number 5384 the digit 8 is worth 80, but in the number 4853 the digit 8 is worth 800.

## Non-calculator methods for addition

### Writing numbers in columns

Write the numbers in tidy columns according to place value.
Add together the numbers of units, tens, hundreds, etc.
If any of these answers are 10 or more, something is carried to the next column.

### Example 1

Work out   4567 + 835.

$$
\begin{array}{r} 4567 \\ + 835 \\ \hline 5402 \\ \hline {\scriptstyle 1\ 1\ 1} \end{array}
$$

$$
\begin{array}{r} 4567 \\ + 835 \\ \hline 2 \\ \hline {\scriptstyle 1} \end{array}
$$
7 + 5
= 12
which is
2
carry 1

$$
\begin{array}{r} 4567 \\ + 835 \\ \hline 02 \\ \hline {\scriptstyle 1\ 1} \end{array}
$$
6 + 3
+ carried 1
= 10
which is
0
carry 1

$$
\begin{array}{r} 4567 \\ + 835 \\ \hline 402 \\ \hline {\scriptstyle 1\ 1\ 1} \end{array}
$$
5 + 8
+ carried 1
= 14
which is
4
carry 1

$$
\begin{array}{r} 4567 \\ + 835 \\ \hline 5402 \\ \hline {\scriptstyle 1\ 1\ 1} \end{array}
$$
4
+ carried 1
= 5

### Using a number line

A number line shows a different method for adding numbers.
With practice you should not need to draw a number line.

### Example 2

Work out   26 + 37.

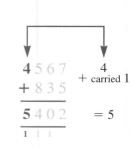

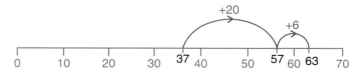

26 + 37   is the same as   37 + 26.
37 + 20 = 57   (adding 20)
57 +  6 = 63   (adding 6)
So,   26 + 37 = 63.

## Working in context

1. Identify the calculation required by the question.
2. Do the calculation.
3. Give the answer to the question using a short sentence.

### Example 3

In Year S3 the class attendances were as follows:

28   30   27   30   25

What was the total attendance?

```
   2 8
   3 0
   2 7
   3 0
 + 2 5
 -----
 1 4 0
   1 2
```

The total attendance was 140.

## Non-calculator methods for subtraction

### Writing numbers in columns

Write the numbers in columns according to place value.

The order in which the numbers are written down is important.

Then, in turn, subtract the numbers of units, tens, hundreds, etc.

If the subtraction in a column cannot be done, because the number being subtracted is greater, borrow 10 from the next column.

Work out   $7238 - 642$.

```
 6 11 1
 7̷ 2̷ 3 8
 - 6 4 2
 -------
 6 5 9 6
```

**Units:** $8 - 2 = 6$

**Tens:** $3 - 4$ cannot be done, so borrow 10 from the 2 in the next column.
Now $10 + 3 - 4 = 9$.

**Hundreds:** $1 - 6$ cannot be done, so borrow 10 from the 7 in the next column.
Now $10 + 1 - 6 = 5$.

**Thousands:** $6 - 0 = 6$.

> You can use addition to check your subtraction.
>
> Does $6596 + 642 = 7238$?
> ```
>   6 5 9 6
>  +  6 4 2
>  -------
>   7 2 3 8
>     1 1
> ```

### Example 4

(a)
```
 0 16 15 1
 1̷ 7̷ 6̷ 2
 - 8 7 3
 -------
   8 8 9
```

(b)
```
   9 9
 2 9̷ 9̷ 1
 3̷ 0̷ 0̷ 6
 - 1 8 4 7
 ---------
   1 1 5 9
```

(c)
```
       9
 8 9̷ 10 1
 9̷ 0̷ 1̷ 2
 - 5 6 7 8
 ---------
   3 3 3 4
```

> Addition is the opposite (inverse) operation to subtraction.
> If $a - b = c$, then $c + b = a$.

*Check the answers by addition.*

## Practice Exercise 18.1

Do not use a calculator for this exercise.

1. How much does it cost to buy:
   (a) a drink and a doughnut,
   (b) a drink and a packet of crisps?

Café Enfant
*Price List*
Drink................... 54p
Doughnut............ 35p
Packet of Crisps.. 27p

2. Draw a number line for each of the following sums and work out the answers.
   (a) 14 + 15      (b) 18 + 25      (c) 7 + 36      (d) 24 + 29

3. Work these out by writing the numbers in columns.
   (a) 765 + 23    (b) 27 + 56    (c) 76 + 98    (d) 324 + 628
   (e) 1273 + 729    (f) 3495 + 8708    (g) 67 + 89 + 45    (h) 431 + 865 + 245

4. Marcus drove 1754 miles on his holiday. His milometer reading was 38 956 at the start. What was his milometer reading at the end?

5. The table shows the number of tickets sold each day last week at a cinema.

| Mon | Tue | Wed | Thu | Fri | Sat | Sun |
|-----|-----|-----|-----|-----|-----|-----|
| 125 | 87 | 95 | 105 | 278 | 487 | 201 |

   How many tickets were sold altogether?

6. The last four attendances at a football stadium were:
   21 004,   19 750,   18 009,   22 267
   What was the total attendance?

7. Here is a number line for 43 − 16.
   (a) What is 43 − 10?
   (b) What is 43 − 16?

8. Draw a number line for each of the following questions and work out the answers.
   (a) 58 − 26      (b) 44 − 17      (c) 37 − 19      (d) 51 − 25

9. Mandy wins £1000. She spends £185 on a DVD player. How much has she got left?

10. Work these out by writing the numbers in columns. Use addition to check your answers.
    (a) 978 − 624    (b) 843 − 415    (c) 1754 − 470    (d) 407 − 249
    (e) 5070 − 2846    (f) 2345 − 1876    (g) 8045 − 1777    (h) 10 000 − 723

11. A car park has spaces for 345 cars. On Tuesday 256 spaces are used. How many spaces are not used?

12. (a) Ricky buys a bunch of spring onions.
       He pays with £1.
       How much change is he given?
    (b) Liz buys a cucumber and a lettuce.
        She pays with £5.
        How much change is she given?

Salad Specials

| | |
|---|---|
| Cucumber | 89p each |
| Lettuce | 75p each |
| Spring onions | 63p a bunch |

13. A shop records the number of tins of soup it has on its shelves.

| | Tomato | Oxtail | Chicken |
|---|--------|--------|---------|
| Start of the week | 67 | 54 | 81 |
| End of the week | 28 | 36 | 26 |

    (a) How many tins of each type of soup did the shop sell?
    (b) How many tins of soup did the shop sell altogether?

**14.** The table shows the milometer readings for three cars at the start and end of a year.

| | Car A | Car B | Car C |
|---|---|---|---|
| Start | 2501 | 55667 | 48050 |
| End | 10980 | 67310 | 61909 |

Which car has done the most miles in the year?

## Short multiplication

**Short multiplication** is when the multiplying number is less than 10,   e.g. 165 × 7.
One method multiplies the units, tens, hundreds, etc. in turn.

```
  1 6 5
×     7
-------
1 1 5 5
  1 4 3
```

**Units:**   7 × 5 = 35,   which is 5 carry 3.
**Tens:**   7 × 6 = 42 + carried 3 = 45,   which is 5 carry 4.
**Hundreds:**   7 × 1 = 7 + carried 4 = 11,   which is 1 carry 1.
There are no more digits to be multiplied by 7, the carried 1 becomes 1 thousand.

### Example 5

(a)
```
  1 6 2
×     4
-------
  6 4 8
  2
```

(b)
```
  9 0 7 1
×       7
---------
6 3 4 9 7
    4
```

(c)
```
  4 8 3 5
×       8
---------
3 8 6 8 0
  6 2 4
```

## Multiplying a whole number by 10, 100, 1000 ...

When you multiply a whole number by:
**10**     The units become 10s,     the 10s become 100s,     the 100s become 1000s, and so on.
**100**     The units become 100s,   the 10s become 1000s,   the 100s become 10 000s, and so on.
**1000**   The units become 1000s, the 10s become 10 000s, the 100s become 100 000s, and so on.

### Example 6

(a)   753 × 10 = 7530
(b)   753 × 100 = 75 300
(c)   753 × 1000 = 753 000

We can show these multiplications in a table.

| 100 000s | 10 000s | 1000s | 100s | 10s | Units | |
|---|---|---|---|---|---|---|
| | | | 7 | 5 | 3 | |
| | | 7 | 5 | 3 | 0 | ←753 × 10 |
| | 7 | 5 | 3 | 0 | 0 | ←753 × 100 |
| 7 | 5 | 3 | 0 | 0 | 0 | ←753 × 1000 |

100 = 10 × 10
Multiplying a number by 100 is the same as multiplying the number by 10 and then by 10 again.

*Explain any patterns you can see.*

# Multiplying a whole number by multiples of 10 (20, 30, 40, ...)

Work out   753 × 20.

This can be written as:

$$753 \times 20 = 753 \times 10 \times 2$$

| 20 = 10 × 2 |

$$= 7530 \times 2$$
$$= 15\ 060$$

## Long multiplication

**Long multiplication** is used when the multiplying number is greater than 10,   e.g. 24 × 17.

Work out   24 × 17.

```
      2 4
    × 1 7
    ─────
    1 6 8   ←24 × 7 = 168
  + 2 4 0   ←24 × 10 = 240
  ─────
    4 0 8
```

A standard non-calculator method for doing long multiplication multiplies the number by:
● the units figure, then
● the tens figure, then
● the hundreds figure, and so on.
All these answers are added together.

| **Example 7** | **Example 8** | **Example 9** |
|---|---|---|

**Example 7**
```
      1 4 5
    ×   6 2
    ───────
      2 9 0   ←145 × 2
  + 8 7 0 0   ←145 × 60
  ─────────
    8 9 9 0
```

**Example 8**
```
        2 7 3
      ×  2 3 4
      ───────
        1 0 9 2   ←273 × 4
        8 1 9 0   ←273 × 30
  +   5 4 6 0 0   ←273 × 200
  ───────────
      6 3 8 8 2
```

**Example 9**
```
          2 4 3 6
        × 1 2 4 7
        ─────────
          1 7 0 5 2   ←2436 × 7
          9 7 4 4 0   ←2436 × 40
          4 8 7 2 0 0   ←2436 × 200
  +   2 4 3 6 0 0 0   ←2436 × 1000
  ─────────────
      3 0 3 7 6 9 2
```

## Practice Exercise 18.2

Do not use a calculator for this exercise.

1. I get 8 doughnuts for £1. How many doughnuts will I get for £5?

2. When John uses a store card he gets 4 points for every pound he spends.
   He spends £18. How many points does he get?

3. A machine makes 24 jigsaws in an hour. How many jigsaws will it make in 6 hours?

4. Linda is paid 3p for each leaflet she delivers. She delivers 184 leaflets.
   How much is she paid?

5. Look at these prices.
   (a)  What is the cost of 5 pencils?
   (b)  What is the cost of 6 pens?
   (c)  What is the total cost of 4 pens and 7 pencils?

Pencil 12p
Pen 19p

6. Work these out using a method you find easiest.
   (a)  21 × 4        (b)  17 × 5        (c)  36 × 7        (d)  183 × 3
   (e)  264 × 8       (f)  3179 × 5      (g)  4012 × 6      (h)  6012 × 7

7. A caretaker puts out 7 rows of chairs. There are 13 chairs in each row.
   How many more chairs are needed for 120 chairs to be put out?

8. Write down the answers to the following questions.
   You do not have to show any working.
   (a) $132 \times 10$     (b) $123 \times 100$     (c) $47 \times 1000$     (d) $384 \times 100$

9. Here is a price list from an office catalogue.
   (a) What is the cost of 10 desks?
   (b) What is the cost of 100 chairs?
   (c) What is the total cost of 100 desks and 1000 chairs?

   Desk £120
   Chair £59

10. A bag of compost costs £12. One square metre of turf costs £7.
    (a) What is the cost of 10 bags of compost?
    (b) What is the cost of $100 \, \text{m}^2$ of turf?
    (c) What is the total cost of 100 bags of compost and $1000 \, \text{m}^2$ of turf?

11. There are 7 classrooms in a school.
    In each classroom there are 30 chairs and 20 tables.
    Find the total number of (a) chairs, (b) tables.

12. Work out.
    (a) $357 \times 20$     (b) $632 \times 30$     (c) $537 \times 40$
    (d) $260 \times 50$     (e) $186 \times 70$     (f) $239 \times 90$

13. On the first night of the show, 70 tickets and 40 programmes are sold.
    How much money is paid in total
    for the tickets and programmes?

    PLAYHOUSE THEATRE
    PRESENT
    CABARET
    Tickets: £19     Programmes: £3

14. There are 400 metres in one lap of a running track.
    How many metres are there in 25 laps?

15. Work out.
    (a) $17 \times 12$    (b) $23 \times 15$    (c) $142 \times 32$    (d) $276 \times 324$
    (e) $2143 \times 342$    (f) $5718 \times 545$    (g) $2143 \times 1274$    (h) $2548 \times 1368$

16. A box holds 12 tins of soup. How many tins will 18 boxes hold?

17. A computer prints 17 symbols on a line. How many symbols will it print on 15 lines?

18. A gardener buys 36 flower pots at 25 pence each. What is the total cost?

19. A restaurant charges £23 for dinner. What is the total charge for 42 dinners?

20. A company is organising a Christmas party for 128 workers.
    Each worker must pay £12 towards the cost.
    Work out the total amount paid by workers.

21. Here is part of a price list.
    What is the total cost of 14 desks and 23 cabinets?

    Office Supplies
    Desk £126
    Cabinet £149

## Short division

The process of dividing a number by a number less than 10 is called **short division**.
Short division relies on knowledge of the Multiplication Tables.
What is $32 \div 8$, $42 \div 7$, $72 \div 9$, $54 \div 6$ ?

Work out $882 \div 7$.

> You may set your working out like this:
>
> $$7 \overline{)8\,{}^18\,{}^42} = 126$$

$$7 \overline{)8\,{}^18\,{}^42}$$
$$\quad 1\ 2\ 6$$

Starting from the left:
$8 \div 7 = 1$ remainder 1,  which is 1 carry 1.
$18 \div 7 = 2$ remainder 4,  which is 2 carry 4.
$42 \div 7 = 6$, with no remainder.

So, $882 \div 7 = 126$.

You can check your division by multiplying.
*Does* $126 \times 7 = 882?$

> Multiplication is the opposite (inverse) operation to division.
> If $a \div b = c$, then $c \times b = a$.

### Example 10

Work out $1470 \div 6$.

$$6 \overline{)1\,4\,{}^27\,{}^30}$$
$$\quad\ 2\ 4\ 5$$

$1470 \div 6 = 245$

### Example 11

Pencils are boxed in packs of 5.
I have 87 pencils.
How many boxes can I fill?

$87 \div 5$   $5 \overline{)8\,{}^37}$
$$\qquad\quad 1\ 7 \text{ remainder } 2$$

I can fill 17 boxes.
There will be 2 pencils left over.

## Dividing a whole number by 10 or 100

When you divide a whole number by:
**10**   The 10s  become units,  the 100s  become 10s,  the 1000s   become 100s, and so on.
**100**   The 100s become units,  the 1000s become 10s,   the 10 000s become 100s, and so on.

### Example 12

(a)  $7530 \div 10 = 753$
(b)  $12\,400 \div 100 = 124$

| 10 000s | 1000s | 100s | 10s | Units |
|---------|-------|------|-----|-------|
|         | 7     | 5    | 3   | 0     |
|         |       | 7    | 5   | 3     | ←$7530 \div 10$

*Explain any patterns you can see.*

## Practice Exercise 18.3        Do not use a calculator for this exercise.

1.  Calculate these divisions. Show your working clearly.
    State the remainder if there is one.
    Use multiplication to check your answers.
    (a)  $85 \div 5$      (b)  $471 \div 3$      (c)  $816 \div 6$      (d)  $455 \div 6$
    (e)  $3146 \div 8$      (f)  $824 \div 4$      (g)  $9882 \div 9$      (h)  $80\,560 \div 4$

2. A lollipop costs 7p. Maxine has 95p.
   (a) How many lollipops can she buy?
   (b) What amount of money will she have left?

3. Two tins of cat food cost 98p.
   What is the cost of one tin?

4. Flower pots cost £5 each. I have £30.
   How many flower pots can I buy?

5. Pam buys 3 watches for £42.
   How much is each watch?

6. Work out.
   (a) $4560 \div 10$   (b) $465\,000 \div 1000$   (c) $64\,000 \div 1000$   (d) $65\,400 \div 100$

7. Raffle tickets cost 10p each. Jo has 60 pence.
   How many raffle tickets can she buy?

8. What number should be put in the box to make each of these statements correct?
   (a) $56\,400 \div \square = 564$   (b) $\square \div 1000 = 702$   (c) $35\,000 \div \square = 3500$

## Problems involving number

The number skills you have met so far can be applied to practical situations.

### Example 13

Harold loads 5 parcels each weighing 3 kg and 4 parcels each weighing 7 kg onto a trolley.
The unloaded trolley weighs 18 kg.
What is the total weight of the trolley and the parcels?

Total weight $= (5 \times 3) + (4 \times 7) + 18\,kg$
$= 15 + 28 + 18\,kg$
$= 61\,kg$

Set your working out clearly so that someone else can follow what you are doing.

The total weight of the trolley and parcels is 61 kg.

*How could a calculator be used to answer this problem?*

## Practice Exercise 18.4

You should be able to do this exercise without using your calculator.
Having completed the exercise use a calculator to check your working.

1. Claire is 16 cm taller than Rachel. Their heights add up to 312 cm.
   How tall is Rachel?

2. A box containing 6 packets of tea weighs 750 g. Each packet of tea weighs 120 g.
   What is the weight of the box?

3. Look at this price list.

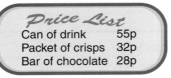

**Price List**
Can of drink        55p
Packet of crisps    32p
Bar of chocolate    28p

(a) What change does Harry get from £2, if he buys 2 bars of chocolate and a can of drink?

(b) How much does Harry save if he buys a packet of crisps and a can of drink instead of 2 bars of chocolate and a can of drink?

4. The caretaker set out 17 rows of chairs. There are 15 chairs in each row.
How many more chairs are needed to provide seats for 280 people?

5. A roll of wire is 550 cm long. From the roll, Hilary cuts 3 pieces which each measure 85 cm and 4 pieces which each measure 35 cm.
How much wire is left on the roll?

6. A box, which contains 48 matches, has a total weight of 207 g.
If each match weighs 4 g, what is the weight of the empty box?

## Key Points

▶ The numbers  0, 1, 2, 3, 4, 5, …  can be used to count objects.
Such numbers are called **whole numbers**.

**You should be able to:**

▶ Read and write whole numbers expressed in figures and words.

▶ Order whole numbers and recognise the place value of each digit in a number.

▶ Carry out accurately non-calculator methods for addition and subtraction.

▶ Carry out multiplication by a number less than 10 (short multiplication).

▶ Multiply whole numbers by 10, 100, 1000, … and by 20, 30, 40, …

▶ Carry out division by a number less than 10 (short division).

▶ Divide whole numbers by 10, 100.

▶ Carry out long multiplication.

## Review Exercise 18

Do not use a calculator for this exercise.

1. Which of these numbers are even numbers?

| 6 | 9 | 12 | 21 | 77 | 110 |

2. Using the digits  2,  3  and  7  make as many three-digit numbers as you can.
Use each digit just once in each three-digit number,  e.g. 237.
Put your three-digit numbers in descending order.
How many of your numbers are even numbers?

3. Gaby stated:  *"The sum of three consecutive numbers is always an odd number."*
By means of an example, show that this statement is not true.

4. In the game of darts the scores of the three darts are added together.
   These are then taken away from the current total to calculate the new total.
   In each case work out the score of the three darts and the new total.

|  | Current Total | 1st dart | 2nd dart | 3rd dart | Score | New Total |
|---|---|---|---|---|---|---|
| (a) | 501 | 60 | 18 | 19 | [  ] | [  ] |
| (b) | 420 | 19 | 42 | 39 | [  ] | [  ] |
| (c) | 301 | 50 | 57 | 11 | [  ] | [  ] |

5. Work out the following. Show your working.
   (a) 465 + 12 + 1582    (b) 2465 − 1878    (c) 718 × 9    (d) 1446 ÷ 6

6. A school has 843 pupils. How many are boys if there are 459 girls?

7. A plank of wood is 396 cm in length.
   The plank is cut into two pieces.
   One piece is 28 cm longer than the other.
   How long is the shorter piece of wood?

8. Adrian is 6 kg lighter than Richard. Their weights add up to 152 kg.
   How heavy is Richard?

9. One thousand chocolate biscuits are packed in boxes of 6.
   (a) How many full boxes will there be?
   (b) How many biscuits will be left over?

10. How many chews costing 6p each can I buy for 90p?

11. A company has 47 shops. Each shop employs 28 people.
    How many people are employed altogether?

12. The total weight of a carton which contains 6 eggs is 520 g.
    The carton weighs 70 g.
    What is the weight of each egg?

13. A cupboard is 90 cm wide.
    It is placed between two walls which are 160 cm apart.
    The gap between the cupboard and each wall is the same.
    What is the size of the gap?

14. The table shows the maximum number of people that can be carried on some buses.

    (a) How many people can 4 minibuses carry?
    (b) How many people can 5 coaches carry?
    (c) How many people can 9 double-decker buses carry?
    (d) A trip for 174 people is planned.
        4 coaches are ordered.
        How many empty seats will there be?

| Minibus | 17 |
| Coach | 55 |
| Double-Decker Bus | 74 |

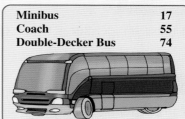

# 19 Negative Numbers

In Chapter 18 we used a number line to show whole numbers.
This number line can be extended to include **negative whole numbers**.

Negative whole numbers, zero and positive whole numbers are called **integers**.
−5 can be read as "minus five" or "negative five".

A number written without a sign before it is assumed to be positive.
+5 has the same value as 5.
Real-life situations which use negative numbers include temperature, bank accounts and depths below sea level.

*Can you think of any other situations where negative numbers are used?*

## Ordering numbers

**The thermometer**

| | |
|---|---|
| −5°C is colder than −1°C. | 2°C is warmer than −3°C. |
| −3°C is colder than 1°C. | 4°C is warmer than −5°C. |
| −4°C is colder than 0°C. | 0°C is warmer than −3°C. |
| 2°C is colder than 4°C. | 5°C is warmer than 2°C. |

As you move up the thermometer the temperatures become warmer. | As you move down the thermometer the temperatures become colder.

**The number line**

| | |
|---|---|
| −5 is less than −1. | 2 is more than −3. |
| −3 is less than 1. | 4 is more than −5. |
| −4 is less than 0. | 0 is more than −3. |
| 2 is less than 4. | 5 is more than 2. |

As you move from left to right along the number line the numbers become bigger. | As you move from right to left along the number line the numbers become smaller.

### Example 1

List these temperatures from coldest to hottest:  3°C,  5°C,  −2°C,  0°C,  −4°C.

−4°C,  −2°C,  0°C,  3°C,  5°C.

### Example 2

List these numbers in ascending order (from lowest to highest):  50,  −41,  −18,  −11,  28,  9.

−41,  −18,  −11,  9,  28,  50.

## Practice Exercise **19.1**

1. Copy and complete these sentences using the words 'colder' or 'warmer' as appropriate.
   (a)  −2°C is …… than −5°C.  (b)  −1°C is …… than   4°C.
   (c)   2°C is …… than −4°C.  (d)  −10°C is …… than −5°C.

2. What temperatures are shown by these thermometers?
   (a)

   (b)

3. Copy and complete these sentences using the words 'less' or 'more' as appropriate.
   (a)  −3 is …… than   2.  (b)   1 is …… than  −5.
   (c)  −4 is …… than −1.  (d)  −4 is …… than −10.

4. At midnight on New Year's Day the temperatures in some cities were as shown:

   | | | | |
   |---|---|---|---|
   | **Edinburgh −7°C** | **London 0°C** | **Moscow −22°C** | **New York −17°C** |
   | | **Rome 3°C** | **Colombo 21°C** | **Cairo 15°C** |

   (a)  Which city recorded the highest temperature?
   (b)  Which city recorded the lowest temperature?
   (c)  List the temperatures from coldest to hottest.

5. List these numbers from lowest to highest.
   (a)  31,  −78,  51,  −39,  −16,  −9,  11
   (b)  5,  1,  −1,  −3,  −5,  −2,  0,  2,  4
   (c)  99,  −103,  104,  5,  −3,  52,  −63,  −19

6. List these numbers in descending order:
   30,  10,  −30,  −50,  −20,  0,  40

7. List these numbers in ascending order:
   27,  −30,  17,  0,  −15, −10,  8

## Subtracting a larger number from a smaller number

Work out   3 − 5.

> To work out smaller number − larger number:
> ● Do the calculation the other way round.   3 − 5   becomes   5 − 3.
> ● Put a minus sign in front of the answer.   So,   3 − 5 = −2.

This is the same as starting at 3 on a number line and going 5 places to the left, to get to −2.

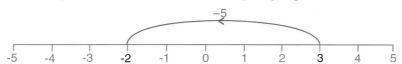

## Example 3

Work out  $7 - 13$ .

Do the calculation the other way round.
$$13 - 7 = 6$$
Then place a minus sign in front of the answer.
$$\text{So,}\ 7 - 13 = -6$$

## Example 4

Alec has £50 in his bank account. He writes a cheque for £80. What is his new balance?

His new balance is given by the calculation   £50 − £80.
$$80 - 50 = 30.$$
$$\text{So,}\ \ 50 - 80 = -30.$$
The new balance is −£30.
This means that Alec's account is overdrawn by £30.

## Practice Exercise 19.2  Do not use a calculator for this exercise.

1. Use the number line to work out the following.

   (a)  $4 - 3$
   (b)  $1 - 3$
   (c)  $2 - 4$
   (d)  $5 - 9$
   (e)  $3 - 6$
   (f)  $6 - 10$

2. Draw a number line to show each of these statements.
   (a)  $4 - 6 = -2$
   (b)  $3 - 4 = -1$
   (c)  $7 - 10 = -3$

3. Work out the following.
   (a)  $1 - 4$
   (b)  $3 - 5$
   (c)  $5 - 8$
   (d)  $10 - 12$
   (e)  $4 - 7$
   (f)  $8 - 12$
   (g)  $13 - 20$
   (h)  $24 - 36$
   (i)  $10 - 20$
   (j)  $23 - 30$
   (k)  $29 - 50$
   (l)  $20 - 21$

4. What number should be put in the box to make each of these statements correct?
   (a)  $7 - \square = -2$
   (b)  $\square - 6 = -5$
   (c)  $9 - \square = -3$
   (d)  $-3 - 7 = \square$
   (e)  $\square - 50 = -20$
   (f)  $10 - \square = -5$

5. Mr Armstrong has £25 in the bank.
   He writes a cheque for £100.
   What is his new balance?

6. The temperature inside a fridge is 6°C above zero.
   The temperature inside a freezer is 5°C below zero.
   By how many degrees is the temperature inside the freezer below the temperature inside the fridge?

7. At midnight, the temperature in Montrose is 3°C below freezing and in Dumfries the temperature is 2°C above freezing.
   What is the difference in temperature between Montrose and Dumfries?

8. Brad is 8 cm shorter than Alex and Cath is 9 cm taller than Alex.
   By how many centimetres is Cath taller than Brad?

9. Adrian is 5 kg heavier than Tim. Matt is 3 kg lighter than Tim.
   What is the difference in weight between Matt and Adrian?

**10.** Negative numbers can be used for depths below sea level.

Use negative numbers to answer the following.
(a) At what depth is the diver?
(b) At what depth is the treasure chest?

What is the difference in height between
(c) the helicopter and the parachutist,
(d) the diver and the jellyfish,
(e) the diver and the treasure chest,
(f) the bird and the jellyfish,
(g) the parachutist and the treasure chest,
(h) the kite and the jellyfish,
(i) the helicopter and the kite,
(j) the diver and the helicopter,
(k) the bird and the treasure chest?

| | |
|---|---|
| Helicopter | 160 m above |
| Parachute | 100 m above |
| Bird | 50 m above |
| Kite | 30 m above |
| | Sea level |
| Jellyfish | 20 m below |
| Diver | 80 m below |
| Treasure chest | 200 m below |

## Addition and subtraction using negative numbers

Think of the number line as a series of stepping stones.

What is  $-4 - 5$ ?

Using the number line:
  Start at $-4$.
$-5$ means move 5 stones to the **left**.
$$-4 - 5 = -9$$

What is  $-4 + 5$ ?

Using the number line:
  Start at $-4$.
$+5$ means move 5 stones to the **right**.
$$-4 + 5 = 1$$

> The first number is the starting point.
> The direction of movement is given by the next sign.
>
> − means move **left**.   + means move **right**.

What is  $-3 - (+7)$ ?

$-3 - (+7)$ is the same as $-3 - 7$.
  Start at $-3$ and move 7 to the **left**.
$$-3 - (+7) = -10$$

What is  $-3 - (-7)$ ?

$-3 - (-7)$ is the same as $-3 + 7$.
  Start at $-3$ and move 7 to the **right**.
$$-3 - (-7) = 4$$

To add or subtract negative numbers:
● Replace double signs with a single sign.
● Start on the number line with the first number.
● Then move left or right according to the single sign.

| |
|---|
| + + can be replaced by + |
| − − can be replaced by + |
| + − can be replaced by − |
| − + can be replaced by − |

Example 5

Work out $2 + (-6)$.

$+ -$ can be replaced by $-$.
$$2 + (-6) = 2 - 6$$
Start at 2 and move 6 to the left.
$$2 + (-6) = -4$$

Example 6

Work out $-2 - (-8)$.

$- -$ can be replaced by $+$.
$$-2 - (-8) = -2 + 8$$
Start at $-2$ and move 8 to the right.
$$-2 - (-8) = 6$$

Example 7

Work out $-4 - (+6)$.

$- +$ can be replaced by $-$.
$$-4 - (+6) = -4 - 6$$
Start at $-4$ and move 6 to the left.
$$-4 - (+6) = -10$$

Example 8

Work out $-4 + (-3) + 6 - (-5) - (+3)$.

Replace all double signs.
$$= -4 - 3 + 6 + 5 - 3$$
$$= 1$$

## Practice Exercise 19.3    Do not use a calculator for this exercise.

1.  Work out.
    (a)  $-3 + (+5)$
    (b)  $5 + (-4)$
    (c)  $-2 + (-7)$
    (d)  $-1 + (+9)$
    (e)  $7 + (-3)$
    (f)  $15 + (-20)$
    (g)  $-11 + (+4)$
    (h)  $11 + (-4)$
    (i)  $8 + (-7)$
    (j)  $-8 + (-7)$
    (k)  $3 + (+3) + (-9)$
    (l)  $-7 + (-5) + 6$

2.  Work out.
    (a)  $8 - (-5)$
    (b)  $-4 - (-10)$
    (c)  $10 - (+3)$
    (d)  $6 - (-1)$
    (e)  $-5 - (-10)$
    (f)  $-4 - (+8)$
    (g)  $-7 - (-6)$
    (h)  $7 - (-6)$
    (i)  $-2 - (+9)$
    (j)  $2 - (-9)$
    (k)  $5 - (+5) + 9$
    (l)  $-10 - (-6) + 4$

3.  Work out.
    (a)  $-3 - (-8)$
    (b)  $5 + (-2)$
    (c)  $7 - (+4)$
    (d)  $-9 - (-5) + (-3)$
    (e)  $7 + (-8) - (+5)$
    (f)  $-2 - (-7) - 6$

4.  Work out.
    (a)  $10 + 5 - 8 + 6 - 7$
    (b)  $12 + 8 - 15 + 7 - 20$
    (c)  $30 - 20 + 12 - 50$
    (d)  $6 + 12 - 14 - 4$
    (e)  $37 - 23 - 24 - 25$
    (f)  $12 + 13 + 14 - 20$

5.

| Edinburgh $-7°C$   Moscow $-22°C$   New York $-17°C$ |
| Rome $3°C$   Cairo $15°C$ |

What is the difference in temperature between
    (a)  Edinburgh and Rome,
    (b)  Edinburgh and New York,
    (c)  Moscow and New York,
    (d)  Moscow and Cairo?

6.  The temperature inside a freezer was $-23°C$.
    After two hours the temperature had risen by $8°C$.
    What is the temperature in the freezer then?

## Multiplying and dividing negative numbers

You will need to know these rules for multiplying and dividing negative numbers:

| When multiplying: | $+ \times + = +$ | $- \times - = +$ | $+ \times - = -$ | $- \times + = -$ |

| When dividing: | $+ \div + = +$ | $- \div - = +$ | $+ \div - = -$ | $- \div + = -$ |

### Example 9

Work out $(+7) \times (-5)$.

Signs: $+ \times - = -$
Numbers: $7 \times 5 = 35$
So, $(+7) \times (-5) = -35$.

### Example 10

Work out $(-4) \times (-8)$.

Signs: $- \times - = +$
Numbers: $4 \times 8 = 32$
So, $(-4) \times (-8) = 32$.

### Example 11

Work out $(+8) \div (-2)$.

Signs: $+ \div - = -$
Numbers: $8 \div 2 = 4$
So, $(+8) \div (-2) = -4$.

**Work logically:**
Work out the sign first.
Then work out the numbers.

### Example 12

Work out $(-36) \div (-3)$.

Signs: $- \div - = +$
Numbers: $36 \div 3 = 12$
So, $(-36) \div (-3) = 12$.

## Practice Exercise 19.4

Do not use a calculator for this exercise.

1.  (a) $(+7) \times (+5)$     (b) $(-7) \times (+5)$     (c) $(-7) \times (-5)$
    (d) $5 \times (+2)$        (e) $(+5) \times (-2)$     (f) $(-5) \times (-2)$
    (g) $(-1) \times (-1)$     (h) $8 \times (-3)$        (i) $(-8) \times (+3)$
    (j) $(-5) \times 9$        (k) $(-8) \times (-8)$     (l) $(-7) \times 6$
    (m) $(-7) \times (-6)$     (n) $8 \times (-10)$       (o) $(-8) \times (+10)$
    (p) $(-4) \times (-8)$

2.  (a) $(-8) \div (+2)$       (b) $(-8) \div (-2)$       (c) $(+20) \div (+4)$
    (d) $(+20) \div (-4)$      (e) $(-20) \div (+4)$      (f) $(-20) \div (-4)$
    (g) $(+18) \div (+3)$      (h) $(-18) \div (+3)$      (i) $(-24) \div (-6)$
    (j) $(+24) \div (-3)$      (k) $(-30) \div (-5)$      (l) $(-30) \div (+6)$

3.  In a multiple choice test there are:

      5 marks for a right answer   and   $-3$ marks for a wrong answer.

    For example: A student has 8 questions right and 17 wrong. What is his overall mark?
      $8 \times 5 + 17 \times -3 = 40 + -51 = 40 - 51 = -11$

    In a 25-question test these students have the following right and wrong answers.
    They can leave a question out rather than guess a wrong answer.

| | Ahmed | Bridget | Chris | Dileep | Evan |
|---|---|---|---|---|---|
| Right | 10 | 12 | 6 | 7 | 9 |
| Wrong | 8 | 13 | 17 | 18 | 16 |

    (a) How many marks did each student score?
    (b) Put the students in order from first to fifth.

## Key Points

▶ The number line can be extended to include **negative whole numbers**.

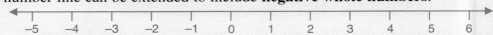

▶ Negative whole numbers, zero and positive whole numbers are called **integers**.

▶ $-5$ can be read as "minus five" or "negative five".
A number written without a sign before it is assumed to be positive.
$+5$ has the same value as 5.

▶ To add or subtract negative numbers: Replace double signs with the single sign.

> $+ +$ can be replaced by $+$     $- -$ can be replaced by $+$
> $+ -$ can be replaced by $-$     $- +$ can be replaced by $-$

▶ You should be able to multiply and divide negative numers.

## Review Exercise 19

You should be able to do this exercise without a calculator.

1. List these temperatures from coldest to hottest.
   (a) $23°C$,   $-28°C$,   $-3°C$,   $19°C$,   $-13°C$.
   (b) $20°C$,   $-15°C$,   $-20°C$,   $0°C$,   $-5°C$,   $10°C$.

2. Calculate.
   (a) $-7 - 11$      (b) $-7 + 11$      (c) $-7 - (-11)$

3. The temperature inside an igloo is $-5°C$.
   The temperature outside the igloo is $17°C$ cooler.
   What is the temperature outside the igloo?

4. The temperature of an iceberg is $-13°C$.
   The temperature of the sea is $15°$ warmer than the iceberg.
   What is the temperature of the sea?

5. Dan has £26 in his bank account. He buys a jacket for £60 and pays by cheque.
   If the cheque is accepted by his bank how much will his account be overdrawn?

6. A multichoice test has 20 questions. For each question the mark given is:

   > $+2$ for a correct answer,    $-1$ for a wrong answer.
   > 0 if the question is not attempted.

   (a) What is the lowest mark that could be scored on the test?
   (b) Tim attempts all the questions and gets 10 correct.
       Naomi attempts 13 questions and gets 8 correct.
       Who scores the better mark? Explain your answer.

7. The temperatures at Athens and Moscow are taken at the same time.
   Athens $8°C$     Moscow $-5°C$
   (a) How many degrees colder is Moscow than Athens?
   (b) At the same time, Oslo is $3°C$ colder than Moscow.
       What is the temperature in Oslo?

# 20 Decimals

Numbers and quantities are not always whole numbers.
The number system you met in Chapter 18 can be extended to include **decimal numbers**,
such as tenths, hundredths, thousandths, and smaller numbers.
A **decimal point** is used to separate the whole number part from the decimal part of the number.

This number is read as seventy-three point two six.

| whole number, 73 | → | 73.26 | ← | decimal part, 2 tenths + 6 hundredths (which is the same as 26 hundredths) |

## Place value

In the number 1.53
the digit 1 is worth 1 unit $= 1$
the digit 5 is worth 5 tenths $= 0.5$
the digit 3 is worth 3 hundredths $= 0.03$

| 1 unit = 10 tenths |
| 1 tenth = 10 hundredths |
| 1 hundredth = 10 thousandths ... and so on. |

$$1.53 = 1 + 0.5 + 0.03$$

The number 1.53 can be represented by a diagram.

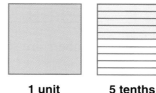 

**1 unit**  **5 tenths**  **3 hundredths**

## Ordering decimals

Compare the numbers   52.359   and   52.36.   Which number is the bigger?

You can use a grid to compare the numbers.

| tens | units | • | tenths | hundredths | thousandths |
|------|-------|---|--------|------------|-------------|
| 5 | 2 | • | 3 | 5 | 9 |
| 5 | 2 | • | 3 | 6 | |

Start by comparing the digits with the greatest place value, the tens.
Both numbers have   5 tens,     so move down to compare the units.
Both numbers have   2 units,     so move down to compare the tenths.
Both numbers have   3 tenths,   so move down to compare the hundredths.
52.359 has 5 hundredths but 52.36 has 6 hundredths.

So, 52.36 is bigger than 52.359.

A similar method can be used to place a list of decimal numbers in order.

**Example 1**

What numbers are arrows *A*, *B* and *C* pointing to on this scale?

There are 10 marks between 2 and 3.
Each mark represents 0.1.

Arrow *A*: 2.2          Arrow *B*: 2.6          Arrow *C*: 2.9

**Example 2**

What numbers are arrows *P*, *Q* and *R* pointing to on this scale?

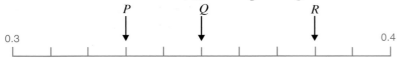

There are 10 marks between 0.3 and 0.4.
Each mark represents 0.01.

Arrow *P*: 0.33          Arrow *Q*: 0.35          Arrow *R*: 0.38

> The scale shows the main numbers. The distance between the main numbers is divided up using marks. To read a scale you must first work out what the distance between two marks represents.

## Practice Exercise 20.1

1. 2.564 = 2 + 0.5 + 0.06 + 0.004.   Write these numbers in the same way.
   (a) 4.7          (b) 5.55          (c) 7.62          (d) 37.928          (e) 7.541

2. Write down the numbers shown by these diagrams.
   (a)           (b)

3. On these scales, what numbers are shown by the arrows?
   (a)
   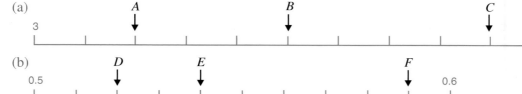
   (b)

4. (a) Copy the number line.

   8          9          10

   (b) Draw and label arrows to show the following numbers.
       (i)  *A* at 8.6          (ii)  *B* at 7.8          (iii)  *C* at 9.5

5. List the following decimals in ascending order.
   (a) 3.1,   3.01,   3.001,   3.15,   3.2.
   (b) 3.567,   3.657,   3.576,   3.675.
   (c) 0.1,   0.55,   0.45,   0.5,   0.15.

6. Compare the numbers   93.07   and   93.072.   Which is the smaller number?

# Non-calculator method for addition of decimals

Write the numbers in tidy columns according to place value.
This is easily done by keeping the decimal points in a vertical column.
Start the addition from the right, just as you did for whole numbers.
Use the same method for carrying as well.

**Example 3**

Work out   7.3 + 10.9.

```
   7 . 3
+ 1 0 . 9
─────────
 1 8 . 2
   ₁
```

**Example 4**

Work out   42.6 + 0.75 + 9.

```
  4 2 . 6
    0 . 7 5
+   9 . 0
─────────
  5 2 . 3 5
   ₁ ₁
```

> You can write 9 as 9.0 or 9.00 to keep your figures tidy.
> This does not change the value of the number.
> 42.6 can be written as 42.60.

## Practice Exercise 20.2

Do this exercise without using your calculator, showing your working clearly.
Having completed the exercise you can use a calculator to check your answers.

1.  Work out.
    (a)  3.6 + 15.2    (b)  2.6 + 3.8    (c)  14.8 + 3.5    (d)  23.4 + 9.7
    (e)  5.14 + 3.72   (f)  8.36 + 4.74  (g)  6.48 + 5.9    (h)  11.8 + 5.69
    (i)  7.065 + 5.384 (j)  17.93 + 8.09 (k)  5.06 + 27.3   (l)  12.7 + 5.463

2.  The length of a car is 4.7 metres.
    The length of a trailer is 2.45 metres.
    What is the total length of the car and trailer?

3.  Last week, Matt bought 17.6 litres of petrol on Tuesday and 18.5 litres of petrol
    on Saturday. How many litres of petrol did Matt buy last week?

4.

| 3.2 | 4.1 | 1.6 | 2.5 | 0.8 |

    When added together, which two of these numbers give:
    (a)  the highest total,    (b)  the lowest total,    (c)  a total closest to 5?

5.  Work out.
    (a)  6.54 + 0.27 + 0.03    (b)  2.22 + 0.78 + 0.07    (c)  79.1 + 7 + 0.23
    (d)  5.564 + 0.017 + 10.2  (e)  9.123 + 0.71 + 6.2    (f)  16 + 2.98 + 5.9

6.  In bobsleigh the times of four runs are added together.

| Team A records: | 37.03 sec | 37.76 sec | 36.89 sec | 37.25 sec |
| Team B records: | 36.87 sec | 37.51 sec | 37.03 sec | 38.12 sec |
| Team C records: | 37.27 sec | 37.45 sec | 37.64 sec | 36.72 sec |

    (a)  Work out the total time for each team.
    (b)  The team with the lowest time wins. Put the teams in order 1st, 2nd and 3rd.

## Non-calculator method for subtraction of decimals

Write the numbers in tidy columns according to place value.
This is easily done by keeping the decimal points in a vertical column.
Start the subtraction from the right, just as you did for whole numbers.
Use the same method for borrowing as well.

### Example 5

Work out   $5.6 - 3.8$.

$$\begin{array}{r} {}^4\cancel{5}^{1}.6 \\ -\ 3.8 \\ \hline 1.8 \end{array}$$

You can use addition to check your subtraction.
Does   $1.8 + 3.8 = 5.6$?

### Example 6

Work out   $17.1 - 8.72$.

$$\begin{array}{r} {}^6 1\cancel{7}^{10}.\cancel{1}^{1}0 \\ -\ 8.72 \\ \hline 8.38 \end{array}$$

**Useful tip:**
Writing 17.1 as 17.10 can make the working easier. This does not change the value of 17.1.

*Check the answers by addition.*

## Money

1360p can be written as £13.60.

| complete number of pounds, 13 | → £13.60 ← | number of pence, 60 |

£6 can be written as £6.00.

There must be exactly **two** figures after the decimal point when a decimal point is used to record amounts of money.

### Example 7

I buy a newspaper for 45p, a set of batteries for £2.50 and a book of stamps for £2.
What is the total cost?
How much change should I get from £5?

Working in pounds.

$$\begin{array}{r} 0.45 \\ 2.50 \\ +\ 2.00 \\ \hline 4.95 \end{array} \qquad \begin{array}{r} 5.00 \\ -\ 4.95 \\ \hline 0.05 \end{array}$$

The total cost is £4.95.         The change is £0.05 or 5p.

## Other uses of decimal notation

Many measurements are recorded using decimals, including time, distance, weight, volume, etc.
The same rules for addition and subtraction can be applied if all the measurements involved are recorded using the same units.

## Multiplying a decimal number by a whole number

- Ignore the decimal point and multiply the numbers using long multiplication.
- Count the total number of decimal places in the numbers being multiplied together.
- Place the decimal point so that the answer has the same number of decimal places.

## Example 8

Work out   $1.7 \times 4$.

$$\begin{array}{r} 1.7 \\ \times 4 \\ \hline 6.8 \\ \hline ^2 \end{array}$$

1.7 has 1 decimal place.

6.8   The answer has 1 decimal place.

## Example 9

Work out   $8 \times £1.65$.

$8 \times 1.65$   is the same as   $1.65 \times 8$.

$$\begin{array}{r} 1.65 \\ \times 8 \\ \hline 13.20 \\ \hline _5 \ _4 \end{array}$$

1.65 has 2 decimal places.

13.20   The answer has 2 decimal places.

$8 \times £1.65 = £13.20$

## Practice Exercise 20.3

Do this exercise without using your calculator, showing your working clearly.
Having completed the exercise you can use a calculator to check your answers.

1.  Work out.
    (a)  $6.7 - 2.3$
    (b)  $9.47 - 3.24$
    (c)  $7.4 - 2.8$
    (d)  $24.5 - 9.7$
    (e)  $12.48 - 7.52$
    (f)  $37.6 - 16.8$
    (g)  $4.7 - 2.56$
    (h)  $10 - 4.78$
    (i)  $9.57 - 4.567$
    (j)  $9.13 - 7.89$
    (k)  $14.2 - 5.16$
    (l)  $3.1 - 1.204$

2.  Add these amounts of money. Calculate the change from the given amount.
    (a)  (i)  45p, 63p, 79p, £1.43    (ii)  What is the change from £5?
    (b)  (i)  31p, £0.25, 27p    (ii)  What is the change from £10?

3.  Fred cuts three pieces of wood of length 0.95 m, 1.67 m and 2.5 m
    from a plank 6 m long.
    How much wood is left?

4.  Kevin is 0.15 m shorter than Sally. Sally is 1.7 m tall. How tall is Kevin?

5.  Swimmer A finishes the 100 m freestyle in 51.371 seconds.
    Swimmer B finishes in 52.090 seconds.
    How long after Swimmer A does Swimmer B finish?

6.  Work out.
    (a)  $0.6 \times 2$
    (b)  $1.7 \times 5$
    (c)  $3.2 \times 4$
    (d)  $12 \times 0.3$
    (e)  $5 \times 2.6$
    (f)  $8 \times 2.2$
    (g)  $6 \times 1.8$
    (h)  $4.3 \times 7$
    (i)  $3 \times 9.6$
    (j)  $87 \times 0.4$
    (k)  $15 \times 2.14$
    (l)  $0.024 \times 23$

7.  Work out.
    (a)  $5.6 + 2.8 - 3.1$
    (b)  $2.75 + 3.6 - 1.46$
    (c)  $24.1 + 11.05 - 12.8$
    (d)  $2.65 + 7.278 - 3.6$
    (e)  $15.6 - 4.78 + 6.9$
    (f)  $36.9 - 2.74 + 12.784$

8.  A puzzle costs £1.90. How much will 4 puzzles cost?

9.  A cup of coffee costs £1.15.
    (a)  How much will I have to pay for 7 cups?
    (b)  How much change will I get from £10?

**10.** I buy 5 kites which cost £2.99 each.
   (a) What is the total cost?   (b) How much change will I get from £20?

**11.** Erin buys four cheeseburgers costing £2.85 each and two cans of cola costing 87p each.
   How much change does she get from £20?

## Non-calculator methods for division involving decimals

Use the same method of working as you used for dividing whole numbers.
The decimal point moves vertically to the same position in the answer.

Work out   $9 \div 4$.

$$4 \overline{)9.{}^1 0\, {}^2 0} \qquad 2.2\, 5$$

Starting from the left:
$9 \div 4 = 2$ remainder 1,   which is 2 carry 1.
$10 \div 4 = 2$ remainder 2,   which is 2 carry 2.
$20 \div 4 = 5$

> Noughts are added until the division is finished.

So,   $9 \div 4 = 2.25$.

You can check your division by multiplying.   *Does   $2.25 \times 4 = 9$?*

| Example 10 | Example 11 |
|---|---|
| 8 bandages cost £14. How much does each bandage cost? | Work out   $11.06 \div 7$. |
| You must work out   $14 \div 8$. | $$7 \overline{)1 1.0\, {}^4 6\, {}^5}$$ $$1.5\, 8$$ |
| $$8 \overline{)1 4.{}^6 0\, {}^4 0}$$ $$1.7\, 5$$ | So,   $11.06 \div 7 = 15.8$. |
| One bandage costs £1.75. | |

> Noughts can be added to the end of a decimal.
> Adding noughts does not change the value of the number.
> 14 has the same value as 14.00.
> Continue dividing until either there is no remainder or the required accuracy is obtained.

## Practice Exercise 20.4

Do this exercise without using your calculator, showing your working clearly.
Having completed the exercise you can use a calculator to check your answers.

**1.** Work out.
   (a) $6 \div 5$    (b) $13 \div 2$    (c) $9 \div 4$    (d) $18 \div 5$
   (e) $375 \div 6$    (f) $155 \div 4$    (g) $139 \div 5$    (h) $14 \div 8$

**2.** Work out.
   (a) $9.42 \div 3$    (b) $9.6 \div 5$    (c) $5.04 \div 8$    (d) $2.72 \div 4$
   (e) $15.6 \div 6$    (f) $2.456 \div 4$    (g) $2.61 \div 5$    (h) $18.72 \div 9$

**3.** 8 switches cost £26. How much does each switch cost?

**4.** The price of a can of cola in four shops was:   85p,   89p,   78p,   82p
   Find the average price of the cola.

5. A 3-litre bottle of lemonade costs £3.84. What is the cost of 1 litre of lemonade?

6. A pack of 7 tubes of oil paint costs £9.45.
   How much does each tube of oil paint cost?

7. The number of students in six classes on Friday were: 28, 19, 21, 27, 14, 20.
   What was the average number of students in each class?

## Changing decimals to fractions

**How to change a decimal to a fraction:**

Change 0.12 to a fraction.                                      0.12

Write the decimal without the decimal point.                    12
*This will be the numerator (top number).*

The denominator (bottom number) is a power of 10.   $\frac{12}{100}$   | Fractions are covered in further detail in Chapter 22.
*The number of noughts is the same as the number of*
*decimal places in the original decimal.*

Divide both the numerator and denominator by          Divide by 4
the largest possible number.
*This gives the fraction in its simplest form.*          $\frac{3}{25}$

### Example 12

Write the following decimals as fractions in their simplest form.

(a) $0.3 = \frac{3}{10}$

(b) $0.6 = \frac{6}{10} = \frac{3}{5}$

(c) $0.45 = \frac{45}{100} = \frac{9}{20}$

(d) $1.5 = 1 + 0.5$
$= 1 + \frac{5}{10}$
$= 1 + \frac{1}{2}$
$= 1\frac{1}{2}$   | $1\frac{1}{2}$ is called a **mixed number**. It is a mixture of whole numbers and fractions.

## Practice Exercise 20.5

1. Write the following decimals as fractions in their simplest form.
   (a) 0.25      (b) 0.5      (c) 0.75      (d) 0.1

2. Write the following decimals as fractions in their simplest form.
   (a) 0.7      (b) 0.4      (c) 0.01      (d) 0.2
   (e) 0.05     (f) 0.15     (g) 0.52      (h) 0.07
   (i) 0.125    (j) 0.65     (k) 0.6       (l) 0.95

3. Change these decimals into mixed numbers.
   (a) 1.7      (b) 2.3      (c) 1.4       (d) 3.25
   (e) 4.8      (f) 12.1     (g) 16.75     (h) 5.05

## Key Points

▶ A **decimal point** is used to separate the whole number part from the decimal part of the number.

**You should be able to:**

▶ Place decimals in order by considering place value.

▶ Add and subtract decimals, multiply a decimal by a whole number.

▶ Use non-calculator methods for division involving decimals.

▶ Use decimal notation for money and other measures.

▶ Change decimals to fractions.

## Review Exercise 20

1. List the following decimals in order, smallest first.

    | 0.7    0.5    0.8    0.85    0.55 |

2. On these scales, what numbers are shown by the arrows?

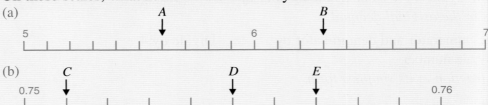

3. Look at these decimals.    | 0.07    0.6    0.09    0.1 |

    (a) Which is the smallest number?    (b) Which is the largest number?

4. List the following decimals in descending order.
    (a) 9.87, 8.79, 9.78, 8.97.    (b) 0.00015, 0.15, 1.5, 0.015.

5. Four parcels weigh 1.6 kg, 0.8 kg, 0.55 kg and 1.25 kg.
   What is the total weight of the parcels?

6. A 4 × 100 m relay team runs the four stages in:
        10.01 s,   9.93 s,   10.15 s   and   9.91 s.
   What is the overall time for the team?

7. Two pieces of wood of length 0.97 m and 1.78 m are sawn from a plank 5.12 m long.
   How much wood is left?

8. Work out.
    (a) 8.215 + 7.6 − 3.55       (b) 16.41 + 8.7 − 3.78
    (c) 12.8 − 3.65 + 4.924      (d) 23.47 + 31.6 − 19.815

9. Work out.
    (a) 1.7 × 3    (b) 7 × 2.4    (c) £3.15 × 4    (d) 5 × £8.45    (e) 35 ÷ 8

10. Write 0.45 as a fraction. Give your answer in its simplest form.

# 21 Approximation *and* Estimation

## Approximation

In real-life it is not always necessary to use exact numbers.
A number can be **rounded** to an **approximate** number.
Numbers are rounded according to how accurately we wish to give details.
For example, the distance to the Sun can be given as 93 million miles.

*Can you think of other situations where approximations might be used?*

## Rounding in real-life problems

In a real-life problem a rounding must be used which gives a sensible answer.

Penny is arranging a BBQ. 50 people have been invited.
She caters for everyone to have one burger.
Burgers are sold in packs of 12.
How many packs of burgers should she buy?

The answer is found by working out   $50 \div 12$.
In 4 packs, there are   $4 \times 12 = 48$ burgers.
In 5 packs, there are   $5 \times 12 = 60$ burgers.
$50 \div 12 = 4$ remainder 2.
Penny must buy 5 packs in order that everybody has one burger.
(In fact she will have 10 left over for those who might want a second burger.)

### Example 1

A year group in a school is going to the
National Museum.
There are 242 students and teachers going.
Each coach can carry 55 passengers.
How many coaches should be ordered?

$242 \div 55 = 4.4$
This should be rounded up to 5.

4 coaches can only carry 220 passengers
$(4 \times 55 = 220)$.

### Example 2

Filing cabinets are to be placed along
a wall.
The available space is 460 cm.
Each cabinet is 80 cm wide.
How many can be fitted in?

$460 \div 80 = 5.75$
This should be rounded down to 5.

Although the answer is nearly 6,
the 6th cabinet would not fit in.

## Practice Exercise 21.1

Try to do this exercise without using a calculator.

1. 49 students are waiting to go to the Sports Stadium.
   A minibus can take 15 passengers at a time.
   How many trips are required?

2. A classroom wall is 700 cm long.
   How many tables, each 120 cm long, could be fitted along the wall?

3. 76 people are waiting to go to the top of Canary Wharf.
   The lift can only take 8 at a time.
   How many times must the lift go up?

4. There are 210 students in a year group.
   They each need an exercise book.
   The exercise books are sold in packs of 25.
   How many packs should be ordered?

5. Car parking spaces should be 2.5 m wide.
   How many can be fitted into a car park which is 61 m wide?

6. A sweet manufacturer puts 17 sweets in a bag.
   How many bags can be made up if there are 500 sweets?

7. Kim needs 26 candles for a cake.
   The candles are sold in packs of 4.
   How many packs must she buy?

## Rounding using decimal places

What is the cost of 1.75 metres of material costing £3.99 a metre?
$$1.75 \times 3.99 = 6.9825$$
The cost of the material is £6.9825 or 698.25p.

As you can only pay in pence, a sensible answer is
£6.98, correct to two decimal places (nearest penny).
This means that there are only two decimal places after the decimal point.

> Often it is not necessary to use an exact answer.
> Sometimes it is impossible, or impractical, to use the exact answer.

## To round a number to a given number of decimal places

> When rounding a number to one, two or more decimal places:
> 1. Write the number using one more decimal place than asked for.
> 2. Look at the last decimal place and
>    - if the figure is 5 or more round up,
>    - if the figure is less than 5 round down.
> 3. When answering a problem remember to include any units and state the degree of approximation used.

### Example 3

Write 2.76435 to 2 decimal places.

Look at the third decimal place. **4**
This is less than 5, so, round down.
Answer 2.76

### Example 4

Write 7.104 to 2 decimal places.

$7.104 = 7.10$ to 2 d.p.
The zero is written down because it shows the accuracy used, 2 decimal places.

Notation: Often decimal place is shortened to d.p.

## Practice Exercise **21.2**

1. Write the number 3.9617 correct to (a) 2 decimal places, (b) 1 decimal place.

2. The display on a calculator shows the result of 34 ÷ 7. What is the result correct to two decimal places?

   `4.857142857`

3. 68.847 kg — The scales show Gary's weight. Write Gary's weight correct to one decimal place.

4. Copy and complete this table.

| Number | 2.367 | 0.964 | 0.965 | 15.2806 | 0.056 | 4.991 | 4.996 |
|---|---|---|---|---|---|---|---|
| d.p. | 1 | 2 | 2 | 1 | 2 | 2 | 2 |
| Answer | 2.4 | | | | | | |

5. Carry out these calculations giving the answers correct to (a) 1 d.p. (b) 2 d.p.
   (i) 6.12 × 7.54
   (ii) 89.1 × 0.67
   (iii) 90.53 × 6.29
   (iv) 98.6 ÷ 5.78
   (v) 67.2 ÷ 101.45

6. In each of these short problems decide upon the most suitable accuracy for the answer. Then calculate the answer. Give a reason for your degree of accuracy.
   (a) One gallon is 4.54596… litres. How many litres is 9 gallons?
   (b) What is the cost of 0.454 kg of cheese at £5.21 per kilogram?
   (c) The total length of 7 equal sticks, lying end to end, is 250 cm. How long is each stick?
   (d) A packet of 6 bandages costs £7.99. How much does one bandage cost?
   (e) Petrol costs 133.9 pence a litre. I buy 15.6 litres. How much will I have to pay?

## Rounding using significant figures

Consider the calculation 600.02 × 7500.97 = 4500732.0194
To 1 d.p. it is 4500732.0, to 2 d.p. it is 4500732.02.
The answers to either 1 d.p. or 2 d.p. are very close to the actual answer and are almost as long.
There is little advantage in using either of these two roundings.
The point of a rounding is that it is a more convenient number to use.
Another kind of rounding uses **significant figures**.
The **most** significant figure in a number is the figure which has the greatest place value.
Consider the number 237.
The figure 2 has the greatest place value. It is worth 200.
So, 2 is the most significant figure.
In the number 0.00328, the figure 3 has the greatest place value.
So, 3 is the most significant figure.

> Noughts which are used to locate the decimal point and preserve the place value of other figures are not significant.

## To round a number to one significant figure

When rounding a number to one significant figure:
1. Start from the most significant figure.
2. Look at the next figure to the right of this and
   - if the figure is 5 or more round up,
   - if the figure is less than 5 round down.
3. Add noughts, as necessary, to locate the decimal point and preserve the place value.

### Example 5

Round the numbers   75,   135,   1478   and   2500   to one significant figure.

| Number | Rounded to 1 sig. fig. |
|--------|------------------------|
| 75     | 80                     |
| 135    | 100                    |
| 1478   | 1000                   |
| 2500   | 3000                   |

**Notation:**
Often significant figure is shortened to sig. fig.

### Example 6

Write   0.000364907   to 1 significant figure.

The figure after the first significant figure 3 is 6.
This is 5 or more, so round up, 3 becomes 4.
So,   0.000364907 = 0.0004   to 1 sig. fig.

Notice that the noughts before the 4 locate the decimal point and preserve place value.

## Choosing a suitable degree of accuracy

In some calculations it would be wrong to use the complete answer from the calculator.
The result of a calculation involving measurement should not be given to a greater degree of accuracy than the measurements used in the calculation.

### Example 7

What is the area of a rectangle measuring 4.6 cm by 7.2 cm?

**Note:**
To find the area of a rectangle: multiply length by breadth.

$4.6 \times 7.2 = 33.12$
Since the measurements used in the calculation (4.6 cm and 7.2 cm)
are given to 1 decimal place, the answer could be as well.
$33.1 \, cm^2$ is a suitable answer.   $33 \, cm^2$, to the nearest whole number, would also be appropriate.

## Practice Exercise 21.3

1. Write these numbers correct to one significant figure.
   - (a)  17
   - (b)  523
   - (c)  350
   - (d)  1900
   - (e)  24.6
   - (f)  0.083
   - (g)  0.086
   - (h)  0.00948
   - (i)  0.0095

2. This display shows the result of   $3400 \div 7$.
   What is the result correct to one significant figure?

   `485.7142857`

3. Carry out these calculations giving the answers correct to 1 sig. fig.
   (a) $672 \times 123$  (b) $6.72 \times 12.3$  (c) $78.2 \times 12.8$
   (d) $7.19 \div 987.5$  (e) $124 \div 65300$

4. A rectangular field measures 18.6 m by 25.4 m.
   Calculate the area of the field, giving your answer to a suitable degree of accuracy.

5. In each of these short problems decide upon the most suitable accuracy for the answer.
   Then work out the answer, remembering to state the units.
   Give a reason for your degree of accuracy.
   (a) Find the area of a rectangle measuring 13.2 cm by 11.9 cm.
   (b) Find the area of a football pitch measuring 99 m by 62 m.
   (c) The total length of 13 tables placed end to end measures 16 m.
       How long is each table?
   (d) Find the area of carpet needed to cover a rectangular floor measuring
       3.65 m by 4.35 m.

## Estimation

It is always a good idea to find an **estimate** for any calculation.
An estimate is used to check that the answer to a calculation is of the right magnitude (size).
If the answer is very different to the estimate then a mistake has possibly been made.

Estimation is done by approximating every number in the calculation to one significant figure.
The calculation is then done using the approximated values.

### Example 8

Estimate $421 \times 48$.

Round 421 to one significant figure: 400
Round 48 to one significant figure: 50
$400 \times 50 = 20\ 000$

*Use a calculator to calculate $421 \times 48$.*
*Comment on your answer.*

### Example 9

Estimate $608 \div 19$.

Round the numbers in the calculation to
one significant figure.
$600 \div 20 = 30$

*Use a calculator to calculate $608 \div 19$.*
*Comment on your answer.*

## Practice Exercise 21.4

1. Last year, Hannah paid these four telephone bills:

   | £48 | £89 | £62 | £103 |

   By using approximations to one significant figure, **estimate** her total telephone bill
   for the year.

2. Bernard plans to buy a conservatory costing £8328 and furniture costing £984.
   (a) By using approximations, estimate the total amount Bernard plans to spend.
   (b) Find the actual cost.

3. Make estimates to these calculations by using approximations to one significant figure.
   (a) (i) $39 \times 21$  (ii) $115 \times 18$  (iii) $797 \times 53$  (iv) $913 \times 59$
   (b) (i) $76 \div 18$  (ii) $597 \div 29$  (iii) $889 \div 61$  (iv) $3897 \div 82$

4. Lilly ordered 39 prints of her holiday photographs.
   Each print cost 52 pence.
   Use suitable approximations to **estimate** the total cost of the prints.
   Show your working.

5. Chairs are arranged in rows.
   There are 18 chairs in each row.
   Estimate the total number of chairs in 27 rows.

6. A book contains 576 pages which are grouped into 32 chapters of equal length.
   Estimate the number of pages in each chapter.

7. Last year Alex used 964 litres of petrol to drive 15 209 kilometres.
   Use suitable approximations to estimate her petrol consumption in kilometres per litre.

8. (a) When estimating the answer to $29 \times 48$,
       the approximations 30 and 50 are used.
       How can you tell that the estimate must be bigger than the actual answer?
   (b) When estimating the answer to $182 \div 13$,
       the approximations 200 and 10 are used.
       Will the estimate be bigger or smaller than the actual answer?
       Explain your answer.

## Accuracy in measurement

No measurement is ever exact.
Measures which can lie within a range of possible values are called **continuous measures**.
The value of a continuous measure depends on the accuracy of whatever is making
the measurement.

Jane is 160 cm tall to the nearest 10 cm.
What are the limits between which her actual height lies?

Height is a continuous measure.
When rounding to the nearest 10 cm:
The minimum value that rounds to 160 cm is 155 cm.
155 cm is the minimum height that Jane can be.

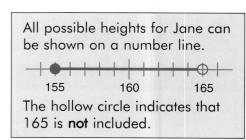

All possible heights for Jane can
be shown on a number line.

The hollow circle indicates that
165 is **not** included.

The maximum value that rounds to 160 cm is 164.999… cm.
164.999… cm is the maximum height that Jane can be.
For ease the value 164.999… cm is normally called 165 cm.

So, Jane's actual height is any height from 155 cm to 165 cm.
This can be written as the inequality:
155 cm $\leqslant$ Jane's height $<$ 165 cm

## Example 10

The length of a pencil is 17 cm to the nearest centimetre.
What are the limits between which the actual length of the pencil lies?

When rounding to the nearest centimetre:

The smallest value that rounds to 17 cm is 16.5 cm.
The largest value that rounds to 17 cm is 17.4999… cm.

For ease, 17.4999… is called 17.5.

So, the actual length of the pencil lies between 16.5 cm and 17.5 cm.

16.5 cm $\leqslant$ length of pencil $<$ 17.5 cm

---

To find the limits:
- Halve the accuracy, $\frac{1}{2}a$.
- Lower limit = estimate $- \frac{1}{2}a$.
- Upper limit = estimate $+ \frac{1}{2}a$.

## Example 11

A concrete block weighs 1.8 kg, correct to the nearest tenth of a kilogram.
What is the minimum possible weight of the concrete block?

Minimum weight = 1.8 kg $-$ 0.05 kg
Minimum weight = 1.75 kg

---

## Practice Exercise 21.5

1. A girl's height is 168 cm, correct to the nearest centimetre.
   What is the minimum possible height of the girl?

2. Harry weighs 49 kg, correct to the nearest kilogram.
   What is the maximum possible weight he could be?

3. The height of a building is 9 m, correct to the nearest metre.
   Copy and complete the inequality:     …… $\leqslant$ height of building $<$ ……

4. A brick weighs 840 g, correct to the nearest 10 g.
   What is the minimum and maximum possible weight of the brick?

5. A piece of cheese weighs 285 grams, correct to the nearest 5 grams.
   What is the maximum possible weight of the piece of cheese?

6. An athlete completed a race in 11.6 seconds, correct to the nearest tenth of a second.
   What is the minimum possible time the athlete could have taken?

7. A pane of glass weighs 9.4 kg, correct to one decimal place.
   What is the minimum possible weight of the pane of glass?

8. A glass contains 24 ml of milk, correct to the nearest millilitre.
   Find the minimum possible number of millilitres in four glasses.

---

## Key Points

▶ In real-life it is not always necessary to use exact numbers. A number can be **rounded** to an **approximate** number. Numbers are rounded according to how accurately we wish to give details. For example, the distance to the Sun can be given as 93 million miles.

▶ In real-life problems a rounding must be used which gives a sensible answer.

► You should be able to approximate using **decimal places**.

> Write the number using one more decimal place than asked for.
> Look at the last decimal place and
> - if the figure is 5 or more round up,
> - if the figure is less than 5 round down.

► You should be able to approximate to the most **significant figure**.

> Start from the most significant figure.
> Look at the next figure to the right of this and
> - if the figure is 5 or more round up,
> - if the figure is less than 5 round down.
> Add noughts, as necessary, to preserve the place value.

► You should be able to choose a suitable degree of accuracy for calculations involving measurement.

► You should be able to use approximations to estimate that the actual answer to a calculation is of the right order of magnitude.

> Estimation is done by approximating every number in the calculation to one significant figure.
> The calculation is then done using the approximated values.

► You should be able to recognise limitations on the accuracy of data and measurements.

## Review Exercise 21

1. A group of 175 people are going to Glasgow. Coaches can take 39 passengers. How many coaches should be ordered?

2. Write these numbers correct to 2 decimal places.
   (a) 28.714   (b) 6.91288   (c) 12.397   (d) 0.0418   (e) 0.00912

3. Round these numbers to 1 significant figure.
   (a) 72   (b) 138   (c) 754   (d) 650   (e) 78   (f) 987

4. The display shows the result of 179 ÷ 7. What is the result correct to:

   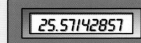

   (a) two decimal places,
   (b) one decimal place,
   (c) one significant figure?

5. Find **estimates** to these calculations by using approximations to one significant figure.
   (a) 86.5 × 1.9   (b) 2016 ÷ 49.8

6. Daniel has a part-time job in a factory.
   He is paid £36 for each shift he works. Last year he worked 108 shifts.
   Estimate Daniel's total pay for the year. You must show all your working.

7. "You require 2700 tiles to tile your swimming pool."
   This figure is correct to the nearest 100.
   What is the greatest number of tiles needed?

 **Fractions**

---

## Activity

(a) Each diagram shows a different way of shading one half of a square.

   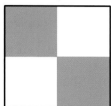

Find some more ways of shading one half of a square.

(b) Each diagram shows a different way of dividing the square into quarters.

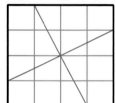 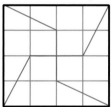 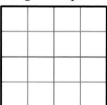 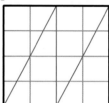

Find some more ways of dividing a square into quarters.

---

## Shaded fractions

What fraction of this rectangle is shaded?

The rectangle is divided into **eight** squares.
The squares are all the same size.
**Three** of the squares are shaded.
$\frac{3}{8}$ of the rectangle is shaded.

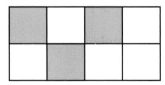

In a fraction:
The top number is called the **numerator**.
The bottom number is called the **denominator**.

### Example 1

What fraction of this rectangle is shaded?

The rectangle is divided into 10 equal parts.
Three of the equal parts are shaded.

So, $\frac{3}{10}$ of the rectangle is shaded.

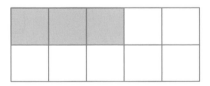

### Example 2

Shade $\frac{2}{5}$ of a rectangle.

Draw a rectangle and divide it into 5 equal parts.
Then shade two of the parts.

1. What fraction of each of these rectangles is shaded?

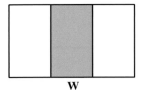 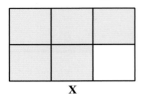 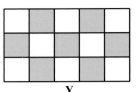 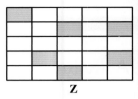

      W            X            Y            Z

2. Make two copies of each rectangle.

   (a) Shade $\frac{1}{4}$ of rectangle A.

   (b) Shade $\frac{3}{4}$ of rectangle A.

   (c) Shade $\frac{1}{5}$ of rectangle B.

   (d) Shade $\frac{3}{5}$ of rectangle B.

   (e) Shade $\frac{1}{2}$ of rectangle C.

   (f) Shade $\frac{3}{4}$ of rectangle C.

   (g) Shade $\frac{2}{3}$ of rectangle D.

   (h) Shade $\frac{6}{9}$ of rectangle D.

   (i) Shade $\frac{1}{3}$ of rectangle E.

   (j) Shade $\frac{3}{12}$ of rectangle E.

   (k) Shade $\frac{3}{7}$ of rectangle F.

   (l) Shade $\frac{12}{28}$ of rectangle F.

**Rectangle A** 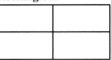       **Rectangle B**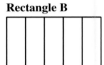

**Rectangle C**        **Rectangle D**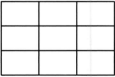

**Rectangle E**        **Rectangle F**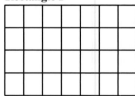

3. What fraction of each of these diagrams is shaded?

   (a)      (b)      (c)      (d)

 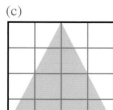 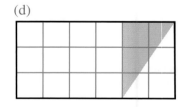

4. What fraction of each of these shapes is shaded?

   (a)      (b)      (c)      (d)      (e)

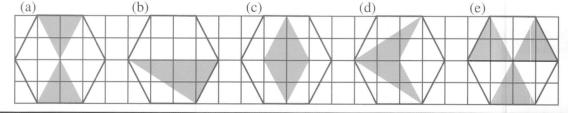

**5.**

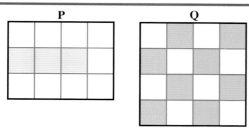

P    Q    R    S

Look at these diagrams.

(a) Which diagram has $\frac{3}{12}$ shaded?    (b) Which diagram has $\frac{1}{4}$ shaded?

(c) Which diagram has $\frac{6}{15}$ shaded?    (d) Which diagram has $\frac{2}{5}$ shaded?

(e) Which diagram has $\frac{1}{2}$ shaded?    (f) Which diagram has $\frac{1}{3}$ shaded?

**6.** You are asked to design a flag.

(a) In one design, $\frac{1}{2}$ of the flag is red and $\frac{1}{3}$ is blue. The rest of the flag is white.
   (i) On squared paper, draw some 2 by 3 rectangles and design possible flags.
   (ii) What fraction of the flag is white?

(b) In another design, $\frac{2}{3}$ of the flag is red and $\frac{1}{4}$ is blue. The rest of the flag is white.
   (i) On squared paper, draw some 3 by 4 rectangles and design possible flags.
   (ii) What fraction of the flag is white?

## Finding fractions of quantities

**Example 3**

Find $\frac{2}{5}$ of £65.

Divide £65 into 5 equal parts.
£65 ÷ 5 = £13.

| 13 | 13 | 13 | 13 | 13 |
|----|----|----|----|----|

Each of these parts is $\frac{1}{5}$ of £65.

Two of these parts are $\frac{2}{5}$ of £65.

| 13 | 13 | 13 | 13 | 13 |
|----|----|----|----|----|

So, $\frac{2}{5}$ of £65 = 2 × £13 = £26.

**Example 4**

A coat costing £138 is reduced by $\frac{1}{3}$.
What is the reduced price of the coat?

Find $\frac{1}{3}$ of £138.

$\frac{1}{3}$ of £138 = £138 ÷ 3 = £46.

So, reduced price = £138 − £46
                  = £92.

## Practice Exercise 22.2    Do not use a calculator for questions 1 to 4.

**1.** Calculate:
(a) $\frac{1}{4}$ of 12    (b) $\frac{1}{5}$ of 20    (c) $\frac{1}{10}$ of 30    (d) $\frac{1}{6}$ of 48    (e) $\frac{2}{5}$ of 20
(f) $\frac{3}{10}$ of 30    (g) $\frac{2}{7}$ of 42    (h) $\frac{5}{9}$ of 36    (i) $\frac{5}{6}$ of 48    (j) $\frac{3}{8}$ of 32

**2.** Richard has 30 marbles. He gives $\frac{1}{5}$ of them away.
(a) How many marbles does he give away?
(b) How many marbles has he got left?

3. Stella has collected 48 tokens. She needs $\frac{1}{6}$ more to claim a prize.
   What is the total number of tokens she needs to claim a prize?

4. Aisha has 36 balloons. She sells $\frac{2}{9}$ of them. How many balloons has she got left?

5. Alfie collects £12.50 for charity. He gives $\frac{3}{5}$ of it to Oxfam.
   How much does he give to other charities?

6. Ken has saved £5.60. Paula has saved $\frac{3}{8}$ more than Ken. How much has Paula saved?

7. In a sale all prices are reduced by $\frac{3}{10}$.
   What is the sale price of a microwave which was originally priced at £212?

8. Lauren and Amelia share a bar of chocolate. The chocolate bar has 24 squares.
   Lauren eats $\frac{3}{8}$ of the bar. Amelia eats $\frac{5}{12}$ of the bar.
   (a) How many squares has Lauren eaten?
   (b) How many squares has Amelia eaten?
   (c) What fraction of the bar is left?

## Fractions and decimals

All fractions can be written as decimals and vice versa.

## Changing decimals to fractions

$0.7 = \frac{7}{10}$    $0.03 = \frac{3}{100}$    $0.009 = \frac{9}{1000}$

0.35 can be written as a fraction.
Using place value:
$0.35 = \frac{3}{10} + \frac{5}{100} = \frac{30}{100} + \frac{5}{100} = \frac{35}{100}$
This can be written as a fraction in its simplest form.
$\frac{35}{100} = \frac{35 \div 5}{100 \div 5} = \frac{7}{20}$    $0.35 = \frac{35}{100} = \frac{7}{20}$

> Write **equivalent fractions** with denominator 100.
> To write an equivalent fraction, multiply the numerator and the denominator by the same number.
> $$\frac{3}{10} = \frac{3 \times 10}{10 \times 10} = \frac{30}{100}$$

### Example 5

Change the following decimals to fractions in their simplest form.
(a) 0.02                          (b) 0.225
(a) $0.02 = \frac{2}{100} = \frac{2 \div 2}{100 \div 2} = \frac{1}{50}$    (b) $0.225 = \frac{225}{1000} = \frac{225 \div 25}{1000 \div 25} = \frac{9}{40}$

## Changing fractions to decimals

### Example 6

Change the following fractions to decimals.

> $\frac{1}{5}$ means $1 \div 5$.
> $1 \div 5$ can be worked out using: short division, long division or a calculator.

(a) $\frac{1}{5}$                          (b) $\frac{11}{20}$

(a) $\frac{1}{5} = 1 \div 5 = 0.2$    (b) $\frac{11}{20} = 11 \div 20 = 0.55$

## Practice Exercise 22.3    Do not use a calculator for questions 1 to 4.

1. Match the decimals in **Box A** with the fractions in **Box B**.

   **Box A:** 0.5, 0.2, 0.75, 0.7, 0.01     **Box B:** $\frac{3}{4}$, $\frac{1}{2}$, $\frac{1}{100}$, $\frac{1}{5}$, $\frac{7}{10}$

2. Change the following decimals to fractions in their simplest form.
   (a)  0.12      (b)  0.6      (c)  0.32      (d)  0.175      (e)  0.45      (f)  0.65
   (g)  0.22      (h)  0.202    (i)  0.28      (j)  0.555      (k)  0.625     (l)  0.84

3. Change the following fractions to decimals.
   (a) (i) $\frac{1}{10}$ (ii) $\frac{3}{10}$ (iii) $\frac{7}{10}$   (b) (i) $\frac{1}{4}$ (ii) $\frac{1}{2}$ (iii) $\frac{3}{4}$
   (c) (i) $\frac{3}{20}$ (ii) $\frac{7}{20}$ (iii) $\frac{19}{20}$   (d) (i) $\frac{4}{25}$ (ii) $\frac{9}{25}$ (iii) $\frac{23}{25}$

4. Change these fractions to decimals.
   (a) $\frac{1}{8}$     (b) $\frac{5}{8}$     (c) $\frac{9}{40}$     (d) $\frac{29}{40}$

5. Change these fractions to decimals. Give your answers correct to two decimal places.
   (a) $\frac{1}{3}$     (b) $\frac{1}{6}$     (c) $\frac{3}{7}$     (d) $\frac{5}{11}$     (e) $\frac{7}{9}$

## Key Points

▶ The top number of a fraction is called the **numerator**.
  The bottom number of a fraction is called the **denominator**.

▶ You should be able to find a fraction of a quantity.

▶ All fractions can be written as decimals.

## Review Exercise 22

1. (a)  What fraction of the
       rectangle is shaded?         (b) Copy and shade $\frac{1}{4}$
                                                        of this rectangle.

2. (a)  What fraction of the diagram has been shaded?
       Give your answer in its simplest form.
   (b)  How many extra squares must be shaded
       so that altogether $\frac{1}{4}$ of the diagram is shaded?

3. A necklace is made from 60 beads.
   $\frac{3}{10}$ of the beads are red.   $\frac{9}{20}$ of the beads are blue.   The rest of the beads are white.
   (a)  How many red beads are on the necklace?
   (b)  How many white beads are on the necklace?

4. Richard has 210 deckchairs for hire.
   On Saturday he rents out $\frac{3}{5}$ of his deckchairs.
   (a)  How many deckchairs does he rent out on Saturday?

   On Sunday he rents out $\frac{5}{6}$ of his deckchairs.
   (b)  How many **more** deckchairs does Richard rent out on Sunday than Saturday?

5. (a)  Change $\frac{3}{8}$ to a decimal.
   (b)  Write $\frac{2}{3}$ as a decimal, giving your answer correct to 2 decimal places.

# 23 Percentages

## The meaning of a percentage

A fraction with denominator 100 has the special name - **percentage**.
'Per cent' means 'out of 100'.
The symbol for per cent is %.
A percentage can be written as a fraction with denominator 100.

> 10% means 10 out of 100.
> 10% can be written as $\frac{10}{100}$.
> 10% is read as '10 percent'.

### Example 1

What percentage of this diagram is shaded?

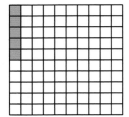

The large square is divided into 100 smaller squares.
5 of the smaller squares are shaded.
$\frac{5}{100}$ of the diagram is shaded.
$\frac{5}{100} = 5\%$
So, 5% of the diagram is shaded.

*What percentage of each of these diagrams is shaded?*

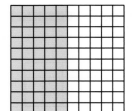 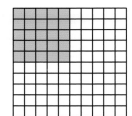 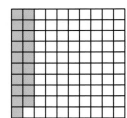 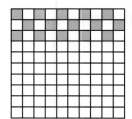

## Changing percentages to decimals and fractions

> To change a percentage to a decimal or a fraction:   **divide by 100**.

### Example 2

Write 38% as a fraction in its simplest form.

38% means '38 out of 100'.
This can be written as $\frac{38}{100}$.
$\frac{38}{100} = \frac{38 \div 2}{100 \div 2} = \frac{19}{50}$
$38\% = \frac{19}{50}$

**Remember:**
To write a fraction in its **simplest form**,
divide both the numerator and
denominator of the fraction by the **largest**
number that divides into them both.

### Example 3

Write 38% as a decimal.

$38\% = \frac{38}{100} = 38 \div 100 = 0.38$

**Remember:**
To change a fraction
to a decimal, divide
the numerator by
the denominator.

### Example 4

Write 0.5% as a decimal.

$0.5\% = \frac{0.5}{100} = 0.5 \div 100 = 0.005$

## Practice Exercise 23.1

Do not use a calculator for questions 1 to 3.

1. What percentage of each diagram is shaded?

(a) 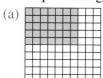  (b)   (c)   (d)

(e) 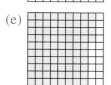  (f)   (g)   (h)

2. (a) Draw a 10 by 10 square on squared paper.
   (i) Calculate $\frac{2}{5}$ of 100.
   (ii) Shade $\frac{2}{5}$ of a 10 by 10 square.
      What percentage of the square is shaded?
   (b) Repeat (a) for the following fractions.
      (i) $\frac{3}{5}$   (ii) $\frac{7}{10}$   (iii) $\frac{9}{20}$   (iv) $\frac{6}{25}$   (v) $\frac{23}{50}$   (vi) $\frac{17}{25}$

3. Copy and complete this table to show the percentages given as:
   (a) fractions in their simplest form,   (b) decimals.

| Percentage | 10% | 20% | 25% | 50% | 75% | 80% |
|---|---|---|---|---|---|---|
| Fraction | $\frac{1}{10}$ | | | | | |
| Decimal | 0.1 | | | | | |

4. Change these percentages to fractions in their simplest form.
   (a) 15%   (b) 5%   (c) 18%   (d) 52%   (e) 23%   (f) 12.5%

5. Change these percentages to decimals.
   (a) 15%   (b) 5%   (c) 47%   (d) 72%   (e) 87.5%   (f) 150%

## Changing decimals and fractions to percentages

To change a decimal or a fraction to a percentage: **multiply by 100**.

### Example 5

Change 0.3 to a percentage.

$0.3 \times 100 = 30$
So, 0.3 as a percentage is 30%.

### Example 6

Change 0.875 to a percentage.

$0.875 \times 100 = 87.5$
So, 0.875 as a percentage is 87.5%.

### Example 7

Change $\frac{7}{10}$ to a percentage.

$\frac{7}{10} \times 100 = 7 \times 100 \div 10$
$= 700 \div 10 = 70\%$

### Example 8

Change $\frac{11}{25}$ to a percentage.

$\frac{11}{25} \times 100 = 11 \times 100 \div 25$
$= 1100 \div 25 = 44\%$

## Comparing fractions

Fractions can be compared by first writing them as percentages.

### Example 9

Ben scored 17 out of 20 in a Maths test and 21 out of 25 in a History test.
Which is Ben's better mark?

Change each mark to a percentage.

Maths: $\frac{17}{20}$    $\frac{17}{20} \times 100 = 17 \times 100 \div 20 = 85\%$

History: $\frac{21}{25}$    $\frac{21}{25} \times 100 = 21 \times 100 \div 25 = 84\%$

So, Ben's better mark was his Maths mark of 85%.

### Practice Exercise 23.2    Do not use a calculator for questions 1 to 3.

1. Copy and complete this table to work out the percentage equivalents of the fractions given.

   | Fraction | $\frac{3}{10}$ | $\frac{2}{5}$ | $\frac{3}{25}$ | $\frac{7}{20}$ |
   |---|---|---|---|---|
   | Percentage | | | | |

2. Copy and complete this table to work out the percentage equivalents of the decimals given.

   | Decimal | 0.7 | 0.45 | 0.05 | 1.2 |
   |---|---|---|---|---|
   | Percentage | | | | |

3. What is $\frac{1}{3}$ as a percentage?

4. Change these fractions to percentages.

   (a) $\frac{17}{50}$   (b) $\frac{12}{25}$   (c) $\frac{30}{200}$   (d) $\frac{4}{5}$   (e) $\frac{135}{500}$   (f) $\frac{13}{20}$   (g) $\frac{2}{3}$   (h) $\frac{2}{9}$

5. Change these decimals to percentages.

   (a) 0.15    (b) 0.32    (c) 0.125    (d) 0.07    (e) 1.12    (f) 0.015

6. Write in order of size, lowest first:

   (a) $\frac{1}{2}$   60%   $\frac{2}{5}$   0.55    (b) 43%   $\frac{9}{20}$   0.42   $\frac{11}{25}$    (c) $\frac{23}{80}$   28%   $\frac{57}{200}$   0.2805

7. Peter scores 96 out of 120. What percentage did he get?

8. Change each of these marks to a percentage.

   (a) Maths:   27 out of 30.    (b) French:   34 out of 40.
   (c) Science:   22 out of 25.    (d) Art:     48 out of 60.

9. Which rectangle has the greater percentage shaded?

   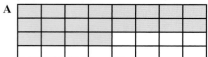 

10. In an ice hockey competition, Team A won 8 out of the 11 games
    they played whilst Team B won 5 of their 7 games.
    Which team has the better record in the competition?

# Finding a percentage of a quantity

> To find 1% of a quantity, divide the quantity by 100.
> To find 20% of a quantity, multiply 1% of the quantity by 20.
> This is the same as the method you would use to find $\frac{20}{100}$ of a quantity.

**Example 10**

Find 3% of £56.

**Step 1:** Divide by 100.
£56 ÷ 100 = £0.56

**Step 2:** Multiply by 3.

$$0.56 \leftarrow 0.56 \text{ has 2 decimal places.}$$
$$\times 3$$
$$\overline{1.68} \leftarrow \text{The answer has 2 decimal places.}$$

So, 3% of £56 = £1.68.

**Example 11**

Find 60% of 300.

$20\% = \frac{1}{5}$, so, $60\% = \frac{3}{5}$.

| Percentage | 10% | 20% | 25% | $33\frac{1}{3}\%$ | 50% |
|---|---|---|---|---|---|
| Fraction | $\frac{1}{10}$ | $\frac{1}{5}$ | $\frac{1}{4}$ | $\frac{1}{3}$ | $\frac{1}{2}$ |

Finding 60% of 300 is the same as finding $\frac{3}{5}$ of 300.

**Step 1:** Divide by 5.
300 ÷ 5 = 60

**Step 2:** Multiply by 3.
60 × 3 = 180

So, 60% of 300 = 180. *Try the examples using a calculator.*

## Practice Exercise 23.3 — Do not use a calculator for questions 1 to 4.

1. Find:
   (a) 10% of 500  (b) 20% of 700  (c) 30% of 200  (d) 25% of 60
   (e) $33\frac{1}{3}\%$ of 36  (f) 75% of 120  (g) 80% of 30  (h) 50% of 28

2. Find:
   (a) 20% of £80  (b) 75% of £20  (c) 30% of £220  (d) 60% of 20 pence

3. There are 450 seats in a theatre. 60% of the seats are in the stalls.
   How many seats are in the stalls?

4. A salesman earns a bonus of 3% of his weekly sales.
   How much bonus does the salesman earn in a week when his sales are £1400?

5. Find:
   (a) 5% of 800  (b) 85% of 20  (c) 12% of 500  (d) 32% of 200
   (e) 30% of 80 kg  (f) 35% of 800 m  (g) 45% of £25  (h) 15% of £350

6. Abbie has 300 marbles. 20% of the marbles are blue. 35% of the marbles are red.
   The rest of the marbles are white.
   (a) How many marbles are (i) blue, (ii) red?
   (b) What percentage of the marbles are white?

7. Bart invests £400 in a building society. He earns 5% interest per year.
   How much interest does he get in one year?

8. Jenny gets a 15% discount on a theatre ticket. The normal cost is £18.
   How much does she save?

9. Dipak earns £350 per week. He gets a wage rise of 3%.
   How much extra does he earn each week?

10. (a) In a school of 1200 pupils 45% are boys. How many pupils are girls?
    (b) 30% of the girls at this school are under 13. How many girls are under 13?

11. A dozen biscuits weigh 720 g.
    The amount of flour in a biscuit is 40% of the weight of a biscuit.
    What is the weight of flour in **each** biscuit?

## Percentage increase and decrease

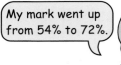
My mark went up from 54% to 72%.

My mark went up from 42% to 60%.

### Sadik and Chandni took Maths tests in October and June
*Who has made the most improvement?*

They have both improved by a score of 18%, so by one measure they have both improved equally. Another way of comparing their improvement is to use the idea of a **percentage increase**.

$$\text{Percentage increase} = \frac{\text{actual increase}}{\text{initial value}} \times 100\%$$

Comparing percentage increases is the best way to decide whether Sadik or Chandni has made the most improvement. *Explain why.*

**For Sadik**
% increase = $\frac{18}{54} \times 100\% = 33.3\%$

**For Chandni**
% increase = $\frac{18}{42} \times 100\% = 42.9\%$

Both calculations are correct to one decimal place.

A **percentage decrease** can be calculated in a similar way.

$$\text{Percentage decrease} = \frac{\text{actual decrease}}{\text{initial value}} \times 100\%$$

**Remember:** To calculate % increase or % decrease always use the initial value.

### Example 12

A shop buys pens for 15 pence and sells them for 21 pence.
What is their percentage profit?

Percentage profit is the same as percentage increase.

Actual profit = 21 pence − 15 pence = 6 pence.

$$\% \text{ profit} = \frac{\text{actual profit}}{\text{initial value}} \times 100$$

$$\% \text{ profit} = \frac{6}{15} \times 100 = 40\%$$

### Example 13

Pam buys a micro-scooter for £24.
She sells the micro-scooter for £15.
What is her percentage loss?

Percentage loss is the same as percentage decrease.

Actual loss = £24 − £15 = £9.

$$\% \text{ loss} = \frac{\text{actual loss}}{\text{initial value}} \times 100$$

$$\% \text{ loss} = \frac{9}{24} \times 100 = 37.5\%$$

## Practice Exercise **23.4**

1. A shop buys calculators for £10 and sells them for £12.
   Find the percentage profit.

2. Geri's wages of £8 per hour are increased to £10 per hour.
   Find the percentage increase in her earnings.

3. A man buys a boat for £25 000 and sells it for £18 000.
   Find his percentage loss.

4. In October, Sam scored 50% in an English test. In January he improved to 66%.
   In the same tests, Becky scored 40% and 56%.
   Who has made the most improvement? Explain your answer.

5. The rent on Gail's flat increased from £90 to £120 per week.
   (a) Find the percentage increase in her rent.

   At the same time Gail's wages increased from £280 per week to £310 per week.
   (b) Find the percentage increase in her wages.
   Comment on your answers.

6. The value of car A when new was £13 000.
   The value of car B when new was £16 500.
   After one year the value of car A is £11 200 and the value of car B is £13 500.
   Calculate the percentage loss in the values of cars A and B after one year.

7. During 2010, the population of a village decreased from 323 to 260.
   Find the percentage decrease in the population.

8. At the start of May a flower was 12.3 cm high. In May it grew by 14.5%.
   At the start of July it was 16.7 cm high.
   What was its percentage growth during June?

## Key Points

▶ 'Per cent' means 'out of 100'. The symbol for per cent is %. 10% can be written as $\frac{10}{100}$.

▶ | To change a percentage to a decimal or a fraction: **divide by 100**. |

   For example:  18%  as a decimal is  $18 \div 100 = 0.18$.
              18%  as a fraction is  $\frac{18}{100}$  which in its simplest form is  $\frac{9}{50}$.

▶ | To change a decimal or a fraction to a percentage: **multiply by 100**. |

   For example:  0.12  as a percentage is  $0.12 \times 100 = 12\%$.
              $\frac{3}{25}$  as a percentage is  $\frac{3}{25} \times 100 = 3 \times 100 \div 25 = 12\%$.

▶ Percentages can be used to compare fractions.

► You should be able to find a percentage of a quantity with and without a calculator.
►

$$\text{Percentage increase} = \frac{\text{actual increase}}{\text{initial value}} \times 100\%$$

$$\text{Percentage decrease} = \frac{\text{actual decrease}}{\text{initial value}} \times 100\%$$

**Review** Exercise 23    Do not use a calculator questions 1 to 3.

1.  (a)  What percentage of these squares is shaded?

(b)  Copy and shade 15% of this diagram.

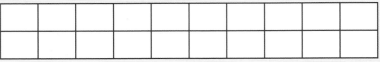

2.  Toby's last ten holidays were spent in the following countries.

What percentage of Toby's holidays were spent in England?

3.  Find:  (a)  20% of £80      (b)  75% of 60 minutes      (c)  2% of £128

4.  (a)  Write  0.47  as a percentage.      (b)  Write  $\frac{7}{20}$  as a percentage.

5.  A bag contains 60 beads.
    (a)  Emily uses 30% of the beads to make a necklace.
         How many beads does she use?
    (b)  Laura uses 12 beads to make a bracelet.
         What percentage of the beads does she use?

6.  There are 800 houses on an estate.  45% of the houses are detached.
    (a)  How many detached houses are on the estate?

    520 of the houses on the estate have garages.
    (b)  What percentage of the houses on the estate have garages?

7.  On Monday peaches cost 15p each.  On Tuesday peaches cost 12p each.
    What is the percentage reduction in price?

8.  45% of the books on a shelf in the library are reference books.
    $\frac{2}{5}$ of the books are science fiction.
    The rest of the books on the shelf are revision guides.
    What percentage of the books on the shelf are revision guides?

9.  The price of a micro-scooter is reduced by 10%.
    In a sale, the new price is reduced by a further 10%.
    By what percentage has the original price of the micro-scooter been reduced in the sale?

# 24 Time *and* Speed

The time of day is given in terms of hours, minutes and sometimes seconds.
There are 24 hours in each day, 60 minutes in each hour and 60 seconds in each minute.

## 24-hour clock and 12-hour clock times

The time can be given using the 12-hour clock or the 24-hour clock.

The watch and the digital clock both show the same time.
The time on the watch is 5.45 pm using 12-hour clock time.
The digital clock shows 5.45 pm as 1745 using 24-hour clock time.

> **12-hour clock times**
> Times before midday are given as am.
> Times after midday are given as pm.

> **24-hour clock times**
> The first two figures give the hours.
> The last two figures give the minutes.

### Example 1

A digital TV tuner uses 24-hour clock times.

(a) What time is shown by the tuner at 6.30 pm?
(b) The tuner is set to record a programme from 1120 to 1645.
What are these times in 12-hour clock time?

(a) 6.30 pm is equivalent to 1830.

> **12-hour to 24-hour clock times**
> Times before midday:
>     use the same figures.
> Times after midday:
>     add 12 to the hours.

(b) 1120 is equivalent to 11.20 am.
1645 is equivalent to 4.45 pm.

> **24-hour to 12-hour clock times**
> Times before midday:
>     use the same figures and include **am**.
> Times after midday:
>     subtract 12 from the hours and include **pm**.

### Example 2

A motorist left Dumfries at 10.50 am and arrived in St Andrews at 1.20 pm.
How long did the journey take?

**Method 1** (subtraction)

```
  1 3 . 2 0
  1 0 . 5 0
  ─────────
```

1. Write the times as 24-hour clock times.
2. Subtract the minutes.
   $20 - 50$ cannot be done.

```
    2  6 0
  1 3̸ . 2 0
  1 0 . 5 0
  ─────────
    2 . 3 0
```

Exchange 1 hour for 60 minutes.
$60 + 20 - 50 = 30$ minutes.

3. Subtract the hours.
$12 - 10 = 2.$

**Method 2** (adding on)

| | |
|---|---|
| 10.50 to 11.00 = | 10 minutes |
| 11.00 to 13.00 = 2 hours | |
| 13.00 to 13.20 = | 20 minutes |
| Total time      = | 2 hours 30 minutes |

The journey took 2 hours 30 minutes.

1. Write these 12-hour clock times in 24-hour clock time.

    (a)   10.30 am      (b)   10.30 pm      (c)   1.45 am      (d)   1.45 pm      (e)   11.50 pm

2. Write these 24-hour clock times in 12-hour clock time.

    (a)   1415          (b)   0525          (c)   2320          (d)   1005          (e)   1705

3.    The clock shows the time an alarm goes off in the morning.
    What time does the alarm go off:
    (a)   in 12-hour clock time,
    (b)   in 24-hour clock time?

4. The clocks show the time a school starts in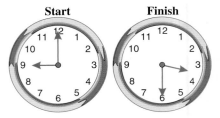
    the morning and finishes in the afternoon.
    (a)   Write these times in 12-hour clock time.
    (b)   Write these times in 24-hour clock time.
    (c)   How long is the school day?

5.    A video is set to record a film using 24-hour clock time.
    The start and finish times are shown.
    (a)   Write these times in 12-hour clock time.
    (b)   How long did the film last?

6. The times of some Monday afternoon ITV programmes are shown.

    | **12 30** News | **1 20** Three minutes |
    | **12 55** Shortland Street | **1 25** Home and Away |

    (a)   Give the times of these programmes using 24-hour clock time.
    (b)   How many minutes does Shortland Street last?

7. A train left Dunblane at 1013 and arrived in Edinburgh at 1117.
    (a)   At what time did the train leave in 12-hour clock time?
    (b)   How long did the journey take?

8. A coach left Glasgow at 0940 and arrived in London at 1432.
    (a)   What was the arrival time in 12-hour clock time?
    (b)   How many minutes did the journey take?

9. A plane left Edinburgh at 11.10 am and arrived in Paris at 1.25 pm.
    (a)   What was the arrival time in 24-hour clock time?
    (b)   How long did the journey take?

10. A coach leaves Blackpool at 2.20 pm to travel to Greenock.
    The journey takes 5 hours 30 minutes.
    At what time does the coach reach Greenock?
    Give your answer in
    (a)   12-hour clock time,          (b)   24-hour clock time.

11. A plane flies from Edinburgh to London City Airport.
    The plane leaves Edinburgh at 1115. The flight takes 80 minutes.
    At what time does the plane arrive in London?
    Give your answer in    (a)  24-hour clock time,        (b)  12-hour clock time.

12. Mrs Hill took 2 hours 56 minutes to drive from Dumfries to Dunbar.
    She left Dumfries at 1045. At what time did she arrive in Dunbar?
    Give your answer in    (a)  24-hour clock time,        (b)  12-hour clock time.

## Timetables

Bus and rail timetables are usually given in 24-hour clock time.
Michael and Sarah visited the Severn Valley Railway when they were on holiday.
Here is part of a rail timetable.

| Kidderminster | 1035 | 1115 | 1155 | 1240 | 1325 | 1410 |
| Bewdley | 1050 | 1130 | — | 1300 | — | 1430 |
| Arley | 1105 | 1148 | — | 1318 | 1403 | 1448 |
| Highley | 1114 | 1158 | — | 1328 | — | 1458 |
| Hampton Loade | 1125 | 1210 | — | 1340 | 1425 | 1510 |
| Bridgnorth | 1140 | 1225 | 1310 | 1355 | 1440 | 1525 |

Some trains do not stop at every station. This is shown by a dash on the timetable.

*How many minutes does the journey take on the 1035 train from Kidderminster to Arley?*

*Jean catches the 1155 train from Kidderminster to Bridgnorth.*
*What is her arrival time in 12-hour clock time?*
*How long does the journey take?*

*Alex lives in Bewdley.*
*What is the time of the last train he can catch to keep an appointment in Bridgnorth at 1.15 pm?*

## Practice Exercise 24.2

1.  The times of rail journeys from Linlithgow to Glasgow are shown.

| Linlithgow | 1403 | 1433 | 1503 |
| Polmont | 1409 | 1439 | 1509 |
| Falkirk | 1414 | 1444 | 1514 |
| Glasgow | 1436 | 1507 | 1537 |

    (a)  Richard catches the 1403 from Linlithgow to Glasgow.
        (i)   How many minutes does the journey take?
        (ii)  What is his arrival time in 12-hour clock time?
    (b)  Kate catches the 1439 from Polmont to Falkirk.
        (i)   How many minutes does the journey take?
        (ii)  What is her arrival time in 12-hour clock time?

**2.** The times of some trains from Atown to Newtown are shown.

| Atown | 0702 | 0802 | 0857 | 0900 | 0957 | 1102 | 1257 |
|---|---|---|---|---|---|---|---|
| Beetown | — | — | 0908 | — | 1008 | — | 1308 |
| Deeside | 0715 | 0815 | 0912 | — | 1012 | — | 1312 |
| Kayville | 0745 | 0845 | 0943 | 0940 | 1043 | 1141 | 1342 |
| Oldtown | 0805 | 0905 | 1003 | — | 1103 | 1201 | 1403 |
| Newtown | 0834 | 0934 | 1032 | 1025 | 1132 | 1230 | 1432 |

(a) John catches the 0745 from Kayville to Newtown.
How many minutes does the journey take?

(b) Aimee catches the 0857 from Atown to Newtown.
How long does the journey take?

(c) Sarah catches the 1257 from Atown to Kayville.
What is her arrival time using the 12-hour clock?

(d) Keith wants to be in Newtown by 1030.
What is the latest train he can catch from Deeside?

**3.** The times of some bus journeys are shown.

| Selkirk | 1725 | 1755 | 1834 | 1855 |
|---|---|---|---|---|
| Galashiels | 1740 | 1815 | 1902 | 1915 |
| Stow | — | 1837 | — | 1937 |
| Newtongrange | — | 1906 | — | 2003 |
| Edinburgh | — | 1937 | — | 2034 |

(a) Harry catches the bus at 1725 from Selkirk to Galashiels.
   (i) How many minutes does the journey take?
   (ii) What is his arrival time in 12-hour clock time?

(b) Rachel lives in Galashiels.
She is going to a show in Edinburgh which starts at 8.45 pm.
   (i) What is the time of the latest bus she can catch from
Galashiels to Edinburgh?
   (ii) How many minutes does Rachel have to get to the theatre after the bus
arrives in Edinburgh?

(c) Gareth catches the 1755 bus from Selkirk to Newtongrange.
How long does the journey take?
Give your answer in minutes.

**4.** The table shows the express train services from Here to There.

| Here | 1109 | 1204 | 1313 | 1413 |
|---|---|---|---|---|
| Partway | 1201 | 1300 | 1359 | 1456 |
| There | 1247 | 1345 | 1445 | 1540 |

(a) Which train takes the longest time to travel from Here to There?

(b) Which trains take the same time to travel from Partway to There?

**5.** The table shows the train services from Carlisle to Edinburgh.

| Carlisle | 1104 | 1211 | 1303 | 1411 | 1502 | 1611 |
|---|---|---|---|---|---|---|
| Lockerbie | — | 1230 | — | 1430 | — | 1630 |
| Haymarket | 1214 | 1333 | 1416 | 1534 | 1617 | 1731 |
| Edinburgh | 1221 | 1339 | 1421 | 1539 | 1621 | 1739 |

(a) Liz catches the 1230 from Lockerbie to Edinburgh.
How long does the journey take?

(b) Harold needs to be in Haymarket before half-past two in the afternoon.
What is the latest train he can catch from Carlisle?

(c) Ella arrives at Lockerbie station at 1.45 pm.
    (i) What time is the next train to Edinburgh?
    (ii) How long does she have to wait for the train?

(d) Which train takes the longest time to travel from Haymarket to Edinburgh?

**6.** The timetable shows some rail journeys from Mallaig to Glasgow.

| Mallaig | 1010 | 1605 | 1815 | |
|---|---|---|---|---|
| Glenfinnan | 1058 | 1653 | 1903 | |
| Fort William | 1132 | 1728 | 1937 | 1950 |
| Rannoch | 1241 | 1836 | | 2103 |
| Glasgow | 1530 | 2131 | | 0020 |

(a) Nick catches the 1058 from Glenfinnan to Rannoch.
    (i) What is his time of arrival in 12-hour clock time?
    (ii) How long does the journey take?

(b) Anne-Marie arrives at Mallaig station at 5.45 pm.
What time is the next train to Glasgow?

Anne-Marie has to change trains at Fort William.

(c) How long does she have to wait at Fort William?

(d) What time does Anne-Marie arrive in Glasgow?
Give your answer in 12-hour clock time.

(e) How long, in hours and minutes, was her journey from Mallaig to Glasgow?

## Speed

**Speed** is a measurement of how fast something is travelling.
It involves two other measures, **distance** and **time**.
Speed can be calculated using this formula.

$$\text{Speed} = \frac{\text{Distance}}{\text{Time}}$$

> **Speed** can be thought of as the **distance** travelled in **one unit of time** (1 hour, 1 second, ...)

Speed can be measured in:
    kilometres per hour (km/h),   metres per second (m/s),   miles per hour (mph),   and so on.

## Average speed

When the speed of an object is **constant** it means that the object doesn't slow down or go faster.

However, in many situations, speed is not constant.
For example:

A sprinter needs time to start from the starting blocks
and is well into the race before running at top speed.
A plane changes speed as it takes off and lands.

In situations like this the idea of **average speed** can be used.

The formula for average speed is:

$$\text{Average speed} = \frac{\text{Total distance travelled}}{\text{Total time taken}}$$

The formula linking speed, distance and time can be rearranged and remembered as:

| | |
|---|---|
| (average) **speed** = (total) **distance** ÷ (total) **time** | $S = D \div T$ |
| (total) **distance** = (average) **speed** × (total) **time** | $D = S \times T$ |
| (total) **time** = (total) **distance** ÷ (average) **speed** | $T = D \div S$ |

### Example 3

Robert drives a distance of 260 km.
His journey takes 5 hours.
What is his average speed on the journey?

$$\text{Speed} = \frac{\text{Distance}}{\text{Time}}$$

$$\text{Speed} = \frac{260}{5}$$

$$\text{Speed} = 52 \text{ km/h}$$

$\frac{\text{Distance}}{\text{Time}}$ units are $\frac{\text{km}}{\text{h}}$, which is written as km/h.

$\frac{260}{5}$ means 260 ÷ 5

### Example 4

Lisa drives at an average speed of 80 kilometres per hour on a journey that takes 3 hours.
What distance has she travelled?

$$\text{Distance} = \text{Speed} \times \text{Time}$$

$$\text{Distance} = 80 \times 3$$

$$\text{Distance} = 240 \text{ km}$$

So in 3 hours she travels 240 km.

Speed × Time units are $\frac{\text{km}}{\text{h}} \times$ h, which gives km.

### Example 5

A cheetah takes 4 seconds to travel 100 m.
What is the speed of the cheetah?

$$\text{Speed} = \frac{\text{Distance}}{\text{Time}}$$

$$\text{Speed} = \frac{100}{4}$$

$$\text{Speed} = 25 \text{ m/s}$$

Distance is given in metres.   Time is given in seconds.
$\frac{\text{Distance}}{\text{Time}}$ units are $\frac{\text{m}}{\text{s}}$, which is written as m/s.

**Practice** Exercise **24.3**

1. John cycles 16 miles in 2 hours.
   What is his average speed in miles per hour?

2. Sue runs 21 km in 3 hours.
   What is her average speed in kilometres per hour?

3. Joe swims 100 m in 4 minutes.
   What is his average speed in metres per minute?

4. Calculate the average speed for each of the following journeys in kilometres per hour.

   | | Total distance travelled | Total time taken |
   |---|---|---|
   | (a) | 60 km | 3 hours |
   | (b) | 100 km | 2 hours |
   | (c) | 10 km | $2\frac{1}{2}$ hours |

5. Jackie runs 15 km in $1\frac{1}{2}$ hours.
   What is her average speed in kilometres per hour?

6. Beverley walks for 2 hours at an average speed of 4 km/h.
   How many kilometres does she walk?

7. Howard cycles for 5 hours at an average speed of 6 miles per hour.
   How far does he cycle?

8. Aubrey runs at 6 km/h for $\frac{1}{2}$ hour.
   How far does he run?

9. Calculate the total distance travelled on each of the following journeys.

   | | Total time taken | Average speed |
   |---|---|---|
   | (a) | 3 hours | 50 km/h |
   | (b) | 2 hours | 43 km/h |
   | (c) | $\frac{1}{2}$ hour | 80 km/h |

10. Penny cycles to work at an average speed of 18 km/h.
    She takes 20 minutes.
    How far does she cycle to work?

11. A car travels 120 km in 2 hours.
    (a) What is its average speed in kilometres per hour?
    (b) How many hours would the car take to travel 120 km if it had gone twice as fast?

12. Liam drives for 60 km at an average speed of 40 km/h.
    He starts his journey at 9.50 am.
    At what time does his journey end?

## Further problems involving speed

### Example 6

The Scottish Pullman travels from London to York, a distance of 302.8 km in 1 hour 45 minutes.
It then travels from York to Edinburgh, a distance of 334.7 km in 2 hours 30 minutes.
Calculate the average speed of the train between London and Edinburgh.

Total distance travelled = 302.8 + 334.7 = 637.5 km

Total time taken = 1 hr 45 mins + 2 hr 30 mins = 4 hr 15 mins = 4.25 hours

Average speed = $\frac{637.5}{4.25}$ = 150 km/h

## Practice Exercise 24.4

1. On the first part of a journey a car travels 140 km in 3 hours.
   On the second part of the journey the car travels 160 km in 2 hours.
   (a) What is the total distance travelled on the journey?
   (b) What is the total time taken on the journey?
   (c) What is the average speed of the car over the whole journey?

2. Lisa runs two laps of a 400 m running track.
   The first lap takes 70 seconds. The second lap takes 90 seconds.
   What is her average speed over the two laps?

3. Chandni runs from Axton to Farley and then from Farley to Wareham.

   | **Axton to Farley** | **Time taken:** | 1 hr 20 min | **Distance:** 20 km |
   | **Farley to Wareham** | **Average speed:** 0.2 km/min | | **Distance:** 12 km |

   (a) Calculate Chandni's average speed over the whole journey.
   (b) Chandni left Axton at 10.50 am.
   At what time did she arrive in Wareham?

4. A cheetah runs at a constant speed of 90 km/h for 6 seconds.
   How many metres does the cheetah run?

5. The distance from the Sun to the Earth is about 150 million kilometres.
   It takes light from the Sun about 500 seconds to reach the Earth.
   Calculate the approximate speed of light in metres per second.

6. Angela, Ben and Cathy drive from Glasgow to London.
   Angela takes 12 hours 30 minutes driving at an average speed of 64 km/h.
   Ben drives at an average speed of 100 km/h.
   (a) How long does Ben take?

   Cathy takes 7 hours 12 minutes.
   (b) What is Cathy's average speed?

7. Ron runs 400 m in 1 minute 23.2 seconds.
   Calculate his average speed in
   (a) metres per second,       (b) kilometres per hour.

## Key Points

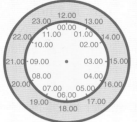

▶ Time can be given using either the
**12-hour clock** or the **24-hour clock**.
When using the 12-hour clock:
  times **before** midday are given as am,
  times **after** midday are given as pm.

▶ **Timetables** are usually given using the 24-hour clock.

▶ **Speed** is a measurement of how fast something is travelling.
It involves two other measures, **distance** and **time**.
In situations where speed is not constant, **average speed** is used.

$$\text{Speed} = \frac{\text{Distance}}{\text{Time}}$$

$$\text{Average speed} = \frac{\text{Total distance travelled}}{\text{Total time taken}}$$

▶ The formula linking speed, distance and time can be rearranged and remembered as:

| | |
|---|---|
| (average) **speed** = (total) **distance** ÷ (total) **time** | $S = D \div T$ |
| (total) **distance** = (average) **speed** × (total) **time** | $D = S \times T$ |
| (total) **time** = (total) **distance** ÷ (average) **speed** | $T = D \div S$ |

## Review Exercise 24

1. A television programme starts at 8.15 pm. It lasts for 135 minutes.
   What time does the programme finish?

2. The table shows the train services from Thurso to Inverness.

   | Thurso   | 0648 | 0841 | 1305 | 1629 |
   |----------|------|------|------|------|
   | Kinbrace | 0737 | —    | 1353 | 1717 |
   | Brora    | 0816 | 1002 | 1432 | 1754 |
   | Lairg    | 0852 | 1038 | 1508 | 1830 |
   | Dingwall | 1003 | 1145 | 1617 | 1938 |
   | Inverness| 1035 | 1213 | 1648 | 2009 |

   (a) Moira catches the 1432 from Brora to Inverness.
       How long does the journey take?
   (b) Iain lives in Kinbrace. He has an appointment in Dingwall at noon.
       (i) What train should he catch from Kinbrace?
       (ii) How long will he have to wait before his appointment?
   (c) Alex wants the quickest journey time from Thurso to Inverness.
       Should he catch the 0648 or the 1629? You must show your working.

3. Mr Rees took 2 hours to drive from Dumfries to Livingston.
   His average speed was 41 miles per hour.
   What is the distance from Dumfries to Livingston?

4. Last month, Mr Carmichael flew from Aberdeen to New York.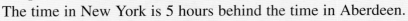
   His plane took off at 0705 and the flight took 6 hours.
   The time in New York is 5 hours behind the time in Aberdeen.
   As soon as the plane landed in New York, he telephoned home.
   (a) What was the time in Aberdeen when Mr Carmichael phoned?
       Give your answer in 12-hour clock time.
   (b) What was the time in New York when the plane landed?
       Give your answer in 24-hour clock time.

5. The diagram shows the distances, in miles, between some junctions on a motorway.

   West ←———— **22** ——— **20** ——— **23** ——— **12** ——— **24** ————→ East

   A coach is travelling east.
   At 1040 it passes junction 22 and at 1110 it passes junction 24.
   Calculate the average speed of the coach in miles per hour.

6. The chart shows the distances, in kilometres, between some towns.

   Ayr

   | 220 | Hawick | | | |
   |-----|--------|---|---|---|
   | 200 | 290 | Oban | | |
   | 190 | 175 | 205 | St Andrews | |
   | 415 | 430 | 250 | 325 | Ullapool |

   (a) Gill takes 5 hours to drive from Ullapool to Oban.
       Work out her average speed in kilometres per hour.
   (b) Matt cycled from Hawick to St Andrews at an average speed of 25 km/h.
       How long did the journey take?
   (c) Alec says: *"If I drive at an average speed of 45 km/h, I can get from Ayr to*
       *Ullapool in less than 9 hours."* Is he right? You must show your working.

7. Lorraine has a jet-ski ride.
   She travels at an average speed of 28 km/h for half an hour.
   How far does she travel?

8. A coach takes a quarter of an hour to travel 20 km on a motorway.
   What is the average speed of the coach in kilometres per hour?

9. Kath has to drive 17 km to work. Calculate her average speed for the journey when
   she leaves home at 0750 and gets to work at 0820.

10. Alex cycles at an average speed of 12 miles per hour for 15 minutes.
    How far does she cycle?

11. Nick started his journey at 0945. He travelled 175 km at an average speed of 50 km/h.
    At what time did his journey end?

12. Kelly cycles 36 kilometres in 4 hours 30 minutes.
    Calculate her average speed in kilometres per hour.

 # Ratio *and* Proportion

 Some faces are SMILERS.  Some faces are GLUMS.

In a group of 10 faces the **ratio** of SMILERS to GLUMS is 3 : 2.
This means that for every three SMILERS there are two GLUMS.

> For the ratio 3 : 2
> say '3 to 2'.

In the group there are 6 SMILERS and 4 GLUMS.

## Example 1

In a group of 16 faces there are 10 SMILERS and 6 GLUMS.
What is the ratio of SMILERS to GLUMS?

There are 10 SMILERS and 6 GLUMS.
For every 5 SMILERS there are 3 GLUMS.
So the ratio of SMILERS to GLUMS is 5 : 3.

## Simplifying ratios

> To simplify a ratio, divide both of the numbers in the ratio by the **same** number.
> A ratio with whole numbers which cannot be simplified is in its **simplest form**.

### Example 2

Write the ratio 15 : 9 in its simplest form.

15 and 9 can both be divided by 3.
$15 \div 3 : 9 \div 3 = 5 : 3$
5 : 3 cannot be simplified.
The ratio 15 : 9 in its simplest form is 5 : 3.

### Example 3

Write the ratio 2 cm : 50 mm in its simplest form.

2 cm : 50 mm = 20 mm : 50 mm = 20 : 50
Divide both parts of the ratio by 10.
$20 \div 10 : 50 \div 10 = 2 : 5$
The ratio 2 cm : 50 mm in its simplest form is 2 : 5.

> In its simplest form a ratio contains **only** whole numbers. There are **no units**.
> In order to simplify the ratio both quantities in the ratio must be in the **same units**.

## Practice Exercise 25.1

1. In a group of 14 faces there are 10 SMILERS and 4 GLUMS.

   Copy and complete the following.
   (a) For every 5 SMILERS there are ...... GLUMS.
   (b) The ratio of SMILERS to GLUMS is 5 : ....

2. In a group of 30 faces there are 21 SMILERS and 9 GLUMS.
   Copy and complete the following.
   The ratio of SMILERS to GLUMS is ... : 3.

3. In a group of 12 faces there are 9 SMILERS and 3 GLUMS.

   Copy and complete the following.
   (a) For every ...... SMILERS there is 1 GLUM.
   (b) The ratio of SMILERS to GLUMS is ... : 1.

4. (a) Draw 10 faces where the ratio of SMILERS to GLUMS is 4 : 1.
   (b) Draw 12 faces where the ratio of SMILERS to GLUMS is 1 : 3.

5. The ratio of SMILERS to GLUMS is 4 : 3.

   (a) How many SMILERS are there when there are 12 GLUMS?
   (b) How many GLUMS are there when there are 12 SMILERS?
   (c) How many FACES are there when there are ...
       (i) 48 SMILERS,          (ii) 48 GLUMS?

6. How many SMILERS and how many GLUMS are there when ...
   (a) the ratio of SMILERS to GLUMS is 7 : 3 and there are 20 faces?
   (b) the ratio of SMILERS to GLUMS is 3 : 2 and there are 15 faces?

7. Give the simplest form of each of these ratios.
   (a) 3 : 6      (b) 9 : 27    (c) 9 : 12    (d) 10 : 25    (e) 30 : 40
   (f) 22 : 55    (g) 9 : 21    (h) 18 : 8    (i) 36 : 81    (j) 35 : 15

8. A necklace contains 30 black beads and 45 gold beads.
   What is the simplest form of the ratio of black beads to gold beads on the necklace?

9. On Monday a hairdresser uses 800 ml of shampoo and 320 ml of conditioner.
   Write in its simplest form the ratio of shampoo : conditioner used on Monday.

10. Denise draws a plan of her classroom. On her plan Denise uses 2 cm to represent 5 m.
    Write the scale as a ratio in its simplest form.

11. On a map a pond is 3.5 cm long. The pond is actually 52.5 m long.
    Write the scale as a ratio in its simplest form.

12. Write each of these ratios in its simplest form.
    (a) £2 : 50p          (b) 20p : £2.50      (c) £2.20 : 40p      (d) 6 m : 240 cm
    (e) 2 kg : 500 g      (f) 1 kg : 425 g     (g) 90 cm : 2 m      (h) 5 km : 200 m
    (i) 20 seconds : 5 minutes                 (j) $\frac{1}{2}$ minute : 15 seconds

13. Sam spends 90p a week on comics. Tom spends £4 a week on comics.
    Write the ratio of the amounts Tom and Sam spend on comics in its simplest form.

14. An alloy is made of tin and zinc. 40% of the alloy is tin.
    What is the ratio of tin : zinc in its simplest form?

15. A box contains blue biros and red biros. $\frac{1}{3}$ of the biros are blue.
    What is the ratio of blue biros to red biros in the box?

## Equivalent ratios

### Example 4

The ratio of boys to girls in a school is 3 : 4. There are 72 boys.
How many girls are there?

$72 \div 3 = 24$
To find a ratio equivalent to 3 : 4 where the first number in the ratio is 72,
multiply each number in the ratio by 24.
$3 \times 24 : 4 \times 24 = 72 : 96$
The number of girls = 96.

> **Finding equivalent ratios:**
> To find equivalent ratios multiply or divide
> each number in the ratio by the **same** number.

## Practice Exercise 25.2

1. A box contains nuts and bolts in the ratio 1 : 5. There are 30 bolts in the box.
   How many nuts are in the box?

2. To make mortar, a builder mixes sand and cement in the ratio 8 : 3.
   The builder uses 12 kg of cement. How much sand does he use?

3. A school play was attended by 350 pupils. The ratio of males to females was 2 : 3.
   How many males attended the play?

4. The ratio of men to women playing golf one day is 7 : 4. There are 63 men playing.
   How many women are playing?

5. Each of these pairs of ratios are equivalent.
   (a) $3 : 4$ and $9 : n$    (b) $2 : 7$ and $8 : n$    (c) $8 : n$ and $2 : 25$    (d) $25 : n$ and $5 : 4$
   In each case calculate the value of $n$.

6. The heights of two friends are in the ratio 7 : 9. The shorter of the friends is 154 cm tall.
   What is the height of the taller of the friends?

7. Sugar and flour are mixed in the ratio 2 : 3.
   How much sugar is used with 600 g of flour?

## Proportion

Some situations involve comparing **different** quantities.
For example, when a motorist buys fuel, the more he buys the greater the cost.
In this situation the quantities can change but the ratio between the quantities stays the same.
When two different quantities are in the **same ratio** they are said to be in **direct proportion**.

### Example 5

4 cakes cost £1.20. Find the cost of 7 cakes.

4 cakes cost £1.20
1 cake costs    £1.20 $\div$ 4 = 30p
7 cakes cost     30p $\times$ 7 = £2.10
So, 7 cakes cost £2.10.

> This is sometimes called the **unitary method**.
> (a) **Divide** by 4 to find the cost of **1** cake.
> (b) **Multiply** by **7** to find the cost of **7** cakes.

Do not use a calculator for questions 1 to 5.

1. 5 candles cost 80 pence.
   (a) What is the cost of 1 candle?
   (b) What is the cost of 8 candles?

2. Georgina works for 4 hours and earns £28.
   (a) How much does she earn in 1 hour?
   (b) How much does she earn in 10 hours?

3. 5 bananas cost £1.50.
   (a) What is the cost of 1 banana?
   (b) What is the cost of 8 bananas?

4. Gina works for 10 hours and earns £65.
   (a) How much does Gina earn in 1 hour?
   (b) How much does Gina earn in 20 hours?

5. Alistair pays £1.90 for 2 cups of tea.
   How much would he pay for 3 cups of tea?

6. Jean pays £168 for 10 square metres of carpet.
   How much would 12 square metres of carpet cost?

7. Alfie is paid £48.80 for working 4 hours overtime.
   How much would he be paid for 5 hours overtime?

8. Aimee pays £1.14 for 3 kg of potatoes.
   How much would 7.5 kg of potatoes cost?

9. 5 litres of petrol costs £6.50.
   How much would 18 litres of petrol cost?

10. 9 metres of stair carpet cost £83.70.
    How much does 9.6 metres cost?

11. 29 euros is about the same as £20. Sue spends 47 euros.
    How many pounds is this?

12. Mary phones her uncle in New York.
    Phone calls to New York are charged at the rate of £2.20 for a 5-minute call.
    (a) How much would a 7-minute call to New York cost?
    (b) Mary's call cost £5.28. How long was her call?

13. These ingredients are needed to make macaroni cheese for 4 people.

    | Macaroni … 120 g | Cheese … 72 g | Flour … 30 g | Milk … 850 ml |

    (a) How much cheese is needed to make macaroni cheese for 10 people?
    (b) How much milk is needed to make macaroni cheese for 3 people?
    (c) How much macaroni is needed to make macaroni cheese for 7 people?

14. A car travels 6 miles in 9 minutes. If the car travels at the same speed:
    (a) how long will it take to travel 8 miles,
    (b) how far will it travel in 24 minutes?

**15.** 5 litres of paint cover an area of 30 m².
   (a)   What area will 2 litres of paint cover?
   (b)   How much paint is needed to cover 72 m²?

**16.** A school is organising three similar trips to the zoo.

Our trip is on Monday.
45 students are going.
The total cost is £468.

Our trip is on Wednesday.
The total cost is £332.80.

Our trip is on Tuesday.
25 students are going.

   (a)   How much does Tuesday's trip cost?
   (b)   How many students are going to the zoo on Wednesday?

**17.** 50 g of flour and 90 ml of milk are needed to make 8 biscuits.
   (a)   How much flour is needed to make 27 biscuits?
   (b)   How many biscuits can be made with 225 g of flour?

   Some biscuits are made with 300 g of flour.
   (c)   How much milk is needed?

## Key Points

▶ The ratio 3 : 2 is read '3 to 2'.

▶ A ratio is used only to **compare** quantities.
   A ratio does not give information about the exact values of quantities being compared.

▶
   | To simplify a ratio, divide both of the numbers in the ratio by the **same** number.
   A ratio with whole numbers which cannot be simplified is in its **simplest form**. |

▶ To find **equivalent ratios**, multiply or divide each number in the ratio by the
   **same** number.

▶ All quantities in a ratio must have the **same units** before the ratio can be simplified.

▶ When two different quantities are in the **same ratio** the two quantities are in
   **direct proportion.**
   For example, the amount and cost of fuel bought by a motorist are in proportion.

## Review Exercise 25

**1.**   The ratio of SMILERS to GLUMS is 5 : 2.

   (a)   How many SMILERS are there when there are 30 GLUMS?
   (b)   How many GLUMS are there when there are 30 SMILERS?
   (c)   How many FACES are there when there are …
      (i)   40 SMILERS,      (ii)   40 GLUMS?

2. A packet contains 5 white balloons and 15 red balloons.
   What is the ratio of white balloons to red balloons in its simplest form?

3. A tin contains 21 nuts and 28 bolts.
   What is the ratio of nuts to bolts in its simplest form?

4. A sewing box contains pins and needles in the ratio 4 : 1. There are 36 pins in the box.
   How many needles are in the box?

5. The ratio of boys to girls in a school is 4 : 5. There are 80 girls.
   How many boys are there?

6. A bag contains white buttons and red buttons in the ratio 1 : 2.
   The bag contains 24 buttons.
   How many white buttons are in the bag?

7.  I earn £400 per week.  I earn £360 per week.

   The amounts Jenny and James earn is in the ratio of their ages.
   Jenny is 20 years old.
   How old is James?

8. These ingredients are needed to make an apple crumble for 6 people.

   | 540 g apples,   150 g flour,   75 g butter,   75 g sugar |

   (a) How much sugar is needed to make an apple crumble for 4 people?
   (b) How much apple is needed to make an apple crumble for 8 people?

9. (a) A wood contains fir trees and yew trees in the ratio 3 : 4.
       There are 18 fir trees in the wood.
       How many yew trees are in the wood?
   (b) Another wood contains 20 beech trees and 12 ash trees.
       Write, in its simplest form, the ratio of beech trees to ash trees.

10. A plan is drawn using a scale of 2 centimetres to represent 5 metres.
    Write the scale as a ratio in the form 1 : $n$, where $n$ is a whole number.

11. The cost of 8 metres of material is £18.40.
    What is the cost of 5 metres of the same material?

12. A 42-litre paddling pool is filled at the rate of 12 litres of water every 5 minutes.
    How long will it take to fill the pool?

13. The cost of 40 bottles of orange juice is £36.
    (a) What is the cost of 30 bottles of orange juice?
    (b) What is the cost of 65 bottles of orange juice?

14. On a map the distance between two houses is 19 mm.
    The actual distance between the houses is 3.8 km.
    What is the scale of the map?

15. Three kilograms of apples cost £2.91.
    What is the cost of two kilograms of apples?

# 26 Understanding *and* Using Measures

## Metric units

The common metric units used to measure length, mass (weight) and capacity (volume) are shown below.

**Length**
1 kilometre (km) = 1000 metres (m)
1 m = 100 centimetres (cm)
1 cm = 10 millimetres (mm)

**Mass**
1 tonne (t) = 1000 kilograms (kg)
1 kg = 1000 grams (g)

**Capacity and volume**
1 litre = 1000 millilitres (ml)
1 cm³ = 1 ml

**Centi** means hundredth, $\frac{1}{100}$.
  So, a **centi**metre is one hundredth of a metre.
  For example: 2 centimetres = $\frac{2}{100}$ metre.

**Kilo** means thousand, 1000.
  So, a **kilo**gram is one thousand grams.
  For example: 3 kilograms = 3000 grams.

**Milli** means thousandth, $\frac{1}{1000}$.
  So, a **milli**litre is one thousandth of a litre.
  For example: 5 millilitres = $\frac{5}{1000}$ litre.

## Changing from one metric unit to another

Different units can be used to measure the same quantity.
For example:
  The same **length** can be measured using centimetres, kilometres, …
  The same **mass** can be measured using grams, kilograms, …
  The same **capacity** can be measured using litres, millilitres, …

> Changing from one metric unit to another involves multiplying, or dividing, by a power of 10 (10, 100 or 1000).

**Example 1**  |  1 centimetre (cm) = 10 millimetres (mm)

(a)  Change 6.3 cm into millimetres.

To change centimetres into millimetres, multiply by 10.
6.3 × 10 = 63
6.3 cm = 63 mm

(b)  Change 364 mm into centimetres.

To change millimetres into centimetres, divide by 10.
364 ÷ 10 = 36.4
364 mm = 36.4 cm

**Example 2**  |  1 metre (m) = 100 centimetres (cm)

(a)  Change 4.2 m into centimetres.

To change metres into centimetres, multiply by 100.
4.2 × 100 = 420
4.2 m = 420 cm

(b)  Change 850 cm into metres.

To change centimetres into metres, divide by 100.
850 ÷ 100 = 8.5
850 cm = 8.5 m

Example 3

1 kilogram (kg) = 1000 grams (g)

(a) Change 19.4 kg into grams.

To change kilograms into grams, multiply by 1000.
$19.4 \times 1000 = 19\ 400$
$19.4\ \text{kg} = 19\ 400\ \text{g}$

(b) Change 245 g into kilograms.

To change grams into kilograms, divide by 1000.
$245 \div 1000 = 0.245$
$245\ \text{g} = 0.245\ \text{kg}$

## Practice Exercise 26.1

Do not use a calculator for this exercise.

1. Change each of the following lengths into millimetres.
   (a) 6 cm
   (b) 32 cm
   (c) 632 cm
   (d) 8.6 cm
   (e) 0.8 cm
   (f) 0.08 cm
   (g) 4.5 cm
   (h) 0.1 cm

2. Change each of the following lengths into centimetres.
   (a) 90 mm
   (b) 210 mm
   (c) 3500 mm
   (d) 73.5 mm
   (e) 2 mm
   (f) 3.5 mm
   (g) 60 mm
   (h) 0.1 mm

3. Change each of the following lengths into metres.
   (a) 200 cm
   (b) 320 cm
   (c) 4550 cm
   (d) 66 cm
   (e) 8 cm
   (f) 9.8 cm
   (g) 1500 cm
   (h) 1 cm

4. Change each of the following lengths into centimetres.
   (a) 6 m
   (b) 56 m
   (c) 7.6 m
   (d) 23.5 m
   (e) 0.9 m
   (f) 0.07 m
   (g) 1.5 m
   (h) 0.1 m

5. Change each of the following lengths into kilometres.
   (a) 4000 m
   (b) 35 000 m
   (c) 6500 m
   (d) 455 m
   (e) 75 m
   (f) 7 m
   (g) 200 m
   (h) 1 m

6. Change each of the following lengths into metres.
   (a) 6 km
   (b) 32 km
   (c) 650 km
   (d) 3.31 km
   (e) 0.35 km
   (f) 0.085 km
   (g) 1.5 km
   (h) 0.1 km

7. The floor of a corridor is a rectangle, 9.5 m long and 150 cm wide.
   Calculate the area of the floor in:
   (a) square centimetres,
   (b) square metres.

8. A rectangular beach towel measures $1.6\ \text{m} \times 600\ \text{mm}$.
   (a) Calculate the perimeter of the towel in centimetres.
   (b) Calculate the area of the towel in square metres.

9. Calculate the volume of a cuboid which has length 1.5 m, breadth 80 cm and height 300 mm.
   Give your answer in cubic centimetres.

10. A field has sides of length 1.45 km, 950 m, 1.1 km and 70 m.
    Find the perimeter of the field in:
    (a) kilometres,
    (b) metres.

**11.** A metal bar, in the shape of a cuboid, has length 10.5 m, breadth 10.5 cm and height 10.5 mm.
Find the volume of the metal bar in cubic centimetres.

**12.** Change each of the following masses into grams.
(a)  2 kg          (b)  45 kg          (c)  7.5 kg          (d)  42.5 kg
(e)  0.6 kg        (f)  0.025 kg       (g)  5.6 kg          (h)  0.01 kg

**13.** Change each of the following masses into kilograms.
(a)  3000 g        (b)  32 000 g       (c)  9300 g          (d)  220 g
(e)  83 g          (f)  6 g            (g)  1500 g          (h)  4950 g

**14.** Copy and complete each of the following.
(a)  320 000 ml = ...... $l$          (b)  0.32 t = ...... kg  = ...... g
(c)  3200 g = ...... kg = ...... t    (d)  320 mm = ...... cm = ...... m
(e)  32 000 cm= ...... m  = ...... km (f)  3.2 km = ...... m   = ...... cm

**15.** Find the number of kilograms in:
(a)  6 t           (b)  8000 g         (c)  800 g           (d)  0.65 t

**16.** Find the number of metres in:
(a)  4 km          (b)  8000 mm        (c)  8.6 cm          (d)  0.04 km

**17.** Find the number of millilitres in:
(a)  2 $l$         (b)  $\frac{1}{2}$ $l$       (c)  0.85 $l$        (d)  0.03 $l$

**18.** Paint is sold in two sizes:   **Large 2.65 litres.   Small 650 ml.**
Graham has two options.
        **Option A:** Buy 7 large tins.   **Option B:** Buy 28 small tins.
Which option gives the most paint? Explain your answer.

**19.** A can of coke contains 330 ml. How many litres of coke are there in 6 cans?

**20.** Twenty children at a party share equally 1 kg of fruit pastilles.
How many grams of pastilles does each child receive?

**21.** A recipe for a dozen biscuits uses 240 g of flour. James has 1.2 kg of flour.
How many biscuits can he make?

## Choosing an appropriate unit

### Example 4

The Great Wall of China is the longest man-made structure in the world.
It is the only man-made structure that can be seen from space.
What unit should be used for its length?

For very long lengths use the **kilometre**.
The Great Wall of China is actually about 2350 km long.

Example 5

The smallest known mammal is the Kitti's hog-nosed bat.
It is not much bigger than a pea.

(a)  What unit should be used for its mass?

(b)  What unit should be used for its length?

(a)  For very small masses use the **gram**.
     The Kitti's hog-nosed bat actually weighs about 1.5 g.

(b)  For very small lengths use the **millimetre**.
     The length of the Kitti's hog-nosed bat is about 10 mm.

## Practice Exercise 26.2

1.  Give the most appropriate metric unit that you would use to measure the following.

    (a)  The distance from Falkirk to York.    (b)  The distance across a road.

    (c)  The length of your foot.              (d)  The length of your little finger nail.

    (e)  The weight of a bag of potatoes.      (f)  The weight of an egg.

    (g)  The capacity of a bucket.             (h)  The capacity of a medicine bottle.

2.

> **"My teacher's height is about 1.7 mm."**
> This statement is incorrect.

It can be corrected by changing the unit:
"My teacher's height is about 1.7 m."

It can also be corrected by changing the quantity:
"My teacher's height is about 1700 mm."

Each of these statements is also incorrect.

*"Tyrannosaurus, a large meat-eating dinosaur, is estimated to have been about 12 cm long."*

*"The tallest mammal is the giraffe which grows up to about 5.9 mm tall."*

*"My car used 5 ml of petrol on a journey of 35 miles."*

*"The area of the school hall is about 500 mm²."*

Correct each statement:

(a)  by changing the unit,

(b)  by changing the quantity.

> It is a useful skill to be able to estimate length, mass and capacity.
> These facts might help you.
>
> **Length**
> Most adults are between 1.5 m and 1.8 m tall.
> The door to your classroom is about 2 m high.
>
> **Mass**
> A biro weighs about 5 g. A standard bag of sugar weighs 1 kg.
>
> **Capacity**
> A teaspoon holds about 5 ml. A can of pop holds about 330 ml.

**3.** Complete each of the following statements by choosing one of the quantities given.
   (a) A cup holds about … of tea.         (b) The height of a car is about ….
   (c) The weight of this book is about ….  (d) The weight of an elephant is about ….
   (e) The distance from Glasgow to Edinburgh is about ….

> 8 g,  200 ml,  7 *l*,  8 kg,  15 cm,  700 kg,  1.5 m,
> 4 km,  700 g,  80 km,  0.07 *l*,  15 mm

**4.** Which of the following is the best estimate for the diameter of a football?
   2 m,  50 mm,  30 cm,  1.5 m,  0.6 m,  800 mm

**5.** Which of the following would be the best estimate for the capacity of a mug?
   15 m,  1200 ml,  2 *l*,  0.5 *l*,  200 ml,  800 ml

**6.** Give a sensible estimate using an appropriate unit for the following measures:
   (a) the length of a matchstick,       (b) the length of a football pitch,
   (c) the weight of a 30 cm ruler,      (d) the weight of a double decker bus,
   (e) the volume of drink in a glass.

**7.** The diagram, which is drawn to scale, shows a man standing next to a tree.
   Using an appropriate metric unit, estimate the height of the tree.
   State the degree of accuracy that you have used in making your estimate.
   You must show your working.

## Reading scales

### Example 6

(a) Use an appropriate metric unit to measure accurately the length of each of lines **A**, **B** and **C**.
   A ————————————————
   B ——————————————————————
   C ——————————

(b) What is the total length of lines **A**, **B** and **C**?
(c) What is the difference in length between lines **B** and **C**?

(a) Line **A** is 7 cm (or 70 mm) long.
   Line **B** is 12.5 cm (or 125 mm) long.
   Line **C** is 4.6 cm (or 46 mm) long.
(b) 7 + 12.5 + 4.6 = 24.1 cm (or 241 mm).
(c) 12.5 − 4.6 = 7.9 cm (or 79 mm).

Chandni, Jill and Susan measured their weights.
The diagram shows the readings on the scale.
What are each of their weights?

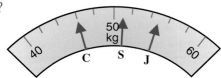

Chandni weighs 46 kg.
Jill weighs 55 kg.
Susan weighs 51 kg.

## Practice Exercise 26.3

1. Measure the lengths of these lines.

   X ————————————————————

   Y ————————

   (a) What is the length of each line in centimetres?
   (b) What is the length of each line in millimetres?

2. Read each of the following scales at pointers **A**, **B** and **C**.

   (a)

   C   B   A

   0 1 2 3 4 5 6 7 8 9 10
   **centimetres**

   (b)

   B   A   C

   30  40  50  60  70  80  90
   **millimetres**

   (c)

   A   B   C

   5   6   7   8   9
   **metres**

3. (a) Read each of the following scales at pointers **A**, **B** and **C**.

   (i)

   (ii)

   (iii)

   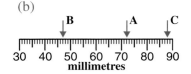

   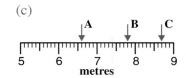

   (iv)

   (v)

   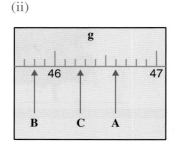

   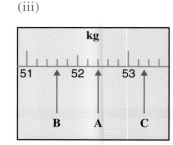

   (b) For each of the above scales work out the difference between the highest and lowest readings.

**4.** What is the temperature shown by pointers **A**, **B** and **C**?

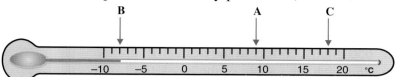

**5.** This diagram shows a speedometer on a car.
What is the speed when the pointer is at
**A**, **B** and **C**?
Give your answers in miles per hour.

## Accuracy in measurement

No measurement is ever exact and measurements given to the nearest whole unit may be inaccurate by up to one half of a unit in either direction.

For example:
Harry weighs 54 kg, correct to the nearest kilogram.
Whole unit = 1 kg.   Possible inaccuracy = 1 kg ÷ 2 = 0.5 kg.
So, Harry's actual weight is any weight from:

   Minimum: 54 kg − 0.5 kg = 53.5 kg.    Maximum: 54 kg + 0.5 kg = 54.5 kg.
This can be written as the inequality:   53.5 kg ≤ Harry's weight < 54.5 kg.

### Example 8

Harry is 1.63 metres tall, to the nearest centimetre.
What is Harry's minimum possible height?
Whole unit = 1 cm.   Possible inaccuracy = 1 cm ÷ 2 = 0.5 cm = 0.005 m.
Harry's minimum height = 1.63 − 0.005 = 1.625 m.

## Practice Exercise 26.4

**1.** The length of a field is 264 metres, correct to the nearest metre.
What is the minimum possible length of the field?

**2.** The weight of a necklace is 32 grams, to the nearest gram.
Copy and complete the inequality   … ≤ weight of necklace < ….

3. A post is 1.6 m in height, correct to the nearest tenth of a metre.
   What are the minimum and maximum possible heights of the post?

4. Jayne runs 4.8 km, correct to the nearest hundred metres.
   What is the minimum distance Jayne has run?

5. A concrete block weighs 650 grams, correct to the nearest 10 grams.
   What are the limits between which the weight of the block lies?

6. What is the minimum time for a race timed at 12.63 seconds,
   measured to the nearest one hundredth of a second?

## Key Points

► The common metric units used to measure length, mass (weight) and capacity (volume) are shown below.

> **Length**
> 1 kilometre (km) = 1000 metres (m)
>       1 m = 100 centimetres (cm)
>       1 cm = 10 millimetres (mm)
>
> **Mass**
> 1 tonne (t) = 1000 kilograms (kg)
>    1 kg = 1000 grams (g)
>
> **Capacity and volume**
> 1 litre = 1000 millilitres (ml)
> $1 \text{ cm}^3 = 1 \text{ ml}$

► You should be able to convert from one metric unit to another.
   Changing from one metric unit to another involves multiplying, or dividing,
   by a power of 10 (10, 100 or 1000).

► You should be able to select an **appropriate unit of measurement**.

► It is a useful skill to be able to **estimate** length, mass and capacity.

► You should be able to read scales accurately.

► You should be able to recognise limitations on the accuracy of measurements.
   A measurement given to the nearest whole unit may be inaccurate by up to half a unit.

## Review Exercise 26

1. Which two weights are the same?
        8 g   8 kg   8000 g   0.8 kg   80 kg

2. Which length is longest?
        0.5 km   50 m   5000 mm   500 cm

3. How many magazines, each 0.6 cm thick, will fit on a bookcase shelf which is exactly 1.2 m wide?

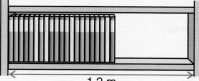

1.2 m

4. One glass of lemonade contains 300 ml.
   How many glasses of lemonade can be poured from a jug which contains 2.4 litres?

5. Ben takes two 5 ml doses of medicine four times a day.
   Ben stops taking the medicine after 5 days.
   Originally, there was $\frac{1}{4}$ of a litre of medicine.
   How much medicine is left?

6. One lap of a running track is 400 m.
   How many laps are run in an 8 km race?

7. Which of the following is the best estimate for the mass of a banana?
   
   1 kg    5 g    250 g    30 g    3 kg    750 g

8. A rectangular strip of card measures 0.8 metres by 5 cm.

   0.8 m

   5 cm

   Calculate the area of the card in:
   (a) square metres,
   (b) square centimetres.

9. A letter weighs 165 g and a parcel weighs 3.6 kg.
   Find the total weight of the letter and the parcel in kilograms.

10. A cuboid has length 3.7 m, breadth 80 cm and height 1600 mm.
    Find the volume of the cuboid, giving your answer in cubic metres.

11. The diagram shows the petrol gauge on a car.
    The arrows show the amount of fuel in the tank at the start and end of a journey.
    No fuel was added during the journey.
    The car's petrol tank holds 60 litres when full.
    Estimate the amount of fuel in the tank:
    (a) at the start of the journey,
    (b) at the end of the journey.
    (c) How much fuel was used for the journey?

12. Tim gives his height as 185 cm, to the nearest centimetre.
    What are the limits between which his true height lies?

13. A blue whale weighs 140 tonnes to the nearest 10 tonnes.
    What is the smallest possible weight of a blue whale?

# 27 Interpreting Graphs

Graphs are used in many real-life situations to represent information.

## Conversion graphs

A **conversion graph** is used to change one quantity into an equivalent quantity.
For example, conversion graphs can be drawn and used to change:

> **weight** – between pounds and kilograms,
> **temperature** – between degrees Celsius and degrees Fahrenheit,
> **currency** – between pounds, £, and euros, €.

### Example 1

Use the Currency Converter Graph to find:

(a)  20 euros in £,
(b)  £4 in euros.

Reading from graph:
(a)  20 euros = £12.50.
(b)  £4 = 6.4 euros.

> If you are given one equivalent value,
> such as 5 miles = 8 kilometres, you
> can draw your own conversion graphs.

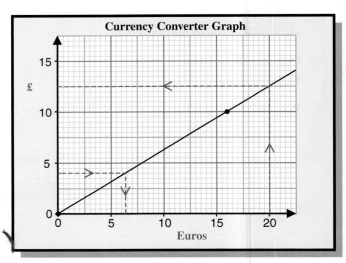

## Practice Exercise 27.1

1.  This conversion graph can be used to change measurements from
    inches into centimetres.

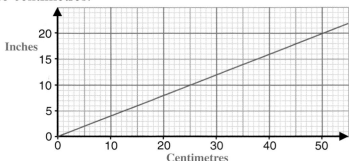

Use the graph to find:

(a)  10 centimetres in inches,      (b)  10 inches in centimetres,
(c)  16 inches in centimetres,      (d)  100 centimetres in inches.

2.  Use   £10 = 16 dollars   to draw a conversion graph for pounds and dollars.
    Use your graph to find:
    (a)  £8 in dollars,                  (b)  10 dollars in £.

3.  Use   5 miles = 8 kilometres   to draw a conversion graph for miles and kilometres.
    Use your graph to find:
    (a)  3.5 miles in kilometres,        (b)  5 kilometres in miles.

4.  Use   10 kilograms = 22 pounds (lb)   to draw a conversion graph for
    kilograms and pounds.
    Use your graph to find:
    (a)  4 kilograms in pounds,        (b)  15 pounds in kilograms.

5.  Use   32°F = 0°C and 212°F = 100°C   to draw a conversion graph for degrees
    Fahrenheit and degrees Celsius.
    Use your graph to find:
    (a)  50°F in degrees Celsius,        (b)  75°C in degrees Fahrenheit.

## Graphs of real-life situations

### Example 2

Craig drew a graph to show the amount of fuel in the family car as they travelled to their
holiday destination.

He also made some notes:

| Part of Graph | Event |
|---|---|
| A | Leave home. |
| A to B | Motorway. |
| B to C | Car breaks down. |
| C to D | On our way again. |
| D to E | Stop for lunch. |
| E to F | Fill tank with fuel. |
| F to G | Country roads. |
| G | Arrive, at last! |

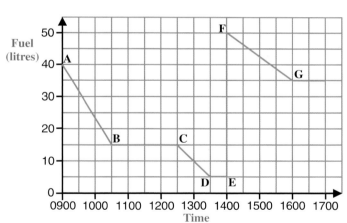

(a)  How much fuel was in the tank at the start of the journey?
(b)  At what time did the car break down?
(c)  How long did the family stop for lunch?
(d)  How much fuel was put into the tank at the garage?
(e)  At what time did the journey end?

(a)  40 litres

(b)  1030

(c)  $\frac{1}{2}$ hour

(d)  45 litres

(e)  1600

*Use the graph to work out how many litres of fuel were used for the journey.*

1. Cans of drink can be bought from a vending machine in the school canteen.
   The graph shows the number of cans in the machine between 1000 and 1500 one day.

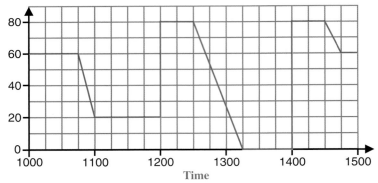

   (a) At 1000 the machine is three-quarters full.
       How many cans does the machine hold when it is full?
   (b) How many drinks were sold between 1045 and 1100?
   (c) The machine was filled up twice during the day.
       At what times was the machine filled up?
   (d) Between what times was the machine empty?
   (e) How many cans of drink were sold altogether between 1000 and 1500?

2. Graphs of the average heights and
   weights for men and women
   are shown.
   (a) John and his wife are both
       170 cm in height.
       Use the graphs to estimate
       the difference in their weights.
   (b) Fred and Mary both weigh 75 kg.
       Use the graphs to estimate
       the difference in their heights.

3. The diagram shows the distance from the starting position
   of a swimmer in a race in a swimming pool.

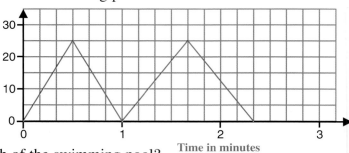

   (a) What is the length of the swimming pool?
   (b) What is the distance of the race?
   (c) How long did the swimmer take to complete the race?

4. The graph illustrates a 10 km cycle race between Afzal and Brian.

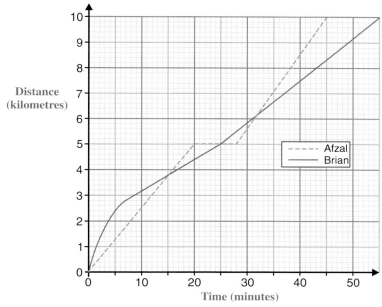

(a) Who was cycling faster at the beginning of the race?
(b) Which cyclist stopped?
(c) How far apart were the cyclists 10 minutes after the start of the race?
(d) Who won the race?

## Comparing data

Bar charts can also be used to compare data.
The table shows how a class of children travelled to school on one day.

| Method of travel | Bus | Cycle | Car | Walk |
|---|---|---|---|---|
| Boys | 2 | 7 | 1 | 5 |
| Girls | 3 | 1 | 5 | 6 |

To make it easier to compare the information given for boys and girls, we can draw both sets of bars on the same diagram, as shown.

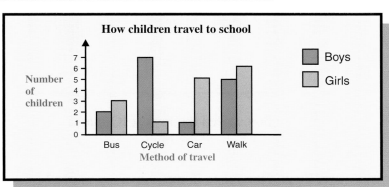

Seven boys cycle to school.
*How many girls cycle to school?*

There are 15 girls in the class and 6 walk to school.
*What percentage of boys walk to school?*

*Compare and comment on the method of travel of these boys and girls.*

1. The bar chart shows information about the sales of fresh and frozen poultry at a butcher's shop on one Saturday.

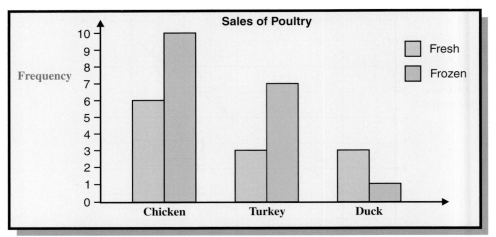

(a) How many frozen chickens were sold?
(b) How many fresh turkeys were sold?
(c) How many ducks were sold altogether?
(d) What fraction of the turkeys sold were frozen?
(e) What percentage of the ducks sold were fresh?

2. The bar chart shows the marks scored by four different boys in both a numeracy test and an IQ test.

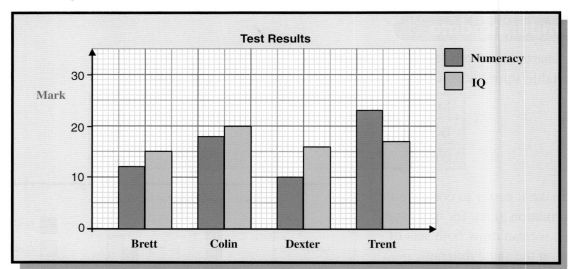

(a) Which boy scored the lowest IQ mark?
(b) Which boy scored the highest mark in numeracy?
(c) What is the range in the IQ marks?
(d) What is the range in the numeracy marks?
(e) The marks are added together to give each boy a total score.
    (i) Which boy had the highest score?
    (ii) Which boy had the lowest score?

**3.** The bar chart shows the reasons given by students for being absent from school on one day.

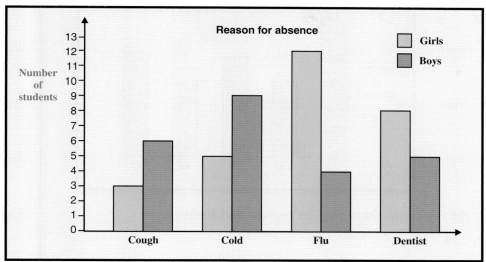

(a) How many girls were absent with flu?
(b) How many boys were absent with a cough?
(c) Which reason for absence was the mode?
(d) Compare and comment on the reasons for absence given by girls and boys.

**4.** The bar chart shows the results of a survey of the shoe sizes of pupils in a Year S4 class.

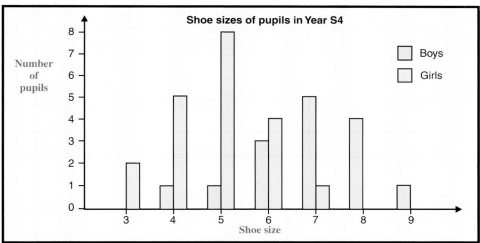

(a) Which size of shoe is the mode for the girls?
(b) Which size of shoe is the mode for the boys?
(c) How many pupils have shoe size 6?
(d) What percentage of boys have shoe size 8 or 9?
(e) What percentage of girls have shoe size 3 or 4?
(f) What is the range of shoe size for girls?
(g) What is the range of shoe size for boys?
(h) Compare and comment on the shoe sizes of boys and girls.

# Finding averages from diagrams

### Example 3

Find the range, mode, median and mean of the ages for the data shown in the bar chart.

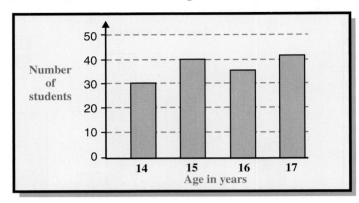

The range is the difference between the highest and lowest ages.

Range = 17 - 14
Range = 3 years

The most common age is shown by the tallest bar.

So, the modal age is 17 years.

Use a table to find the median and the mean.

| Age (years) $x$ | Frequency $f$ | Frequency $\times$ Age $f \times x$ |
|---|---|---|
| 14 | 30 | 420 |
| 15 | 40 | 600 |
| 16 | 36 | 576 |
| 17 | 41 | 697 |
| Totals | $\Sigma f = 147$ | $\Sigma fx = 2293$ |

The middle student is given by: $\dfrac{147 + 1}{2} = 74$

The 74th student in the list has the median age.

The first 70 students are aged 14 or 15 years.
The 74th student has age 16 years.

Median age is 16 years.

$$\text{Mean} = \frac{\text{Total of all ages}}{\text{Number of students}} = \frac{\Sigma fx}{\Sigma f}$$

$\text{Mean} = \frac{2293}{147} = 15.598\ldots$

Mean age is 15.6 years, correct to 1 d.p.

**Practice** Exercise **27.4**

1. Hilary observed customers using the express checkout at a supermarket.

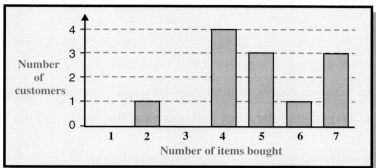

(a) Find the range of the number of items bought.
(b) What is the mode of the number of items bought?
(c) Work out the median number of items bought.
(d) Calculate the mean number of items bought.

2. During one week, the following numbers of sizes of a particular style of shoe were sold.

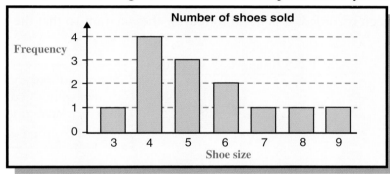

(a) Find the range of the shoe sizes sold.
(b) Which size is the median?
(c) Which size is the mode?
(d) Calculate the mean size. Comment on your answer.

3. (a) Find the range and mode of these prices.
   (b) Calculate the median and mean price of a small carton of milk.

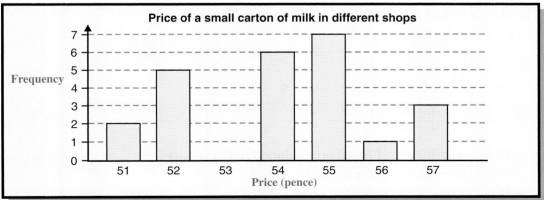

## Stem and leaf diagrams

Data can also be represented using a **stem and leaf diagram**.

**Example 4**

The times, in seconds, taken by 20 students to complete a puzzle are shown.

| 15 | 9 | 23 | 32 | 17 | 12 | 27 | 19 | 26 | 15 |
| 20 | 11 | 24 | 31 | 10 | 17 | 15 | 28 | 33 | 18 |

Construct a stem and leaf diagram to represent this information.

> A stem and leaf diagram is made by splitting each number into two parts.

As the data uses 'tens' and 'units', the stem will represent the 'tens' and the leaf will represent the 'units'.

To draw the stem and leaf diagram begin by drawing a vertical line.

The digits to the left of the line make the **stem**.

The digits to the right of the line are the **leaves**.

> The first number is 15.
> Next to the stem of 1 record 5.

> 9 is recorded as 0 9

```
0 | 9
1 | 5  7  2  9  5  1  0  7  5  8
2 | 3  7  6  0  4  8
3 | 2  1  3
```

Once the data has been recorded, it is usual to redraw the diagram so that the leaves are in numerical order.

```
                    1 | 5   means 15 seconds
---------------------------------------------
0 | 9
1 | 0  1  2  5  5  5  7  7  8  9
2 | 0  3  4  6  7  8
3 | 1  2  3
```

> Stem and leaf diagrams are often drawn without column headings in which case a key is necessary.
> e.g. 1 | 5   means 15 seconds

## Practice Exercise 27.5

1. The amount of petrol, in litres, bought by 20 motorists is shown.

| 16 | 23 | 27 | 10 | 35 | 42 | 26 | 25 | 24 | 17 |
| 23 | 41 | 33 | 35 | 25 | 19 | 16 | 31 | 12 | 29 |

   Construct a stem and leaf diagram to represent this information.

2. David did a survey to find the cost, in pence, of a loaf of bread.
   The stem and leaf diagram shows the results of his survey.

```
                         6 | 7   means 67 pence
------------------------------------------------
6 | 7  9
7 | 1  1  2  9  9  9
8 | 2  5  9
9 | 0
```

   (a) How many loaves of bread are included in the survey?
   (b) What is the range of the prices?
   (c) Which price is the mode?

3. The stem and leaf diagram shows the distribution of marks for a test marked out of 50.

| Boys | | | | Girls | | | 1 | 7 means 17 marks |
|---|---|---|---|---|---|---|---|---|

| Boys | | | | | stem | Girls | | | | | | |
|---|---|---|---|---|---|---|---|---|---|---|---|---|
| | | | | | 0 | 9 | | | | | | |
| | | | 6 | 2 | 1 | 0 | 1 | 2 | 7 | | | |
| | 7 | 6 | 4 | 3 | 2 | 1 | 3 | 5 | 5 | 6 | 7 | 8 |
| 9 | 5 | 3 | 2 | 0 | 3 | 2 | 5 | 9 | | | | |
| | | | 5 | 1 | 4 | 1 | | | | | | |
| | | | | 0 | 5 | | | | | | | |

(a) What is the lowest mark for the girls?
(b) What is the highest mark for the boys?
(c) How many of these boys and girls scored more than 25 marks?
(d) Compare and comment on the marks for boys and girls.

4. The stem and leaf diagram shows the heights, in centimetres, of 20 different pairs of shoes.

| | | | | 2 | 7 means 2.7 cm |
|---|---|---|---|---|---|

| stem | | | | | | | |
|---|---|---|---|---|---|---|---|
| 1 | 8 | | | | | | |
| 2 | 0 | 1 | 4 | 5 | 6 | 6 | 7 |
| 3 | 1 | 4 | 5 | 5 | 6 | 9 | |
| 4 | 0 | 2 | 2 | 5 | | | |
| 5 | 4 | | | | | | |
| 6 | 0 | | | | | | |

(a) Find the range in the heights of heels.
(b) Find the median height of a heel on a shoe.

## Time series

The money spent on shopping **each day**, the gas used **each quarter** and the rainfall **each month** are all examples of **time series**.
A time series is a set of readings taken at time intervals.

A time series is often used to monitor progress and to show the **trend** (increases and decreases) so that future performance can be predicted.
The type of graph used in this situation is called a **line graph**.

This graph shows the temperature of a patient taken every half-hour.

Only the plotted points show **known values**. Lines are drawn to show the **trend**.

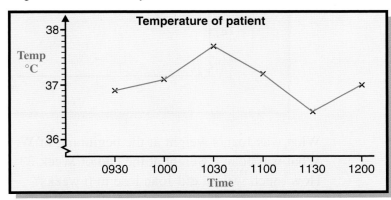

*What is the highest temperature recorded?*

*Explain why the graph can only be used to give an **estimate** of the patient's temperature at 1115.*

1. The number of cars sold by a car dealer is recorded each month.
   The line graph shows the results for the first six months of a year.

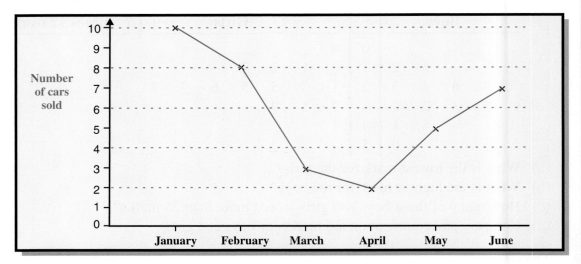

   (a) How many cars were sold in February?
   (b) In which months were more than 5 cars sold?
   (c) Explain why you cannot estimate how many cars were sold halfway through April.

2. Joan is a member of Weight Watchers.
   She records her weight at the beginning of each week.
   The line graph shows a record of her weight for six weeks.

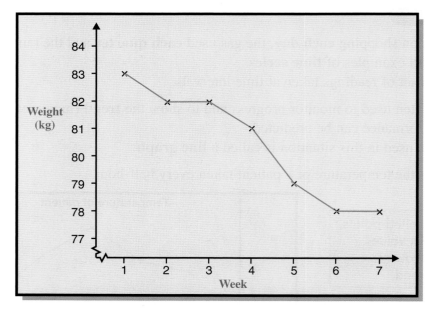

   (a) What was Joan's weight at the beginning of Week 2?
   (b) What was Joan's weight at the end of Week 2?
   (c) How much weight did Joan lose in 6 weeks?
   (d) In which week did Joan's weight first fall below 80 kg?

3. The midday temperature at a seaside resort was recorded each day for one week. The line graph shows the results.

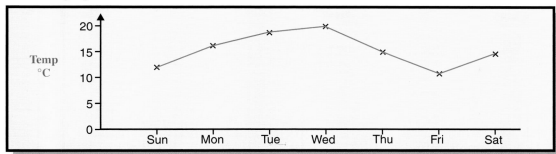

(a) What was the midday temperature on Thursday?
(b) Explain why you cannot use this line graph to estimate the temperature at midnight on Monday.

4. The graph shows the amount of money in Jayne's savings account at the end of each month, for six months.

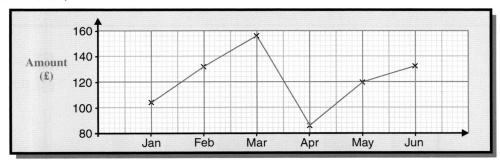

(a) Use your graph to estimate the amount in her account in the middle of February.
(b) Explain what happened to the account between March and April.

## Key Points

▶ A graph used to change from one quantity into an equivalent quantity, such as pounds into kilograms, is called a **conversion graph**.

▶ You should be able to interpret graphs arising from real-life situations.

▶ You should be able to extract data from a bar chart and use it to make comparisons between grouped data.

▶ You should be able to find averages from data presented in diagrams.

▶ A **stem and leaf diagram** is used to present data in its original form.

▶ A **time series** is a set of readings taken at time intervals.

▶ A **line graph** is used to show a **time series**.
Only the plotted points represent actual values.
Points are joined by lines to show the **trend**.

1. The cost of removals includes a fixed amount and a charge per kilometre for the distance moved. The graph shows the cost, in £, for removals up to a distance of 50 kilometres.

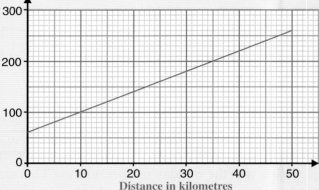

Use the graph to find:
   (a) the cost of removals for a distance of 20 kilometres,
   (b) the distance moved when the cost of removals is £200,
   (c) the fixed amount charged.

2. A group of children were asked how many hours they had spent watching television on a particular Sunday. The bar chart shows the results.

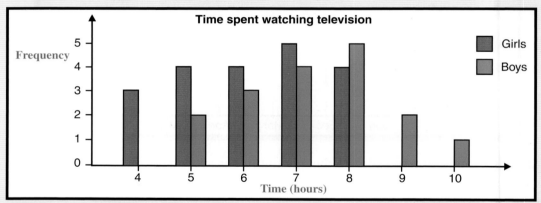

   (a) What was the modal time for the girls?
   (b) What was the range in time for the boys?
   (c) How many boys watched television for more than 8 hours?
   (d) (i) How many girls were included in the survey?
       (ii) What percentage of the girls watched television for 6 hours?
   (e) Compare and comment on the time spent watching television for these boys and girls.

3. Each year, on his birthday, a teenager records his height. The table shows the results.

| Age (yrs) | 13 | 14 | 15 | 16 | 17 | 18 | 19 |
|---|---|---|---|---|---|---|---|
| Height (cm) | 145 | 151 | 157 | 165 | 174 | 179 | 180 |

   (a) Draw a line graph to represent this information.
   (b) Use your graph to estimate:
       (i) the height of the teenager when he was $14\frac{1}{2}$ years of age,
       (ii) the age of the teenager when he reached 160 cm in height.

**4.** A group of students took part in a quiz on the Highway Code.
The bar chart shows their scores.

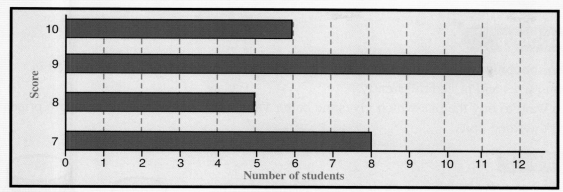

(a) Which score is the mode?
(b) What is the median score?
(c) How many students took part in the quiz?
(d) Calculate the mean score.

**5.** The graph represents a coach journey from Dundee.

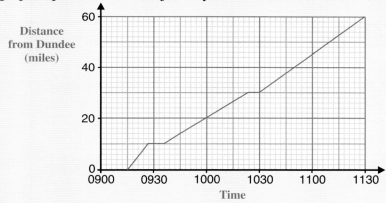

The coach completed its journey at 1130.
(a) At what time did the coach leave Dundee?
(b) How far did the coach travel?
(c) How many times did the coach stop on the journey?
(d) What was the average speed of the coach between 1030 and 1130?

**6.** The stem and leaf diagram shows the marks obtained by 30 candidates in a
navigation test.

2 | 3   represents 23 marks

|   |   |   |   |   |   |   |   |   |
|---|---|---|---|---|---|---|---|---|
| 2 | 3 | 8 | 9 |   |   |   |   |   |
| 3 | 0 | 2 | 3 | 4 | 5 | 6 | 6 | 7 | 8 |
| 4 | 1 | 4 | 5 | 6 | 7 | 8 | 8 | 9 | 9 |
| 5 | 0 | 0 | 0 | 0 | 3 | 6 | 8 | 9 |
| 6 | 0 |   |   |   |   |   |   |   |

(a) Write down the highest mark.
(b) What is the mode mark?
(c) Find the median mark.
(d) Find the range of the marks.

The pass mark for the test was 35 marks.
(e) How many candidates passed the test?

# 28 Making Decisions

## Best buys

When shopping we often have to make choices between products which are packed in various sizes and priced differently.

If we want to buy the one which gives the better value for money we must compare prices using the same units.

### Example 1

Peanut butter is available in small or large jars, as shown.
Which size is the better value for money?

Compare the number of grams per penny for each size.
Small: 250 ÷ 58 = 4.31… grams per penny.
Large: 454 ÷ 106 = 4.28… grams per penny.

The small size gives more grams per penny and is better value.

## Practice Exercise 28.1

In each question you must show all your working.

1.  Milk is sold in 1 pint, 2 pint and 4 pint containers.
    The cost of a 1 pint container is 55p, the cost of a 2 pint container is £1.02 and the cost of a 4 pint container is £1.68.
    (a)  How much per pint is saved by buying a 2 pint container instead of two 1 pint containers?
    (b)  How much per pint is saved by buying a 4 pint container instead of two 2 pint containers?

2.  Mushroom soup is sold in two sizes.
    A small tin costs 43p and weighs 224 g.   A large tin costs 89p and weighs 454 g.
    Which size gives more grams per penny?

3.  Strawberry jam is sold in two sizes.
    A small pot costs 52p and weighs 454 g.   A large pot costs 97p and weighs 822 g.
    Which size gives more grams per penny?

4.  Jars of pickled onions are sold at the following prices:
    460 g at 65p   or   700 g at 98p.
    Which size is better value for money?

5.  Honey is sold in two sizes.
    A large pot costs £1.98 and weighs 454 g.   A small pot costs 86p and weighs 185 g.
    Which size is better value for money?

6.  Cottage cheese costs 85p for 120 g, £1.55 for 250 g and £6 for 1 kg.
    Which size is the best value for money?

7. Two bottles of sauce are shown.
   Which size gives better value for money?

Small
285 g
38p

Medium
567 g
74p

8. Toothpaste is sold in small, medium and large sizes.
   The small size contains 75 ml and costs 85p.
   The medium size contains 125 ml and costs £1.45.
   The large size contains 180 ml and costs £2.05.
   Which size is the best value for money?

## Finance

You will probably have to make many decisions involving finance.
The cost of living includes many bills for services provided to our homes.
Electricity, gas and telephone. Which provider should you choose?
You may have to decide between paying cash or using credit facilities when buying items for the home or for personal use.

### Example 2

Mrs Davis receives a quarterly bill for electricity.
The standing charge for the quarter is £10.40 and she has used 469 units of electricity at 7.85p per unit.
How much is her electricity bill?

Cost of units used:   $469 \times 7.85p = 3681.65p$
                   $= 3682p$, to the nearest penny.

Electricity bill = standing charge + cost of units used
            $= £10.40 + £36.82$
            $= £47.22$

> The actual cost is rounded to the nearest penny.
> Change the cost of units to £.

Her electricity bill is £47.22

## Practice Exercise 28.2

1. Last year the Evans family received four quarterly gas bills.

   | | | | |
   |---|---|---|---|
   | **March:** | **£184.26** | **June:** | **£102.00** |
   | **September:** | **£ 83.49** | **December:** | **£130.25** |

   (a) What was their total bill for the year?
   (b) The family can pay for their gas by 12 equal monthly instalments.
       How much would each instalment be?

2. Mrs Cotton uses 1064 units of electricity during one quarter.
   (a) Find the cost of her electricity bill if each unit costs 7.85 pence and the quarterly charge is £10.40.
   (b) Mrs Cotton considers changing her supplier.
       She sees an offer of 8.55 pence per unit and a standing charge of £5.20 per quarter.
       Would Mrs Cotton have saved money by changing supplier?
       You must show all the working to support your decision.

3. A gas company uses the following rule for changing units of gas to therms.

   | MULTIPLY THE NUMBER OF UNITS BY 1032 AND DIVIDE BY 1000 |
   | --- |

   Each quarter, the company charges 58p per therm of gas used plus a standing charge of £12.50.
   The diagram shows the gas meter readings at the start and end of a quarter.

   Start             End

   (a) How many units of gas were used during the quarter?
   (b) Use the rule to calculate the number of therms used.
   (c) Find the total gas bill for the quarter.

   Another company make a different offer.

   | GAS BILL = NUMBER OF UNITS USED × 59P |
   | --- |

   (d) Is this a better offer? You must show working to support your decision.

4. The table shows the monthly payments for loans.

   |  | 12 MONTHS | 24 MONTHS |
   | --- | --- | --- |
   | LOAN, £ | Monthly repayment | Monthly repayment |
   | 5000 | 492.95 | 287.20 |
   | 3000 | 295.79 | 172.32 |
   | 2000 | 197.15 | 114.88 |

   Marc takes out a loan for £3000 over a period of 12 months.
   Holly takes out a loan for £5000 over a period of 24 months.
   (a) What is the difference in their monthly repayments?
   (b) What is the total amount that Holly has to repay?

5. George wants to insure his house valued at £284 000 and its contents valued at £27 500.
   He gets offers from two insurance companies.
   The annual premiums for the insurance are:

   | COMPANY A | COMPANY B |
   | --- | --- |
   | Buildings: £1.35 per £1000 of cover.<br>Contents: 56p per £100 of cover. | Buildings + Contents:<br>£1.70 per £1000 of cover. |

   Which company should George choose? Show working to support your decision.

**6.** The table shows the cost of posting a letter.

| | Weight | 1st class | 2nd class |
|---|---|---|---|
| Letter | 0 - 100 g | 60p | 50p |
| Large letter | 0 - 100 g | 90p | 69p |
| | 101 - 250 g | £1.20 | £1.10 |
| | 251 - 500 g | £1.60 | £1.40 |

Find the total cost of posting:

(a) A letter weighing 65g by 2nd class post and a large letter weighing 168g by 1st class post.

(b) Find the difference in cost between sending a large letter weighing 78g by 1st class post and by 2nd class post.

**7.** How much more is paid when the motorboat is bought on credit terms instead of cash?

**MOTOR BOAT**
Cash price...£12 800
Credit terms...
Deposit of 30% of cash price
plus 36 monthly payments of £295

## Two-way tables

The results of a survey can be recorded on data-collection sheets and then collated using frequency or grouped frequency tables.
We can also illustrate data using **two-way tables**.

A two-way table is used to illustrate the data for two different features (variables) in a survey.

### Example 3

The two-way table shows the results of a survey.

| Wear glasses | Boys | Girls |
|---|---|---|
| Yes | 4 | 3 |
| No | 14 | 9 |

(a) How many boys wear glasses?
(b) How many children wear glasses?
(c) How many children were surveyed?
(d) Do the results prove or disprove the hypothesis: *"**More boys wear glasses than girls**"*?

(a) 4

(b) 4 + 3 = 7

(c) 4 + 3 + 14 + 9 = 30

(d) Disprove. Boys: $\frac{4}{18} \times 100 = 22\%$, Girls: $\frac{3}{12} \times 100 = 25\%$.

> **Remember:**
> Percentages are a useful way of comparing fractions.

1. The two-way table shows information about the ages of people in a retirement home.

| | Age (years) | | | | |
|---|---|---|---|---|---|
| | 60 - 64 | 65 - 69 | 70 - 74 | 75 - 79 | 80 and over |
| Men | 0 | 2 | 5 | 8 | 1 |
| Women | 2 | 5 | 6 | 5 | 6 |

   (a) How many men are aged 75 - 79?
   (b) How many men are included?
   (c) How many people are aged 75 or more?
   (d) How many people are included?
   (e) What percentage of these people are aged 75 or more?

2. The two-way table shows information about a class of pupils.

| | Boys | Girls |
|---|---|---|
| Can swim | 14 | 8 |
| Cannot swim | 6 | 2 |

   (a) How many boys can swim?
   (b) How many boys are in the class?
   (c) What percentage of the boys can swim?
   (d) What percentage of the girls can swim?
   (e) Do the results prove or disprove the hypothesis:
       **"More boys can swim than girls"**?
   Explain your answer.

3. The two-way table shows the results of a survey to test the hypothesis:
   **"More girls are left-handed than boys."**

| Left-handed | Boys | Girls |
|---|---|---|
| Yes | 3 | 2 |
| No | 18 | 12 |

   Do the results prove or disprove the hypothesis? Explain your answer.

4. In a survey, 100 people were asked:   **"Would you like to be taller?"**

   > 58 of the people asked were men.
   > 65 of the people asked said, "Yes."
   > 24 of the women asked said, "No."

   (a) Construct a two-way table to show the results of the survey.

   (b) A newspaper headline stated:

   > **Over 80% of men would like to be taller.**

   Do the results of the survey support this headline?
   Give a reason for your answer.

## Misleading graphs

Television programmes, newspapers and advertisements frequently use graphs and diagrams to present information.

Many of the graphs and diagrams they use are well presented and give a fair interpretation of the facts. Others are deliberately drawn to mislead.

You, the viewer and consumer, are often left to decide how accurate and genuine the information actually is.

Look at the graph opposite.
*Why is it misleading?*

You should notice that the vertical scale does not begin at zero.
The actual increase in profits is only £200 but the graph makes it appear much more.

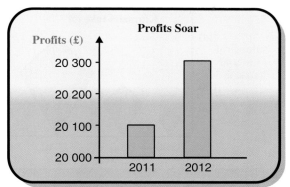

This type of diagram might be used to encourage people to invest their savings with a particular company. Can you think of other uses?

## Practice Exercise 28.4

1. This graph is drawn to compare the money raised for charity by two schools.

   School A has raised £400.
   School B has raised £500.

   Why is the graph misleading?

   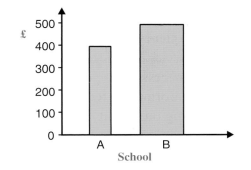

2.
   ### PASS WITH US
   Our learners only need an average of
   8 lessons before they can take the driving test.

   Give a reason why this advertisement may be misleading.

3. This diagram is used to compare the average price of a house in two different years.
   Why is the diagram misleading?

   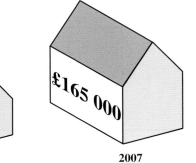

   Big growth in house prices   £150 000

   £165 000

   2005            2007

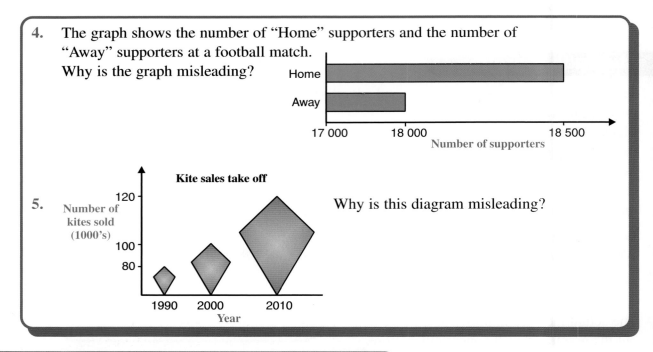

4. The graph shows the number of "Home" supporters and the number of "Away" supporters at a football match. Why is the graph misleading?

5. Why is this diagram misleading?

## Using probability to make decisions

In Chapter 10 we estimated probability using **relative frequency**.

> The relative frequency of an event is given by:
>
> $$\text{Relative frequency} = \frac{\text{Number of times the event happens in an experiment (or in a survey)}}{\text{Total number of trials in the experiment (or observations in the survey)}}$$

It is not always necessary to perform an experiment or make observations.
Sometimes the information required can be found in past records.
You are then using probability to help you make decisions.

### Example 4

Jamie does the following experiment with a bag containing 2 red and 8 blue counters.

> **Take a counter from the bag at random.**
> **Record the colour then put the counter back in the bag. Repeat this for 100 trials.**

Jamie calculates the relative frequency of getting a red counter every 10 trials and shows his results on a graph. Draw a graph showing the results that Jamie might get.
This is the sort of graph that Jamie might get.

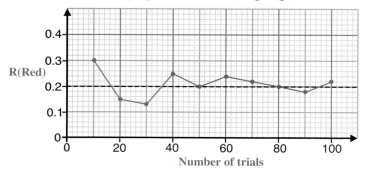

The dotted line shows the **calculated probability**.

$P(Red) = \frac{2}{10} = 0.2$

As the number of trials increases, relative frequency gives a better estimate of calculated probability.

*Try Jamie's experiment yourself and see what sort of results you get.*

## Practice Exercise 28.5

1. A counter is taken from a bag at random.
   Its colour is recorded and the counter is then put back in the bag.
   This is repeated 300 times.
   The number of red counters taken from the bag after every 100 trials is shown in the table.

   | Number of trials | Number of red counters |
   |---|---|
   | 100 | 52 |
   | 200 | 102 |
   | 300 | 141 |

   (a) Calculate the relative frequency after each 100 trials.
   (b) Estimate the probability of taking a red counter from the bag.
   (c) In the long run, is it more likely or less likely that a red counter is taken from the bag? Explain your answer.

2. Marie likes skiing and is planning a skiing holiday.
   She finds a table showing the probability of good conditions on the ski slopes in each month of the year.

   | Jan | Feb | Mar | Apr | May | Jun | Jul | Aug | Sep | Oct | Nov | Dec |
   |---|---|---|---|---|---|---|---|---|---|---|---|
   | 0.9 | 0.85 | 0.6 | 0.2 | 0.1 | 0 | 0 | 0 | 0 | 0 | 0.7 | 0.85 |

   (a) In which months would you not expect to be able to ski?
   (b) In which month of the year is the best skiing conditions?
   (c) It is possible to book a very cheap skiing holiday in April and May. Explain why.
   (d) In which three months of the year are skiing holidays likely to be the most expensive?

3. Shuffle a pack of playing cards.
   Pick 3 cards at random from the pack.

   | Record: | Event |
   |---|---|
   | N | No picture card |
   | P | At least 1 picture card |

   A picture card is a Jack, Queen or King.
   Replace the 3 cards, shuffle the pack and repeat the experiment.
   Do the experiment 100 times in total.
   Before you begin, estimate the probability of selecting at least 1 picture card each time the experiment is done.

   Find the value of $\dfrac{\text{number of times P occurs}}{100}$ as a decimal fraction.

4. A dice is thrown 600 times. The results of the trials are shown in the table.
   The purpose of the experiment is to decide: "Is the dice fair?"

| Score | 1 | 2 | 3 | 4 | 5 | 6 |
|-------|---|---|---|---|---|---|
| Frequency | 98 | 108 | 94 | 102 | 95 | 103 |

> If the dice is fair, the relative frequency of each score should
> be **approximately** equal to the probability of each score.

(a) Find the relative frequency of scoring each number from 1 to 6.
(b) Use your results from part (a) to describe if the dice is fair or not.

The experiment is repeated with another dice.
The results of 600 trials are shown in this table.

| Score | 1 | 2 | 3 | 4 | 5 | 6 |
|-------|---|---|---|---|---|---|
| Frequency | 88 | 96 | 97 | 98 | 98 | 123 |

(c) Is this dice fair? Show working to support your decision.

## Key Points

▶ When deciding on a **best buy**, compare quantities by using the same units.
For example, find which product gives more grams per penny.

▶ You should be able to make decisions involving **finance** by considering
given information.

▶ You should be able to interpret data given in **two-way tables**.

▶ **Misleading graphs**.
Graphs may be misleading if:   the scales are not labelled,
                               the scales are not uniform,
                               the frequency does not begin at zero.

▶ You should be able to use **probability** to help you make decisions.

## Review Exercise 28

1. The table shows the monthly repayments for different loans.

| Amount of loan | Period of loan (months) | | |
|----------------|------|------|------|
| | 24 | 36 | 60 |
| £5000 | 242.05 | 168.14 | 107.29 |
| £7500 | 363.08 | 252.21 | 160.94 |
| £10 000 | 484.10 | 336.28 | 214.58 |

Davina borrows £7500.
She repays the loan over a period of 60 months.
(a) Calculate the total amount Davina has to repay.
(b) Calculate the amount of interest charged on the loan.

2. Which of these two bottles of "Active" drink is better value for money? You must show your working.

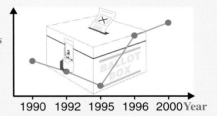

1.5 litre ACTIVE 90p

2 litre ACTIVE £1.30

3. The two-way table shows the results of a spelling test.

|  | Number of spellings correct | | | |
|---|---|---|---|---|
|  | 1 to 5 | 6 to 10 | 11 to 15 | 16 to 20 |
| Male | 1 | 3 | 6 | 5 |
| Female | 0 | 5 | 6 | 9 |

(a) How many females took the test?

(b) How many females got less than 11 spellings correct?

(c) John says, "Males are better at spelling because fewer males got less than 11 spellings correct."
Is he right? Give a reason for your answer.

4. The graph shows the votes cast for a political party in five elections.
Why is the graph misleading?

Votes cast

1990  1992  1995  1996  2000  Year

5. A travel agent says,
   **"More women prefer holidays abroad than men."**
The table shows the results of a survey to test this statement.

|  | Men | Women |
|---|---|---|
| Prefer holidays abroad | 18 | 21 |
| Prefer holidays in the UK | 6 | 7 |

Do these results support the statement made by the travel agent?
Explain your answer.

6. A spinner is labelled, as shown. The results of the first 30 spins are given below.

| 1 | 2 | 3 | 3 | 5 | 1 | 3 | 2 | 2 | 4 | 5 | 3 | 2 | 1 | 2 |
| 5 | 2 | 4 | 1 | 5 | 1 | 5 | 2 | 2 | 4 | 2 | 5 | 4 | 2 | 3 |

(a) Copy and complete this table to show the frequency of obtaining each score.

| Score | 1 | 2 | 3 | 4 | 5 |
|---|---|---|---|---|---|
| Frequency |  |  |  |  |  |

(b) Copy and complete this table to show the relative frequency of obtaining each score for the first 30 spins.

| Score | 1 | 2 | 3 | 4 | 5 |
|---|---|---|---|---|---|
| Relative frequency |  |  |  |  |  |

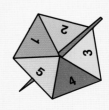

(c) Is the spinner fair? Give a reason for your answer.

# Numeracy

**Try to do questions 1 to 25 without using a calculator.**

1. The temperatures on six days, at noon in February, were:

   7°C    11°C    −3°C    5°C    0°C    −4°C

   (a) Which temperature is the coldest?
   (b) What is the range of the temperatures recorded?
   (c) Find the average temperature recorded.
       Give your answer correct to 2 decimal places.

2. Write these numbers in order, starting with the smallest.

   39    −4    3    120    −15

3. Dave buys these items.
   (a) How much does he have to pay altogether?
   (b) He pays with a £10 note.
       How much change is he given?

   89 pence          £1.47          £1.28

4. (a) What fraction of this shape is shaded?
       Give your answer in its simplest form.

   (b) Copy and shade 20% of this shape.

   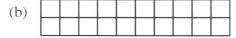

5. (a) Work out $\frac{4}{7}$ of £35.
   (b) Work out the cost of 28 rolls of wallpaper costing £5.18 each.
       Give your answer to the nearest pound.

6. (a) Richard has a dental appointment at 1425.
       What time is his appointment using the 12-hour clock?
   (b) Richard leaves home at 1345. He gets to the dentist at 1417.
       How long did his journey take?

7. (a) Write 10% as a fraction.        (b) Find 10% of £50.

8. Write 86.739:
   (a) to the nearest whole number,
   (b) to one decimal place,
   (c) to two decimal places.

9. The diagram shows a rectangular doormat.
   What is the area of the doormat:   (a) in cm²,    (b) in m²?

   1.5 m

   80 cm

10. Write down the length shown by the pointer.

**11.** Jo measures the lengths, in centimetres, of a sample of runner beans.
The stem and leaf diagram shows the results.

```
                1 | 3   means 13 cm
        1 | 3  5  7  9
        2 | 0  3  4  6  7  7  7  8
        3 | 0  1  1
```

(a) What is the length of the longest runner bean?
(b) How many runner beans are included in the sample?
(c) What is the range of their lengths?
(d) Which length is the median?

**12.** Look at this list of metric units.

| | | | | | |
|---|---|---|---|---|---|
| **centimetre** | **kilogram** | **metre** | **centilitre** | **gram** | **square metre** |
| **litre** | **tonne** | **square centimetre** | **millimetre** | **kilometre** | |

Choose the unit that would be best to use for measuring:
(a) the distance from Ayr to Paisley,
(b) the weight of a double decker bus,
(c) the height of a tree,
(d) the area of carpet needed to cover a floor.

**13.** The conversion graph can be used for changing between miles and kilometres.

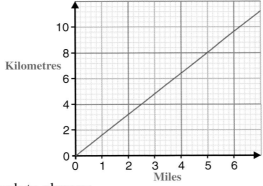

(a) Use the graph to change:
  (i) 4 kilometres to miles,     (ii) 4 miles to kilometres.
(b) Explain how you can use the graph to change 100 miles to kilometres.

**14.** The capacity of a tank is 220 litres, correct to the nearest 5 litres.
Between what limits does the actual capacity lie?

**15.** There are 120 offices in a building.
24 of the offices are not occupied.
What fraction of the offices are occupied?
Give your answer in its simplest form?

**16.** How much bigger is $72 \div 3$ than $72 \div 4$?

17. A group of students were asked which sport they did most.
The bar chart shows the results.

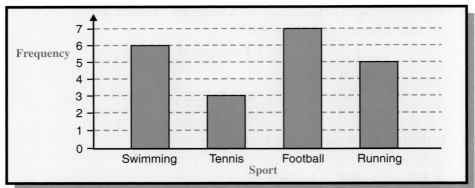

(a) How many students said, "swimming"?
(b) How many students were asked?
(c) Which sport is the mode?

18. A farmer has 32 bags of turnips. Each bag weighs 50 kg. What is the total weight?

19. The table shows the midday temperature in two cities on one day.
(a) How much colder is Moscow than London?
(b) Paris is 5°C colder than London.
What is the temperature in Paris?

| London | 3°C |
| Moscow | −8°C |

20. What number must be put in the box to make each of these statements true?
(a) ☐ × 3 = 15   (b) 3 + ☐ = 11   (c) ☐ − 3 = 7   (d) 3 − ☐ = −5

21. Estimate the value of 98 × 8.2.

22. Joyce wants to calculate $\frac{59.6}{20.2 - 4.9}$.

By writing each of the numbers in Joyce's calculation to the nearest whole number, estimate the answer.

23. (a) Write $\frac{1}{2}$ as a percentage.

(b) Write $\frac{2}{5}$ as a decimal.

(c) Put these fractions in order, smallest first:   $\frac{1}{2}$     $\frac{2}{3}$     $\frac{3}{4}$     $\frac{2}{5}$

(d) Work out $\frac{3}{4}$ of 36.

(e) What fraction of this rectangle is shaded?
Give your answer in its simplest form.

24. The table shows information about a group of children.
(a) One of these children is chosen at random.
What is the probability that the child can swim?
(b) A girl in the group is chosen at random.
What is the probability that she cannot swim?

|  | Boys | Girls |
|---|---|---|
| Can swim | 16 | 19 |
| Cannot swim | 4 | 6 |

(c) Tony says, ***"These results show a higher proportion of girls can swim."***
Is he correct? Give reasons for your answer.

25. (a) Write 0.75 as a percentage.     (b) Write 15% as a fraction in its simplest form.

**You may use a calculator for questions 26 to 37.**

26. A toolbox contains 12 screwdrivers and 30 spanners.
    What is the ratio of screwdrivers to spanners in its simplest form?

27. Laura buys 18 cartons of juice.   She pays with a £10 note.   She gets £2.98 change.
    How much is each carton of juice?

28. (a)   A fence is 2.3 metres high. What is the height of the fence in centimetres?
    (b)   A rule for changing litres into gallons is:

    > **Divide by 4.5**

    A lorry's fuel tank holds 180 litres when it is full.
    Use this rule to work out how many gallons the lorry's fuel tank holds.

29. A survey found the probability of a delivery made by lorry being late is $\frac{2}{9}$.
    Out of 400 scheduled deliveries, how many would you expect to be late?
    Give your answer correct to one significant figure.

30. Eddie drives his lorry 24 miles to deliver a load of car parts.
    He completes the journey in 40 minutes.
    What is Eddie's average speed in miles per hour?

31. Calculate $\frac{594}{19 \times 4}$.   Give your answer to the nearest whole number.

32. The newspaper heading is given to the nearest thousand.
    What is the smallest possible size of the audience?

33. On Monday morning a dentist treated 20 patients.
    (a)   $\frac{1}{4}$ of the patients had a check-up.
          How many of the patients had a check-up?
    (b)   10 patients had a filling.
          What fraction of the patients had a filling? Give your answer in its simplest form.
    (c)   $\frac{3}{10}$ of the patients were children.
          How many patients were children?

34. A hockey pitch is 87 metres long, to the nearest metre.
    (a)   What is the shortest possible length of the hockey pitch?
    (b)   What is the longest possible length of the pitch?

35. A box contains red candles and white candles in the ratio 1 : 4.
    The box contains 30 candles. How many red candles are there?

36. A garage charges £36 per hour.
    What is the charge for a job which takes 1 hour 20 minutes?

37. A farm has 427 acres of land. 135 acres are used for grazing.
    What percentage of the land is used for grazing?

# ANSWERS

## Chapter 1 — Algebraic Expressions

### Practice Exercise 1.1 — Page 1

1. $n + 4$
2. $n - 3$
3. $3n$
4. $m + 6$
5. $m - 12$
6. $8m$
7. $p - 1$
8. $p + 5$
9. $25p$
10. $6k$
11. $5b$ pence
12. $\frac{c}{3}$ pence
13. $\frac{a}{5}$ pence
14. $\frac{36}{g}$
15. (a) $2t$   (b) $10t$

### Practice Exercise 1.2 — Page 2

1. (a) $2y$ (b) $3c$ (c) $5x$
   (d) $7p$ (e) $2t$ (f) $3d$

2. (a) $3n$ (b) $5y$ (c) $p$
   (d) $2r$ (e) $7t + 2y$ (f) $4y$
   (g) $q$ (h) $0$ (i) $-x$
   (j) $3a$ (k) $3b - 2a$ (l) $-t$

3. (a) $10g$ (b) $8m$ (c) $13z$ (d) $4c$
   (e) $7x$ (f) $w$ (g) $0$ (h) $-5y$
   (i) $-5x$ (j) $-14a$ (k) $6b$ (l) $2m$

4. (a) $4x$ (b) $6a$ (c) $9y$ (d) $6u$

5. (a) Can be simplified, $2v$.
   (b) Cannot be simplified, different terms.
   (c) Can be simplified to $3v + 4$.
   (d) Cannot be simplified, different terms.

6. (a) $8x + y$ (b) $w + 2v$ (c) $2a - 2b$
   (d) $5x + 3y$ (e) $3 + 7u$ (f) $p + 4q$
   (g) $3d - 7c$ (h) $2y + 1$ (i) $a + b$
   (j) $4m + n$ (k) $9c - d$ (l) $x + y$
   (m) $6p$ (n) $5 - 5k$ (o) $a + 3$

7. (a) $8a + 3b$ (b) $3p + 3q$ (c) $3m + 2n$
   (d) $x - 2y$ (e) $2x + 3y$ (f) $d + 3$
   (g) $3b - 2a$ (h) $7$ (i) $a + 2b$
   (j) $-2f$ (k) $v - 4w$ (l) $-2 - 5t$
   (m) $4q - 4p$ (n) $1 - 7k$ (o) $c - d + 11$

8. (a) $4x + 2$ (b) $4a + 6b$
   (c) $3x$ (d) $6y + 9$

9. $2x - y + 3y - x + 4 + 2x + 3y - 2$
   $= 3x + 5y + 2$

### Practice Exercise 1.3 — Page 4

1. (a) $3a$ (b) $7b$ (c) $4e$
   (d) $8f$ (e) $6p$ (f) $15q$
   (g) $6y$ (h) $x$ (i) $10a$
   (j) $12b$ (k) $18c$ (l) $21d$

2. (a) $-3x$ (b) $-5x$ (c) $2x$
   (d) $-6x$ (e) $-10a$ (f) $10a$
   (g) $-3c$ (h) $-12c$ (i) $-8a$
   (j) $3f$ (k) $-12p$ (l) $y$

3. (a) $2a$ (b) $12x$ (c) $6g$ (d) $10y$

4. (a) $3(x + 2) = 3x + 6$
   (b) $2(y + 5) = 2y + 10$
   (c) $2(2x + 1) = 4x + 2$
   (d) $3(p + q) = 3p + 3q$

5. (a) $2(x + 5) = 2x + 10$
   (b) $3(a + 6) = 3a + 18$
   (c) $4(y + 3) = 4y + 12$

6. (a) $2(a - 1) = 2a - 2$
   (b) $3(2 - d) = 6 - 3d$
   (c) $4(1 - 2x) = 4 - 8x$

7. 
   $2(q + 2)$ and $2q + 4$
   $2(q - 1)$ and $2q - 2$
   $2(2q + 1)$ and $4q + 2$
   $2(2 - q)$ and $4 - 2q$

8. (a) $2x + 8$ (b) $3t - 6$
   (c) $6a + 2b$ (d) $15 - 10d$
   (e) $3a + 3b$ (f) $6c + 8$
   (g) $6b + 12c$ (h) $6m - 15a$

9. (a) $-3x - 6$ (b) $-3x + 6$
   (c) $-2y + 10$ (d) $-6 + 2x$
   (e) $-15 + 3y$ (f) $-4 - 4a$
   (g) $3 - 2a$ (h) $2d + 6$
   (i) $2b - 6$ (j) $-6p - 9$

10. (a) $2x + 5$ (b) $3a + 11$
    (c) $6w - 17$ (d) $10 + 2p$
    (e) $3q$ (f) $7 - 3t$
    (g) $5z + 8$ (h) $8t + 15$
    (i) $2c - 6$ (j) $5a - 9$
    (k) $3y - 10$ (l) $2x + 6$
    (m) $3 - 2a$ (n) $2d + 6$
    (o) $2b - 6$ (p) $-6p - 9$
    (q) $m - 6$ (r) $5d + 1$

## Practice Exercise 1.4 — Page 6

1. (a) $2x + 2 = 2(x + 1)$
   (b) $3a - 6 = 3(a - 2)$
   (c) $6m + 8 = 2(3m + 4)$
   (d) $5 - 10y = 5(1 - 2y)$
   (e) $8p - 2 = 2(4p - 1)$
   (f) $16r - 12 = 4(4r - 3)$

2. (a) $3p + 6q = 3(p + 2q)$
   (b) $8u - 10v = 2(4u - 5v)$
   (c) $2x + 2y = 2(x + y)$
   (d) $8a - 12b = 4(2a - 3b)$
   (e) $16r + 10s = 2(8r + 5s)$
   (f) $3 - 6p = 3(1 - 2p)$

3. (a) $2(a + b)$       (b) $5(x - y)$
   (c) $3(d + 2e)$      (d) $2(2m - n)$
   (e) $3(2a + 3b)$     (f) $2(3a - 4b)$
   (g) $4(2t + 3)$      (h) $5(a - 2)$
   (i) $2(2d - 1)$      (j) $3(1 - 3g)$
   (k) $5(1 - 4m)$      (l) $4(k + 1)$

1. $6t$ pence

2. $(x + 3)$ years old

3. (a) $3w$
   (b) $w + 2$

4. (a) $6a + 8$
   (b) $2b + 3c + 4$
   (c) $4d + 3f + 2$

5. (a) $2(2a + 1) = 4a + 2$
   (b) $2(3y + 2) = 6y + 4$
   (c) $3(a + b) = 3a + 3b$

6. $12a + 8$ and $4(3a + 2)$

   $4a - 12$ and $4(a - 3)$

   $12 - 4a$ and $4(3 - a)$

   $8 - 12a$ and $4(2 - 3a)$

7. (a) $5y - 20$       (b) $7y + 4$

8. (a) (i) $3(2x - 5)$
       (ii) $7(2 + y)$
   (b) $y + 12$

9. (a) $5x + 8$   (b) $2b - 6$

10. (a) $5(3 - 2a)$
    (b) $2(4 - 3x)$
    (c) $4(4x - 5y)$

## Chapter 2 — Formulae and Patterns

1. (a) 5       (b) 2       (c) 12      (d) 9

2. (a) 10      (b) $-2$    (c) 10      (d) 25

3. (a) 8       (b) 0       (c) 12      (d) 32

4. (a) 24   (b) $-3$   (c) 2   (d) 18   (e) 18

5. (a) 15   (b) 0   (c) 2   (d) 50   (e) 15

1. (a) $-1$    (b) $-4$    (c) $-12$   (d) 3

2. (a) 0       (b) $-8$    (c) $-10$   (d) $-16$

3. (a) $-8$    (b) $-8$    (c) $-12$   (d) 2

4. (a) 12      (b) $-9$    (c) 6

5. (a) $-5$    (b) $-20$   (c) $-45$

1. **17 points**    2. **£190**    3. **26 cm**

4. $T = 97$

5. $X = 8$

6. (a) $M = -7$    (b) $n = 5$

7. (a) $H = 2.5$   (b) $g = 6$

8. (a) $F = 35$    (b) $F = 75$    (c) $F = -15$

9. (a) $V = 26$    (b) $V = 2$     (c) $V = 34$

10. 33

11. 96 m

12. 86°F

13. 138 minutes

1. (a) 17, 21, 25       (b) 14, 16, 18
   (c) 16, 13, 10       (d) 28, 33, 38
   (e) 48, 96, 192      (f) 2, 0, $-2$

2. (a) 8, 14      (b) 10, 22
   (c) 8, 32      (d) 16, $-2$

**3.** (a) Add 7;  37,  44   (b) Add 2;  13,  15
    (c) Add 4;  21,  25   (d) Subtract 5;  11,  6

**4.** (a) 28
    (b) Keep on adding 3 to the last term until
        you get to the 10th term, 28.

**5.** No.
    To find the next number, add 6 to the last term.
    All numbers in the sequence will be odd.

**6.** (a) 2,  1,  $\frac{1}{2}$      (b) 0.9,  1.0,  1.1
    (c) 5,  2.5,  1.25   (d) 29,  47,  76

**7.** (a) Subtract 3;  $-5$,  $-8$,  $-11$
    (b) Divide by 2;  4,  2,  1

## Practice Exercise 2.5 — Page 13

**1.** (a) | 1,  5,  9,  13,  17 |

   (b) | 1,  2,  4,  8,  16 |

   (c) | 40,  35,  30,  25,  20 |

   (d) | 4,  5,  7,  11,  19 |

   (e) | 2,  6,  4,  5,  4.5 |

**2.** (a) | 2,  4,  8 |      (b) | 6,  12,  24 |

   (c) | $-2$,  $-4$,  $-8$ |

**3.** (a) (i) | 36 |  (ii) | 123 |    (b) | 10 |

**4.** | $-6$,  $-27$ |

**5.** (a) | 49,  97 |   (b) | 1537 |

## Practice Exercise 2.6 — Page 15

**1.**

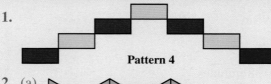

Pattern 4

**2.** (a)

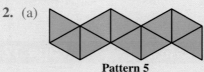

Pattern 5
    (b) Entries are:  2,  4,  6,  8,  10,  12
    (c) Each pattern is made using an even
        number of triangles. 27 is an odd number
    (d) $2p$      (e) 24

**3.** (a) (i) 15  (ii) 30  (iii) 300     (b) $3n$

**4.** (a)

(b) 4      Pattern 4
    (c) Entries are:  5,  9,  13,  17,  21
    (d) $4n + 1$       (e) 81

**5.** (a) (i) 18        (ii) 82
    (b) Pattern 7
    (c) Matches in length of pattern and number
        of verticals both increase by 2 every time.
    (d) $T = 4n + 2$     (e) 202

**6.** (a) (i) 51        (ii) 100
    (b) (i) $P = x + 1$  (ii) $H = 2x$
    (c) 101 posts, 200 horizontal bars.

**7.** (a) 11        (b) Pattern 7    (c) 21
    (d) $m = 2p + 1$   (e) 61

**8.** (a) 27
    (b) Add 5 matches to the number of matches
        used to make the previous pattern.
    (c) Pattern 6

## Review Exercise 2 — Page 17

**1.** 16

**2.** 4

**3.** $P = -18$

**4.** (a) 22        (b) $4d - 6$

**5.** (a) 12        (b) 6 more matches.

**6.** (a) 25, 36, 49   (b) 13, 21, 34

**7.** (a) 23, 27     (b) 43

**8.** (a) 2, 20, 26   (b) 46, 36, 31

**9.** (a) (i) | 21 |  (ii) | 3 |      (b) | 37 |

**10.** (a) | 37,  60 |  (b) | 1,  4 |

**11.** (a) Gregor multiplies the last term by 2,
        $4 \times 2 = 8$
        Fraser adds the next counting number,
        $4 + 3 = 7$
    (b) 512        (c) 46

**12.** (a)

Pattern 4
    (b) Entries are:  8,  10,  12,  14,  16
    (c) $W = 2B + 6$    (d) Pattern 54

**13.** (a) 21,  28,  36
    (b) Add the next counting number.

# Chapter 3 Gradient of a Straight Line

## Practice Exercise 3.1     Page 20

1. Positive gradient: **(1)**, **(3)**, **(7)**
   Negative gradient: **(4)**, **(6)**, **(9)**
   Zero gradient:      **(2)**, **(8)**
   Undefined gradient: **(5)**

2. **(1)** 1,   **(2)** 2,   **(3)** 5,   **(4)** $\frac{4}{3}$,   **(5)** 4,   **(6)** $\frac{2}{3}$

3. **(1)** $-2$,   **(2)** $-1$,   **(3)** $-5$,
   **(4)** $-3$,   **(5)** $-1$,   **(6)** $-\frac{2}{5}$

4. (a) **(5)**, **(7)**, **(11)**    (b) **(8)**    (c) **(3)**

5. (a)    **(1)** 1,             **(2)** $-\frac{3}{4}$,    **(3)** 0,
         **(4)** undefined,    **(5)** $-3$,    **(6)** 0,
         **(7)** $\frac{4}{5}$,             **(8)** $-3$,    **(9)** 1,
         **(10)** undefined,   **(11)** $-4$,   **(12)** $-1$,
         **(13)** 2,            **(14)** 0
   (b)   **(9)**    (c)   **(5)**

## Practice Exercise 3.2     Page 21

1. (a) 3     (b) 1      (c) 2

2. (a) $-2$    (b) $-3$    (c) $-1$

3. (a) 50    (b) $-8$    (c) 2

4. (a) $B$ and $C$   (b) 2   (c) 8   (d) $-2$   (e) 2

## Review Exercise 3     Page 23

1. (a)    **(1)** $-2$, **(2)** 0,     **(3)** 4,    **(4)** $-3$,
         **(5)** 5,    **(6)** $-2$,    **(7)** 3,    **(8)** 0,
         **(9)** undefined,     **(10)** 1,   **(11)** $-4$,
         **(12)** 1
   (b) **(12)**    (c) **(6)**

2. (a) 2     (b) 0      (c) $-1$

3. (a) $-6$    (b) 3      (c) 0      (d) $-10$

# Chapter 4 Circles

## Practice Exercise 4.1     Page 25

1. (a) 12 cm     (b) 24 cm     (c) 39 cm

2. (a) 15 cm     (b) 30 cm     (c) 38.4 cm

3. (a) 37.7 cm    (b) 22.0 cm    (c) 47.1 cm

4. (a) 28.3 cm    (b) 35.2 cm    (c) 100.5 cm

5. 28 cm

6. 75.4 cm

7. 81.7 cm

8. 40.8 cm

9. 57.5 m

10. 5.03 m

11. 31.4 m

## Practice Exercise 4.2     Page 27

1. (a) 75 cm²    (b) 147 cm²    (c) 243 cm²

2. (a) 27 cm²    (b) 75 cm²    (c) 192 cm²

3. (a) 50 cm²    (b) 133 cm²    (c) 452 cm²

4. (a) 32.2 cm²   (b) 45.4 cm²   (c) 530.9 cm²

5. 16 286 mm²

6. 1.13 m²

7. 0.79 m²

8. 50.3 cm²

## Practice Exercise 4.3     Page 29

1. (a) 56.5 cm    (b) 254.5 cm²

2. (a) 26 cm     (b) 55.4 cm²

3. (a) 56.5 cm    (b) 11.3 m

4. 22.0 cm²

5. Circle: 50.3 cm². Semicircle: 47.5 cm²
   The circle is bigger.

6. 21.5 cm²

7. (a) 27 m      (b) 56.7 m²

8. 31 cm

9. (a) 37.7 m    (b) 17 bags

## Review Exercise 4     Page 30

1. (a) 44.0 cm    (b) 56.5 cm

2. (a) 201 cm²    (b) 314 cm²

3. (a) 78.5 cm²    (b) 25.1 cm

4. 15.7 m

5. 125.7 cm²

6. (a) 188.5 cm    (b) 282.7 cm

# Chapter 5 — Areas and Volumes

## Practice Exercise 5.1 — Page 31

1. (a) 9 cm²   (b) 6 cm²   (c) 3.6 cm²
2. (a) 7.2 cm²   (b) 4.16 cm²   (c) 11.52 cm²
3. (a) 3.8 cm²   (b) 8 cm²   (c) 3.24 cm²

## Practice Exercise 5.2 — Page 34

1. (a) 9 cm²   (b) 48 cm²
   (c) 9 cm²   (d) 66 cm²
2. (a) 6 cm²   (b) 20 cm²
   (c) 16 cm²   (d) 42 cm²
3. (a) 18 cm²   (b) 18 cm²   (c) 36 cm²
4. **A** 8 cm²   **B** 12 cm²   **C** 12 cm²
   **D** 9 cm²   **E** 8 cm²   **F** 12 cm²
5. (a) 30 cm²   (b) 10 cm²   (c) 13.5 cm²
6. (a) 20 cm²   (b) 7.5 cm²   (c) 5.75 cm²
7. (a) 30 cm²   (b) 35.75 cm²   (c) 21 cm²
8. 4 cm

## Practice Exercise 5.3 — Page 36

3. (a) 4   (b) 2 faces overlap.
5. (a) Cube, 6, 8, 12
   (b) Cuboid, 6, 8, 12
   (c) Pyramid, 5, 5, 8
   (d) Triangular prism, 5, 6, 9

## Practice Exercise 5.4 — Page 39

1. (a) 6 cm³
   (b) 18 cm³
   (c) 36 cm³
2. (a) (i) 8   (ii) 27
      (iii) 64   (iv) 125
   (b) (i) 24 cm²   (ii) 54 cm²
      (iii) 96 cm²   (iv) 150 cm²
3. (a) 27 cm³,   54 cm²
   (b) 24 cm³,   52 cm²
   (c) 140 cm³,   166 cm²
4. (a) 40 cm³   (b) 140 cm³   (c) 96 cm³
5. (a) 6 cm²,   15 cm³
   (b) 314 cm²,   6280 cm³
   (c) 3.14 cm²,   15.7 cm³

6. (a) 288 cm²   (b) 240 cm³
7. **P**   P = $64\pi$ cm³ = 201.1 cm³
   Q = $63\pi$ cm³ = 197.9 cm³
8. No.   $\pi \times 5 \times 5 \times 10 = 250\pi$ cm³
   $\pi \times 10 \times 10 \times 5 = 500\pi$ cm³

## Review Exercise 5 — Page 41

1. (a) 45 cm   (b) 75 cm²   (c) 10 cm
2. (a) 21 cm²   (b) 66.5 cm²
3. 5 faces
   9 edges
   6 vertices
4. C
5. 787.5 m²
6. (a) 75 cm²   (b) 225 cm³
7. 1040 cm³
8. (b) 480 cm   (c) 600 cm²
   (d) 10 800 cm²   (e) 48 000 cm³

# Chapter 6 — Rotational Symmetry

## Practice Exercise 6.1 — Page 44

1. (a) 2   (b) 3   (c) 4
   (d) 2   (e) 6   (f) 8
2. 1, 1, 3
3. (a)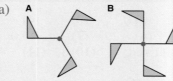
   (b) **A**: 3,   **B**: 4,   **C**: 2
4. (a) N O X Z
   (b) N X Z
5. (a) (b)
6. (a)    (b) 3
7. (a) 2   (b) 1   (c) 2   (d) 4   (e) 1

1. (a) 2
   (b) (6, 5)
   (c) (i) $A(1, 3) \to A'(11, 7)$
       (ii) $B(7, 3) \to B'(9, 3)$
       (iii) $C(11, 7) \to C'(1, 3)$
       (iv) $D(9, 3) \to D'(3, 7)$

2. (a) 4
   (b) (4, 6)
   (c) (i) $P(1, 6) \to P'(7, 6)$
       (ii) $Q(4, 9) \to Q'(4, 3)$
       (iii) $R(7, 6) \to R'(1, 6)$
       (iv) $S(4, 3) \to S'(4, 9)$
   (d) (i) $P(1, 6) \to P'(4, 9)$
       (ii) $Q(4, 9) \to Q'(7, 6)$
       (iii) $R(7, 6) \to R'(4, 3)$
       (iv) $S(4, 3) \to S'(1, 6)$

3. (b) (6, 4)
   (c) 2
   (d) $W'(8, 5)$,   $X'(8, 0)$,   $Y'(4, 3)$,   $Z'(4, 8)$

1. (a) 3      (b) 8      (c) 4
2. (a) 2      (b) 4      (c) 1
3.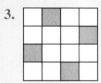

4. (a) 2      (b) 2      (c) 6
5. (a) 2      (b) (2, 2)      (c) $C'(2, 0)$

## Chapter 7   Collecting Data

1. Qualitative.
2. Quantitative, continuous.
3. Quantitative, discrete.
4. Qualitative.
5. Quantitative, discrete.
6. Quantitative, continuous.
7. Quantitative, discrete.
8. Qualitative.
9. Quantitative, discrete.
10. Quantitative, continuous.

1. (a) 15      (b) 21      (c) 4

2. (a)

| Number on dice | Tally |
|---|---|
| 1 | 卌 ‖ |
| 2 | 卌 ‖‖ |
| 3 | 卌 ‖‖‖ |
| 4 | 卌 卌 |
| 5 | 卌 ‖‖‖ |
| 6 | 卌 ‖ |

   (b) 4

3. (a) Frequencies:
      5, 5, 9, 7, 8, 4, 2
   (b) 50 - 59

4. (a) Frequencies:
      0, 4, 10, 8, 6, 2
   (b) 11 - 15 minutes

1. (a) Frequencies:
      4, 5, 7, 4, 5, 5
   (c) 3

2. (b) 7      (c) 3

3. (a) 38      (b) 6
   (c) Monday
   (d)

| Day of birth | Number of boys |
|---|---|
| Sunday | 1 |
| Monday | 3 |
| Tuesday | 4 |
| Wednesday | 4 |
| Thursday | 1 |
| Friday | 5 |
| Saturday | 1 |

4. (a)

| Distance ($m$ metres) | Frequency |
|---|---|
| $5.00 \leqslant m < 5.50$ | 4 |
| $5.50 \leqslant m < 6.00$ | 7 |
| $6.00 \leqslant m < 6.50$ | 9 |
| $6.50 \leqslant m < 7.00$ | 4 |

   (c) $6.00 \leqslant m < 6.50$

5. (a) 36      (b) 24
   (c) 40      (d) 80 - 90 kg

**6.** (a)

| Distance ($m$ miles) | Frequency |
|---|---|
| $0 \leqslant m < 10\,000$ | 9 |
| $10\,000 \leqslant m < 20\,000$ | 8 |
| $20\,000 \leqslant m < 30\,000$ | 6 |
| $30\,000 \leqslant m < 40\,000$ | 7 |

(b) 30    (d) $0 \leqslant m < 10\,000$

**7.** (a) 26    (b) 0    (c) 27    (d) 95

**8.** (a)

| Mark | Frequency |
|---|---|
| 20 and less than 30 | 5 |
| 30 and less than 40 | 8 |
| 40 and less than 50 | 9 |
| 50 and less than 60 | 6 |
| 60 and less than 70 | 2 |

(b) 40 and less than 50    (c) 22

## Review Exercise 7     Page 57

**1.** (a)

| Time ($t$ seconds) | Tally | Frequency |
|---|---|---|
| $0 \leqslant t < 5$ | $\vert\vert\vert$ | 3 |
| $5 \leqslant t < 10$ | $\bcancel{\vert\vert\vert\vert}$ | 5 |
| $10 \leqslant t < 15$ | $\bcancel{\vert\vert\vert\vert}\ \vert\vert\vert$ | 8 |
| $15 \leqslant t < 20$ | $\vert\vert\vert\vert$ | 4 |
| | Total | 20 |

(b) $10 \leqslant t < 15$ seconds

**2.** (a) Frequencies: 1, 3, 8, 12, 4, 2
(b) 3

**3.** (a) Frequencies: 4, 4, 6, 4, 2
(c) 170 - 174 cm

**4.** (a) Frequencies: 8, 7, 4, 6, 4, 1
(c) 1 - 5 hours

## Chapter 8   Averages *and* Range

## Practice Exercise 8.1     Page 60

**1.** (a) 7    (b) 4    (c) 4

**2.** (a) 3    (b) 3

**3.** (a) 1    (b) 2    (c) 3

**4.** (a) 5    (b) 2    (c) 3

**5.** 41p

**6.** (a) 3    (b) 5    (c) 3.5    (d) 4

**7.** (a) 18 kg    (b) 74 kg    (c) 72.4 kg

**8.** (a) 135    (b) 135    (c) 133

**9.** (a) 39    (b) 23    (c) 38.8

## Practice Exercise 8.2     Page 61

**1.** (a) (i) 60 g    (ii) 99 g
(b) Premium more widely spread and heavier.

**2.** (a) (i) 9 minutes    (ii) 9.5 minutes
(b) Trains are more variable,
but less late on average.

**3.** (a) (i) 42 words per minute
(ii) 60 words per minute
(b) First group is quicker on average,
and speeds are less varied than the
second group.

**4.** (a) (i) 0.5 minutes    (ii) 1.95 minutes
(b) Girls a little slower on average
(2.03 minutes) and more varied
(1.0 minutes).

**5.** First Division: Range = 5,   mean = 1.8
Third Division: Range = 6,   mean = 2.7
Third Division - more goals on average and
more spread.

**6.** (a) (i) Roman 1.6%,      Chinese 1.9%,
Egyptian 2.5%,    Greek 1.6%
(ii) Roman 6.48%,    Chinese 6.48%,
Egyptian 6.48%,    Greek 6.38%
(b) Mean silver content is very similar for
all coins. Egyptian coins have largest
variation in silver content.

## Practice Exercise 8.3     Page 64

**1.** (a)

| Number of bottles | 1 | 2 | 3 | 4 |
|---|---|---|---|---|
| Number of houses | 12 | 10 | 5 | 3 |

(b) 1    (c) 2    (d) 1.97

**2.** (a)

| Number of keys | 2 | 3 | 4 | 5 | 6 |
|---|---|---|---|---|---|
| Frequency | 2 | 3 | 8 | 5 | 2 |

(b) 20    (c) 4    (d) 4    (e) 4.1

**3.** (a)

| Wage (£) | 25 | 30 | 35 | 40 | 45 |
|---|---|---|---|---|---|
| Frequency | 6 | 4 | 5 | 1 | 3 |

(b) £20    (c) £25    (d) 19
(e) £30    (f) £620    (g) £32.63

**4.** (a) 2, 2.5, 2.7
(b) 2, 2, 2.1
(c) 0, 5, 4.5

1. Jays:    Mean 1.9,   range 5
   Wasps: Mean 2.4,   range 3
   Wasps scored more on average and had
   less spread.

2. Women: Mean 1.6,   range 6
   Men:     Mean 1.5,   range 2
   Women made more visits to the cinema,
   though the number of visits is more spread.

3. Boys: Mean 2.27,   range 6
   Girls: Mean 2.27,   range 3
   Larger variation in the number of cards
   received by boys.
   Average for boys and girls is the same.

4. Average: Boys 6.2,   Girls 7.2
   Range:   Boys 4,    Girls $4\frac{1}{2}$
   No. Girls' average greater than boys'.
   Correct about variation.

5. (a) MacQuick 20 - 29,   Pizza Pit 30 - 39
   (b) MacQuick - mean 26 years
        (Pizza Pit 36.5 years)
   (c) Exact ages not known.

6. Before: Median 3,   range 4
   After:   Median 3,   range 5
   Would have been better to calculate the means.
   Before 2.2.   After 3.0

1. Mode trainers. Cannot calculate others.

2. Mode 15s,   median 12s,   mean 22.15s
   Median most sensible, not affected by 200 as
   is mean, mode not much use.

3. Mode 81,   median 83,   mean 69.8
   Median most sensible, not affected by 5 and 6
   as is mean, mode not much use.

4. Swimmer A.
   Mean is lower   (A 30.88s, B 31.38s)
   Range less     (A 1.7s, B 15s)
   Median is higher (A 30.9s, B 30.0s)

5. Batsman B.
   Higher median (B 31.5, A 21)
   Higher mean   (B 36, A 35)

6. He should use the median mark.
   The median mark is the middle
   mark, so, half of the students will
   get the median mark or higher.

7. (a) Mode.
        Represents the lowest cost for these data.
   (b) Median.
        Mean affected by **one** much higher cost.
        Mode is equal to the lowest cost.

1. 1.4

2. (a) £22       (b) £27
   (c) Mode is close to lowest of all 11 costs
   and does not represent all the data.

3. (a) 1.75
   (b) 1
   (c) 1
   (d) 5

4. (a) 35      (b) 3      (c) 5.1
   (d) Males have greater range, 6 compared
   with 3. Females have greater average,
   5.1 compared with 3.6.

## Chapter 9    Pie Charts

1.

| Tree | Ash | Beech | Maple |
|---|---|---|---|
| Angle | 120° | 150° | 90° |

2.

| Colour | Angle |
|---|---|
| Brown | 160° |
| Blue | 100° |
| Green | 60° |
| Other | 40° |

3.

| Car | Angle |
|---|---|
| Ford | 90° |
| Saab | 81° |
| Vauxhall | 135° |
| BMW | 54° |

4.

| Cereal | Angle |
|---|---|
| Corn flakes | 125° |
| Muesli | 100° |
| Porridge | 60° |
| Bran flakes | 75° |

5.

| Ice cream | Angle |
|---|---|
| Vanilla | 188° |
| Strawberry | 74° |
| 99 | 98° |

6.

| Takeaway | Angle |
|---|---|
| Fish & chips | 110° |
| Chicken & chips | 136° |
| Chinese meal | 52° |
| Pizza | 62° |

1. (a) 12
   (b) 8
   (c) Hotel

2. (a) 20
   (b) 15
   (c) Sauze d'Oulx

3. (a) France
   (b) 45
   (c) 55
   (d) 20

4. (a) 5
   (b) 2
   (c) 18

5. (a) 14
   (b) 72

6. (a) Heathrow
   (b) 540
   (c) 1080

7. (a) 288
   (b) 174°

1.

| Colour of car | Angle |
|---|---|
| Blue | 100° |
| Green | 30° |
| Red | 80° |
| Silver | 60° |
| White | 90° |

2. (a) N
   (b) Mathematics
   (c) Games, music, science

3. (a)

| Type of music | Frequency |
|---|---|
| A | 17 |
| B | 6 |
| C | 25 |
| D | 12 |
| Total | 60 |

4. (a) 2°

   (b)

| Crop | Number of hectares | Sector angle |
|---|---|---|
| Potatoes | 45 | 90° |
| Wheat | 35 | 70° |
| Barley | 60 | 120° |
| Carrots | 40 | 80° |
| Total | 180 | 360° |

**Chapter**
**10**  Probability

1. (a) **Certain**   (b) **Impossible**  (c) **Evens**
   (d) **Impossible**   (e) **Evens**

2. (a) **Certain**  (b) **Impossible**  (c) **Evens**
   (d) **Evens**   (e) **Impossible**  (f) **Unlikely**

3. (a) **A**   (b) **C**   (c) **B**

4. (a) **T**   (b) **P**   (c) **R**   (d) **S**

5.

1. (a) $\frac{1}{6}$   (b) $\frac{1}{2}$   (c) $\frac{2}{3}$   (d) $\frac{1}{3}$

2. (a) $\frac{1}{3}$   (b) $\frac{2}{3}$   (c) $\frac{2}{3}$

3. (a) $\frac{3}{10}$   (b) $\frac{7}{10}$

4. (a) $\frac{1}{2}$   (b) $\frac{1}{2}$

5. (a) $\frac{1}{12}$   (b) $\frac{1}{6}$

6. (a) $\frac{1}{5}$
   (b) $\frac{1}{5}$
   (c) $\frac{2}{5}$

7. (a) $\frac{1}{2}$   (b) $\frac{1}{4}$   (c) $\frac{1}{52}$

8. (a) $\frac{2}{5}$   (b) $\frac{3}{5}$   (c) 1   (d) 0

9. (a) $\frac{2}{3}$   43 44 45 46
   (b) $\frac{1}{3}$   47 48 49 50
   (c) $\frac{3}{4}$   51 52 53 54

10. (a) $\frac{2}{5}$   (b) $\frac{3}{5}$   (c) $\frac{4}{25}$   (d) $\frac{4}{15}$   (e) $\frac{2}{5}$

11. The events are not equally likely.

12. (a) $\frac{7}{15}$   (b) $\frac{1}{2}$   (c) $\frac{1}{16}$   (d) $\frac{3}{4}$

1. $\frac{7}{25}$   4. $\frac{21}{30} = \frac{7}{10}$

2. $\frac{9}{10}$   5. 25

3. $\frac{3}{10}$   6. (a) 300   (b) 120   (c) 150

1. $\frac{3}{5}$   5. (a) $\frac{2}{7}$   (b) $\frac{8}{13}$

2. 0.4   6. (a) 85%   (b) 150

3. 0.04   7. (a) $\frac{7}{10}$   (b) $\frac{2}{3}$

4. $\frac{47}{50}$   8. 0.6

**9.** (a) $\frac{1}{25}$    (b) $\frac{97}{100}$

**10.** (a) 0.5    (b) 0.3

**11.** (a) (i) The probabilities add up to $\frac{11}{10}$.
     (ii) $\frac{1}{10}$
  (b) (i) $\frac{3}{10}$    (ii) $\frac{7}{10}$    (iii) $\frac{4}{5}$

**12.** (a) $\frac{2}{5}$    (b) $\frac{3}{5}$
  (c) (i) Mutually exclusive -
     there are no blue cubes numbered 1.
     (ii) Not mutually exclusive -
     probability $= \frac{1}{5}$.
  (d) (i) $\frac{3}{5}$    (ii) $\frac{3}{5}$    (iii) $\frac{7}{10}$

**13.** (a) $\frac{2}{5}$
  (b) No.   P(Boy) $= \frac{9}{20}$   P(Girl) $= \frac{11}{20}$

## Review Exercise 10     Page 84

**1.** (a) $\frac{3}{4}$    (b) $\frac{1}{2}$
  (c) $\frac{3}{4}$    (d) $\frac{3}{8}$

**2.** 8

**3.** (a) $\frac{1}{200}$    (b) 10

**4.** (a) $\frac{3}{10}$    (b) $\frac{5}{6}$

**5.** (a) $\frac{1}{3}$    (b) $\frac{1}{15}$    (c) $\frac{11}{24}$
  (d) $\frac{17}{50}$    (e) $\frac{21}{25}$    (f) $\frac{4}{5}$

**6.** (a)

  (b) (i) $\frac{2}{12} = \frac{1}{6}$    (ii) $\frac{10}{12} = \frac{5}{6}$
  (c) $\frac{4}{12} = \frac{1}{3}$

**7.** (a) $\frac{1}{20}$ and $\frac{1}{5}$    (b) 18    (c) 72

## Section Review — Expressions *and* Formulae

### Non-calculator section     Page 86

**1.** (a) (i) 39    (ii) −1
  (b)

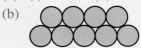

**2.** $2x - 1$

**3.** (a) $3x$ pence    (b) $(x + 7)$ pence

**4.** (a) 8
  (b) 5
  (c) (i) cube
     (ii) cylinder
     (iii) square-based pyramid

**5.** $6m + 2n$

**6.** (a) 5    (b) 1    (c) 1    (d) 1.6

**7.** £59.50

**8.** (a) (1, 2)    (b) 3

**9.** (a)

Pattern 4

  (b)

| Pattern number | 1 | 2 | 3 | 4 |
|---|---|---|---|---|
| Number of squares | 1 | 3 | 5 | 7 |

  (c) 9
  (d) All patterns have an odd number of squares.

**10.** (a) 27    (b) −3    (c) 2.5
  (d) 90    (e) 54

**11.** (a) $3x - 15$    (b) $20p + 10$

**12.** (a) 2    (b) 3    (c) 8

**13.** (a) $2(2a + b)$    (b) $3(2n + 3)$

**14.** (a) $14\,\text{cm}^3$    (b) $30\,\text{cm}^3$    (c) **Q**

**15.** (b) $M(-1, 1)$    (c) 1

**16.** (a) 1H, 2H, 3H, 4H, 5H, 6H,
     1T, 2T, 3T, 4T, 5T, 6T
  (b) $\frac{1}{12}$

**17.** $(15a + 18b)$ pence

**18.** (b) $40\,\text{cm}^2$    (c) $24\,\text{cm}^3$

**19.** 8 cm

**20.** 37.
  Add the last two numbers.

**21.** $3x + 6$

**22.** (a) $12t$ pence    (b) 1

**23.** (a) $\frac{3}{20}$    (b) $\frac{7}{20}$

**24.** (a) $D(5, 2)$    (b) 2    (c) (8, 3.5)

**25.** $24\,\text{cm}^2$

**26.** 24 cm²

**27.** (a)  2°

(b)

| Expense | Cost (£) | Sector angle |
|---|---|---|
| Transport | 35 | 70° |
| Site fee | 45 | 90° |
| Food | 65 | 130° |
| Spending money | 35 | 70° |
| Total | 180 | 360° |

**28.** (a)  24          (b)  −1          (c)  −5

**29.** 35.   Take away the next counting number.

**30.** (a)  170 cm²     (b)  107.8 cm²

**31.** (a)  | 1 hour 57 minutes |

(b)  | 2 hours 1 minute |

**32.** (a)  78.5 cm          (b)  491 cm²

**33.** (a)  $P = 5a + 3b$     (b)  $P = 27.4$

**34.** 108

# Chapter 11
## Straight Line Graphs

**Practice Exercise 11.1**                **Page 91**

**1.** (1)  $x = 1$          (2)  $x = -3$          (3)  $y = 4$
(4)  $y = -1$          (5)  $y = x$

**2.**

**3.** (a)

| $x$ | 0 | 1 | 2 | 3 |
|---|---|---|---|---|
| (i) $y$ | 2 | 3 | 4 | 5 |
| (ii) $y$ | 0 | 2 | 4 | 6 |
| (iii) $y$ | 0 | −1 | −2 | −3 |
| (iv) $y$ | 2 | 1 | 0 | −1 |

**4.** (a)

| $x$ | −1 | 1 | 3 |
|---|---|---|---|
| $y$ | 5 | 1 | −3 |

(c)  (1.5, 0)

**5.** (b)  (0, −2)

**6.** (a)

| $x$ | −2 | −1 | 0 | 1 | 2 |
|---|---|---|---|---|---|
| $y$ | 6 | 5 | 4 | 3 | 2 |

(b)  (i)  $y = 2.5$          (ii)  $y = 4.5$

**7.** (b)  (i)  $y = -5$          (ii)  $x = 0.5$

**8.** (b)  $x = 0.5$

**9.** (b)  (i)  $y = 5$          (ii)  $x = 2.5$
(iii)  $x = -1.5$

**Practice Exercise 11.2**                **Page 93**

**1.** (b)  Same slope, parallel.
y-intercept is different.

**2.** (a)  Gradient 3,   y-intercept −1.

**3.**  | $y = 3x$ |     | $y = 3x + 2$ |

**4.**

| graph | gradient | y-intercept |
|---|---|---|
| $y = 3x + 5$ | 3 | 5 |
| $y = 2x - 3$ | 2 | −3 |
| $y = 4 - 2x$ | −2 | 4 |
| $y = \frac{1}{2}x + 3$ | $\frac{1}{2}$ | 3 |
| $y = 2x$ | 2 | 0 |
| $y = 3$ | 0 | 3 |

**5.** (1)  C     (2)  D     (3)  B     (4)  A

**6.** (a)  £25          (b)  £15 per hour          (c)  £145

**7.** (a)  £3          (b)  £2          (c)  £13

**8.** 50 km/h

**Review Exercise 11**                **Page 94**

**1.** (a)  (1) $y = 2$   (2) $x = -4$   (3) $y = x$
(b)  (−4, 2)

**2.** A: Q,   B: R,   C: P

**3.** (a)                (b)  (3, 4)

**4.** (a)

| $x$ | $-3$ | $0$ | $2$ |
|---|---|---|---|
| $y$ | $0$ | $3$ | $5$ |

(b)

(c) $y = 4.5$

**5.** (a) Gradient 4, $y$-intercept 3    (b) $(0, -2)$

**6.** 20 metres per second.

**7.** (a) **(1)**        (b) 10 days
     (c) **Scaffold Ltd.**, £50

# Chapter 12   Equations *and* Formulae

## Practice Exercise 12.1    Page 96

**1.** (a) $\boxed{3}$ (b) $\boxed{4}$ (c) $\boxed{9}$ (d) $\boxed{16}$

**2.** (a) $x = 4$    (b) $a = 3$    (c) $y = 8$
   (d) $t = 6$    (e) $h = 22$    (f) $d = 1$
   (g) $z = 30$    (h) $p = 0$    (i) $c = 99$
   (j) $x = 2$    (k) $y = 8$    (l) $q = 10$

**3.** (a) $\boxed{5}$ (b) $\boxed{5}$ (c) $\boxed{18}$ (d) $\boxed{21}$

**4.** (a) $a = 4$    (b) $e = 6$    (c) $p = 4$
   (d) $y = \frac{1}{2}$    (e) $d = 10$    (f) $t = 9$
   (g) $m = 28$    (h) $x = 100$

**5.** (a) $\boxed{1}$ (b) $\boxed{4}$ (c) $\boxed{4}$ (d) $\boxed{2}$ (e) $\boxed{3}$ (f) $\boxed{5}$

## Practice Exercise 12.2    Page 97

**1.** 5        **6.** 3

**2.** 14       **7.** 4

**3.** 6        **8.** $\boxed{7}$

**4.** 11      **9.** (a) 2    (b) $2(x + 3) = 2x + 6$

**5.** 4       **10.** (a) 9    (b) $3(x - 2) = 3x - 6$

## Practice Exercise 12.3    Page 99

**1.** (a) $y = 3$    (b) $x = 6$    (c) $a = 10$
   (d) $e = 15$    (e) $d = 11$    (f) $c = 20$
   (g) $x = 2$    (h) $y = 19$    (i) $m = 7$

**2.** (a) $q = 7$    (b) $m = 10$    (c) $n = 16$
   (d) $p = 18$    (e) $x = 31$    (f) $y = 17$
   (g) $a = 2$    (h) $k = 4$    (i) $h = 12$

**3.** (a) $x = 14$    (b) $t = 28$    (c) $f = 18$
   (d) $y = 19$    (e) $b = 7$    (f) $x = 29$
   (g) $m = 4$    (h) $k = 5$    (i) $y = 7$

**4.** (a) $c = 4$    (b) $a = 4$    (c) $f = 3$
   (d) $p = 3$    (e) $h = 5$    (f) $u = 2$

**5.** (a) $p = 4$    (b) $t = 3$    (c) $h = 7$
   (d) $b = 2$    (e) $d = 10$    (f) $x = 6$
   (g) $c = 5$    (h) $n = 3$    (i) $x = 2$

**6.** (a) $a = 12$    (b) $x = 4$    (c) $a = 9$
   (d) $x = 2$    (e) $b = 6$    (f) $x = 4$
   (g) $k = 2$    (h) $b = 3$    (i) $c = 2$
   (j) $c = 7$    (k) $y = 4$    (l) $x = 6$

**7.** (a) $x = -2$    (b) $n = -\frac{1}{2}$    (c) $x = -1$
   (d) $y = -3$    (e) $x = -1$    (f) $x = -3$
   (g) $x = -1\frac{1}{2}$    (h) $x = -4$    (i) $x = -1\frac{1}{2}$

**8.** (a) $d = 30$    (b) $e = 14$    (c) $f = 20$

## Practice Exercise 12.4    Page 100

**1.** (a) $x = 5$    (b) $q = 2$    (c) $t = 3$
   (d) $e = 3$    (e) $g = 4$    (f) $y = 1$
   (g) $x = 2$    (h) $k = 1$    (i) $a = 4$
   (j) $p = 6$    (k) $m = 2$    (l) $d = 5$
   (m) $y = 5$    (n) $u = 3$    (o) $q = 0$

**2.** (a) $d = 8$    (b) $q = 3$    (c) $c = 2$
   (d) $t = 3$    (e) $w = 2$    (f) $e = 3$
   (g) $g = 5$    (h) $z = 4$    (i) $m = -4$
   (j) $a = 5$    (k) $t = -2$    (l) $p = -7$

## Practice Exercise 12.5    Page 101

**1.** (a) $12x$    (b) $x = 15$

**2.** (a) $6k$ kg

   (b) $2\frac{1}{2}$ kg

**3.** $(3y + 15)$ cm    (b) $y = 8$

**4.** (a) $6a + 3$    (b) 7

**5.** (a) $(n - 7)$ years old
   (b) $2n - 7 = 43$. Dominic is 25 years old. Marcie is 18 years old.

**6.** (a) $(4y - 2)$ cm
   (b) 19 cm

## Practice Exercise 12.6    Page 102

**1.** (a) $m = a - 5$    (b) $m = a - x$
   (c) $m = a + 2$    (d) $m = a + b$

**2.** (a) $x = \frac{y}{4}$    (b) $x = \frac{y}{a}$    (c) $x = 2y$
   (d) $x = ay$    (e) $x = \frac{5y}{3}$

3. (a) $p = \frac{1}{2}y - 3$    (b) $p = \frac{t - q}{5}$

    (c) $p = \frac{m + 2}{3}$    (d) $p = \frac{q + r}{4}$

4. $n = \frac{C - 35}{24}$

5. $R = \frac{V}{I}$

6. (a) $d = \frac{P}{4}$      (b) $d = 7$ cm

7. (a) $l = \frac{A}{b}$      (b) $l = 9$ cm

8. (a) (i) $D = ST$
       (ii) $D = 96$ km

   (b) (i) $T = \frac{D}{S}$
       (ii) $T = 2.5$ hours

9. (a) $x = \frac{y - c}{m}$     (b) $x = 0.5$

10. (a) $t = \frac{v - u}{a}$     (b) $t = 2$

11. (a) $b = \frac{2A}{h}$     (b) $b = 6.4$

## Review Exercise 12     Page 103

1. (a) $\boxed{4}$    (b) $\boxed{3}$    (c) $\boxed{6}$    (d) $\boxed{18}$

2. 8

3. (a) $y = 4$    (b) $y = 3$    (c) $y = 7$

4. (a) $m = 7$    (b) $t = 5$

5. (a) 34 years old    (b) 19 years old

6. 7 litres

7. $x = \frac{P + 5}{2}$

8. (a) £17     (b) $n = \frac{C - 500}{15}$    (c) 300

9. (a) $2x$ pence
   (b) £1.98

10. (a) (i) £$(p + 4)$
       (ii) £$(p - 3)$
       (iii) £$(3p + 1)$
   (b) Aimee £12,   Grace £8,   Lydia £5

11. $x = \frac{b + c}{a}$

12. $x = 12$

13. (a) 8 rolls    (b) $p = \frac{5R}{h}$

---

## Chapter 13   Pythagoras' Theorem

### Practice Exercise 13.1     Page 105

1. (a) 10 cm    (b) 25 cm    (c) 26 cm

2. (a) 7.8 cm    (b) 12.8 cm    (c) 10.3 cm

3. (a) $\sqrt{52}$ cm    (b) $\sqrt{20}$ cm

4. (a) 5       (b) 9.22     (c) 13
   (d) 8.06    (e) 7.21

5. (a) $R(9, 7)$    (b) $X(2, 3)$
   (c) $Y(4, 2)$    (d) 2.24

### Practice Exercise 13.2     Page 107

1. (a) 8 cm     (b) 6 cm     (c) 2 cm

2. (a) 6.9 cm    (b) 10.9 cm    (c) 9.5 cm

3. 339 m

4. (a) 6 cm      (b) 36 cm²

5. 3.6 cm

6. (a) 5 m   (b) 16 m   (c) 21 m   (d) 54 m

### Practice Exercise 13.3     Page 108

1. (a) 2.9 cm     3. 10 cm
   (b) 5.7 cm
   (c) 2.1 cm     4. 8.5 cm     7. 6.9 cm
   (d) 2.0 cm     5. 10.6 cm    8. 74.3 cm

2. 17 cm        6. 15 cm     9. 137 m

10. The diagonals of the base should be the same length and measure about 6 m.

### Review Exercise 13     Page 110

1. $PQ = 15$ cm     4. $BC = 3.4$ m

2. $AB = 5$ cm      5. $CD = 5.7$ cm

3. 30 cm          6. 361 m

7. (a) $EF = 9.4$ m
   (b) $DF = 15.5$ m,   $DE = 15.6$ m
     Perimeter $= EF + DF + DE$
              $= 9.4$ m $+ 15.5$ m $+ 15.6$ m
              $= 40.5$ m
     So, perimeter of triangle $DEF$ is greater than 40 m.

## Chapter 14 — Scale Factors *and* Similar Figures

### Practice Exercise 14.1    Page 111

2. (a) $2\frac{1}{2}$    (b) 3

3. (a) 2    (b) $1\frac{1}{2}$

5. (a) 2    (b) $\frac{1}{2}$

6. (a) $\frac{1}{3}$    (b) $\frac{2}{5}$    (c) $2\frac{1}{2}$

7. (a) $\frac{1}{2}$    (b) 3    (c) $\frac{2}{3}$

### Practice Exercise 14.2    Page 114

1. Corresponding lengths not in same ratio.

2. (a) Two circles
   (d) Two squares

3. $a = 4\,\text{cm}, \quad b = 24\,\text{cm}$

4. (a) Scale factor $= \frac{3}{2} = 1.5$
   (b) $x = 1.8\,\text{cm}$
   (c) $a = 120°$

5. 30 cm

6. (a) $x = 1.5\,\text{cm}, \quad y = 2.4\,\text{cm}, \quad a = 70°$
   (b) $x = 5\,\text{cm}, \quad y = 1.5\,\text{cm}, \quad a = 53°$
   (c) $x = 30\,\text{cm}, \quad y = 17.5\,\text{cm}, \quad z = 10\,\text{cm}$

7. 18°

8. 5 cm

9. $x = 16, \quad y = 48$

### Practice Exercise 14.3    Page 116

1. 30 m

2. (a) 2 to 3 = 2 : 3    (b) 9 cm

3. (a) 1 to 50 = 1 : 50    (b) 2.8 cm

4. Original area multiplied by $2^2 = 4$.

5. 2.4 cm

6. Area is quartered.

7. 90 cm²

8. (a) 8 cm
   (b) 96 cm²

9. 8 times original volume.

10. 4000 ml

11. 1.41

### Review Exercise 14    Page 118

2. (a) $\frac{1}{3}$    (b) 3

3. (a) $\frac{1}{3}$    (b) $\frac{1}{3}$    (c) $\frac{1}{3}$

4. $x = 27\,\text{cm}, \quad y = 8\,\text{cm}$

5. Height = 8 m
   Floor area = 2 000 000 cm² = 200 m²

6. (a) 4 cm
   (b) Reduction is $\frac{1}{16}$ of the size of the original photo.

## Chapter 15 — Using Angle Properties

### Practice Exercise 15.1    Page 120

1. (a) $p = 65°$    (b) $p = 73°$    (c) $p = 36°$

2. (a) $q = 35°$    (b) $q = 144°$    (c) $q = 62°$

3. (a) $x = 110°$    (b) $x = 135°$    (c) $x = 30°$

4. (a) $y = 120°$    (b) $y = 150°$    (c) $y = 165°$

5. (a) $g = 133°, \quad h = 47°$
   (b) $m = 96°$
   (c) $j = 127°, \quad k = 53°, \quad l = 37°$

6. (a) $a = 65°$ (alternate angles)
   (b) $b = 115°$ (corresponding angles)
   (c) $c = 105°$ (allied angles)
   (d) $d = 100°$ (alternate angles)

7. (a) $a = 130°, \quad b = 130°$
   (b) $c = 60°, \quad d = 120°$
   (c) $e = 40°, \quad f = 40°$
   (d) $g = 65°, \quad h = 65°$

8. (a) $a = 63°$    (b) $b = 68°, \quad c = 112°$
   (c) $d = 87°$    (d) $e = 124°$

9. (a) $a = 125°, \quad b = 125°$
   (b) $c = 62°, \quad d = 118°, \quad e = 62°$
   (c) $f = 74°, \quad g = 106°$
   (d) $h = 52°, \quad i = 128°$

10. (a) $a = 84°, \quad b = 116°$
    (b) $c = 56°, \quad d = 116°$
    (c) $e = 61°$
    (d) $f = 270°$

### Practice Exercise 15.2    Page 122

1. (a) $\angle QOR = 43°$
   (b) $\angle AOD = 125°$
   (c) $\angle XOQ = 63°$

2. (a) $\angle ABC = 132°$
   (b) $\angle QRS = 126°$
   (c) $\angle ZYV = 141°$
   (d) $\angle LMN = 85°$
   (e) $\angle ABC = 65°$
   (f) $\angle QSP = 105°$, $\angle STU = 105°$

## Practice Exercise 15.3    Page 124

1. (a) $a = 70°$    (b) $b = 37°$
   (c) $c = 114°$    (d) $d = 43°$

2. $x + 45° = 80°$ (ext. $\angle$ of a $\Delta$)
   $x = 80° - 45° = 35°$

3. (a) $a = 120°$    (b) $b = 110°$
   (c) $c = 50°$     (d) $d = 80°$
   (e) $e = 88°$     (f) $f = 55°$

4. (a) $a = 32°$, $b = 148°$
   (b) $c = 63°$
   (c) $d = 52°$, $e = 64°$

5. (a) Isosceles  (b) Equilateral  (c) $\Delta BCE$

6. $AC = BC$, $\angle BAC = \angle ABC$

7. (a) $a = 60°$    (b) $a = 85°$
   (c) $a = 75°$    (d) $a = 50°$

8. $a = 18°$, $b = 144°$, $c = 85°$,
   $d = 116°$, $e = 26.5°$, $f = 153.5°$

9. (a) Equilateral  (b) $60°$  (c) $78°$

10. (a) Isosceles  (b) $74°$  (c) $46°$

11. (a) $\angle BCD = 120°$
    (b) $\angle PRQ = 80°$, $\angle QRS = 160°$
    (c) $\angle MNX = 50°$

## Practice Exercise 15.4    Page 127

1. (a) $a = 90°$    (b) $a = 35°$
   (c) $a = 140°$   (d) $a = 114°$

2. (a) $a = 90°$, $b = 53°$, $c = 37°$
   (b) $d = 42°$, $e = 48°$
   (c) $f = 27°$, $g = 117°$
   (d) $h = 16°$, $i = 99°$, $j = 65°$

3. (a) $a = 36°$, $b = 144°$
   (b) $c = 124°$, $d = 56°$
   (c) $e = 130°$, $f = 23°$, $g = 23°$
   (d) $h = 42°$, $i = 84°$

4. (a) $a = 110°$, $b = 100°$    (b) $c = 95°$
   (c) $d = 46°$                 (d) $e = 96°$

5. $a = 115°$, $b = 44°$

6. $\angle WXY = 72°$, $\angle XYZ = 108°$

7. (a) $a = 62°$
   (b) $b = 54°$, $c = 36°$
   (c) $d = 62°$
   (d) $e = 116°$, $f = 86°$
   (e) $g = 124°$
   (f) $h = 75°$
   (g) $i = 38°$, $j = 42°$
   (h) $k = 55°$, $l = 45°$

8. $A(1, 3)$

9. $(3, 1), (3, 5)$

## Practice Exercise 15.5    Page 129

1. (a) $a = 90°$, $b = 50°$
   (b) $c = 45°$
   (c) $d = 40°$, $e = 54°$
   (d) $f = 20°$

2. (a) $f = 50°$, $g = 65°$
   (b) $h = 130°$, $i = 48°$
   (c) $j = 30°$, $k = 39°$

3. (a) $a = 90°$, $b = 50°$
   (b) $c = 35°$, $d = 35°$
   (c) $e = 90°$, $f = 49°$, $g = 49°$
   (d) $h = 63°$
   (e) $j = 67°$
   (f) $k = 50°$
   (g) $l = 65°$
   (h) $m = 146°$

## Review Exercise 15    Page 131

1. (a) $a = 35°$ (vertically opposite angles)
   (b) $b = 26°$ (supplementary angles)
   (c) $c = 105°$ (angles at a point)

2. (a) $p = 135°$    (b) $q = 45°$    (c) $r = 55°$

3. $a = 82°$
   Sum of angles in a quadrilateral $= 360°$.

4. (a) $a = 65°$    (b) $b = 54°$
   (c) $c = 113°$   (d) $d = 124°$

5. (a) $a = 75°$, $b = 50°$
   (b) $c = 60°$, $d = 120°$
   (c) $e = 24°$, $f = 156°$

6. $(6, 2), (6, 8)$

7. (a) Trapezium  (b) $\angle PSR = 62°$

8. $a = 30°$, $b = 60°$, $c = 42°$, $d = 78°$

9. (a) $a = 90°$, $b = 45°$
   (b) $c = 30°$, $d = 120°$

## Practice Exercise 16.1     Page 133

1. (a) $h = 2.27$ m     (b) $h = 4.02$ m
   (c) $h = 8.02$ m

2. (a) $x = 1.5$ cm     (b) $x = 3.0$ cm
   (c) $x = 5.8$ cm

3. (a) $BC = 3.4$ m     (b) $AC = 11.4$ m

4. (a) $BC = 4.7$ cm
   (b) $\angle ACB = 55°$,   $AB = 7.0$ cm

## Practice Exercise 16.2     Page 135

1. (a) $a = 62.1°$     (b) $a = 25.0°$
   (c) $a = 50.9°$

2. (a) $x = 52.3°$     (b) $x = 60.5°$
   (c) $x = 61.4°$

3. (a) $\angle QPR = 23.6°$
   (b) $\angle PRQ = 64.7°$
   (c) $\angle QPR = 21.8°$
   (d) $\angle QRP = 24.0°$,   $\angle QPR = 66.0°$

## Practice Exercise 16.3     Page 136

1. (a) $l = 7.0$ m     (b) $l = 7.5$ m
   (c) $l = 4.9$ m

2. (a) $x = 6.5$ cm     (b) $x = 5.3$ cm
   (c) $x = 10.6$ cm

3. (a) $AB = 7.62$ m
   (b) $AB = 17.48$ m
   (c) $AB = 66.86$ m
   (d) $\angle ABC = 17.2°$,   $AB = 25.70$ m

## Practice Exercise 16.4     Page 138

1.

| | $\sin p$ | $\cos p$ | $\tan p$ |
|---|---|---|---|
| (a) | $\frac{5}{13}$ | $\frac{12}{13}$ | $\frac{5}{12}$ |
| (b) | $\frac{7}{25}$ | $\frac{24}{25}$ | $\frac{7}{24}$ |
| (c) | $\frac{4}{5}$ | $\frac{3}{5}$ | $\frac{4}{3}$ |

2. (a) $p = 40.9°$     (b) $p = 38.0°$
   (c) $p = 38.8°$     (d) $p = 53.3°$
   (e) $p = 39.7°$     (f) $p = 35.5°$

3. 4.33 cm

4. 72.5°,   72.5°,   34.9°

5. (a) $a = 5.8$ cm     (b) $a = 6.5$ cm
   (c) $a = 4.2$ cm     (d) $a = 3.8$ cm
   (e) $a = 4.7$ cm     (f) $a = 4.0$ cm

6. $WX = 13.1$ cm

7. $PQ = 4.5$ cm

8. $CD = 9.4$ cm

## Practice Exercise 16.5     Page 140

1. 21.4 m

2. 40.1 m

3. (a) 135 m     (b) 53.5°

4. 51.3°

5. 959 m

## Review Exercise 16     Page 141

1. (a) $a = 7.2$ cm     (b) $b = 48.8°$
   (c) $c = 13.5$ cm

2. (a) $BE = 9.5$ cm     (b) $AE = 7.4$ cm
   (c) 38.8 cm

3. (a) $AC = 6.0$ cm     (b) $CE = 1.7$ cm

4. (a) $RQ = 2.8$ cm     (b) $\angle SPR = 19.8°$

5. 31.0°

| | |
|---|---|
| **Chapter** **17** | Scatter Graphs |

## Practice Exercise 17.1     Page 143

1. (a) 72
   (b) (i) English 40, French 78
       (ii) French could be her first language.

2. (a) 39 000 miles
   (b) Older cars tend to have higher mileages.
   (c) (i) 2 years, 40 000 miles
       (ii) Hire car

3. (a) **B**     (b) **C**     (c) **D**

4. (b) Positive correlation
   (c) Different conditions, types of road, etc.

5. (b) Negative correlation
   (c) Points are close to a straight line.

**6.** (a) Negative    (b) Positive
   (c) No correlation    (d) Positive
   (e) Negative

**7.** (b) Scatter of points suggests that there is no correlation.

## Practice Exercise 17.2    Page 145

**1.** (b) Positive correlation    (d) 5.0 to 5.1 kg

**2.** (b) Negative correlation    (d) 38 minutes

**3.** (b) Negative correlation
   (d) (i) 27 to 28    (ii) 91 to 92 kg

**4.** (b) (i) 87 - 88    (ii) 49 - 50
   (c) (ii), as estimated value is within the range of known values.

**5.** (b) Scatter of points suggests correlation is close to zero.

## Review Exercise 17    Page 147

**1.** **A**: 3, **B**: 1, **C**: 2.

**2.** (a) Negative    (b) Positive    (c) Zero

**3.** (c) 1.67 m

**4.** (b) Negative correlation.
   (d) £2400 - £2600

## Section Review   Relationships

### Non-calculator section    Page 148

**1.** (a) $12m$
   (b) (i) $y = 8$    (ii) $a = 8$

**2.** (a) $g = 4.5$    (b) $g = 4$
   (c) $g = 3.5$

**3.** (a) (i) $x = 100°$.
       Angles on a straight line add up to 180°.
     (ii) obtuse
   (b) $y = 60°$

**4.** (b) Positive correlation
   (d) Plotted points close to line of best fit.

**5.** (a) $x = 5$    (b) $x = -2$
   (c) $x = 3$

**6.** $x = \dfrac{22 - 4a}{3}$

**7.** (a) **P** and **S**    (b) (i) 8 cm    (ii) 2.75 cm²

**8.** (a) $2t - 3$    (b) (i) $x = 7$    (ii) $t = 1.5$

**9.** $x = 41°$,   $y = 58°$

**10.** (a) $x = 2$    (b) $x = 4$

**11.** (a) (i)

| $x$ | −2 | −1 | 0 | 1 | 2 | 3 |
|---|---|---|---|---|---|---|
| $y$ | −1 | 1 | 3 | 5 | 7 | 9 |

   (c) $(-1, 1)$

**12.** (a) $x = 54°$
   (b) (i) $y = 63°$    (ii) Alternate angles

**13.** (a) $20x$ grams    (b) $x = 180$

**14.** $G(0, 5)$, $H(10, 0)$

**15.** (a) $x = \dfrac{y - 10}{5}$
   (b) (i) $t = 21$    (ii) $x = 8$

**16.** $a = 38° + 67° = 105°$
   Exterior angle of a triangle
   = sum of opposite two interior angles.

**17.** (a) $2x$ pence
   (b) $3(x + 5)$ pence
   (c) 16 pence

**18.** (a) $\angle ROT = 70°$
   (b) $\angle OTR = 55°$
   (c) $\angle QTS = 55°$

## Section Review   Relationships

### Calculator section    Page 150

**19.** (a) $x = 100$    (b) $x = -3\frac{1}{2}$

**20.** $t = \dfrac{v - u}{10}$

**21.** (a) $(5a + 3)$ cm
   (b) $5a + 3 = 23$,   $a = 4$

**22.** (a) $QS = 25$ m    (b) $QR = 15$ m
   (c) 66 m

**23.** (a) $a = 38.7°$    (b) $a = 44.4°$

**24.** 79.8 m

**25.** 264 cm

**26.** $a = 153°$,   $b = 52°$,   $c = 65°$

**27.** 2.8 cm

**28.** Gradient: $-2$,   $y$-intercept: 5

**29.** (a) $x = 5.6\,\text{cm}$      (b) $x = 7.5\,\text{cm}$

**30.** 44.4 m

**31.** 15 cm

**32.** 5.0 m

**33.** $a = 115°$,   $b = 50°$

**34.** 7

**35.** (a) $x = 123°$,   $x + 57° = 180°$, allied angles.
  (b) (i) Trapezium.
     113° and 67° are allied angles.
     Opposite sides are parallel.
    (ii) $y = 60°$

# Chapter 18 — Whole Numbers

## Practice Exercise 18.1    Page 153

**1.** (a) 89p
  (b) 81p

Café Enfant Price List
Drink.................. 54p
Doughnut........... 35p
Packet of Crisps.. 27p

**2.** (a) 29    (b) 43    (c) 43    (d) 53

**3.** (a) 788    (b) 83    (c) 174    (d) 952
  (e) 2002    (f) 12 203    (g) 201    (h) 1541

**4.** 40 710

**5.** 1378

**6.** 81 030

**7.** (a) 33    (b) 27

**8.** (a) 32    (b) 27    (c) 18    (d) 26

**9.** £815

**10.** (a) 354    (b) 428    (c) 1284    (d) 158
  (e) 2224    (f) 469    (g) 6268    (h) 3277

**11.** 89

**12.** (a) 37p
  (b) £3.36

Salad Specials
Cucumber      89p each
Lettuce       75p each
Spring onions 63p a bunch

**13.** (a) Tomato 39, Oxtail 18, Chicken 55
  (b) 112

**14.** Car C.   A: 8479   B: 11643   C: 13859

## Practice Exercise 18.2    Page 156

**1.** 40

**2.** 72

**3.** 144

**4.** £5.52

**5.** (a) 60p
  (b) £1.14
  (c) £1.60

Pencil 12p    Pen 19p

**6.** (a) 84    (b) 85    (c) 252
  (d) 549    (e) 2112    (f) 15 895
  (g) 24 072    (h) 42 084

**7.** 29

**8.** (a) 1320    (b) 12 300
  (c) 47 000    (d) 38 400

**9.** (a) £1200
  (b) £5900
  (c) £71 000

Desk    £120
Chair   £59

**10.** (a) £120    (b) £700    (c) £8200

**11.** (a) 210 chairs    (b) 140 tables

**12.** (a) 7140    (b) 18 960    (c) 21 480
  (d) 13 000    (e) 13 020    (f) 21 510

**13.** £1450

**14.** 10 000

**15.** (a) 204    (b) 345
  (c) 4544    (d) 89 424
  (e) 732 906    (f) 3 116 310
  (g) 2 730 182    (h) 3 485 664

**16.** 216

**17.** 255

**18.** £9

**19.** £966

**20.** £1536

**21.** £5191

Office Supplies
Desk      £126
Cabinet   £149

## Practice Exercise 18.3    Page 158

**1.** (a) 17
  (b) 157
  (c) 136
  (d) 75 remainder 5
  (e) 393 remainder 2
  (f) 206
  (g) 1098
  (h) 20 140

**2.** (a) 13    (b) 4 pence

**3.** 49p

**4.** 6

**5.** £14

**6.** (a) 456    (b) 465    (c) 64    (d) 654

**7.** 6

**8.** (a) ⟦100⟧
  (b) ⟦702 000⟧
  (c) ⟦10⟧

## Practice Exercise 18.4    Page 159

1. 148 cm
2. 30 g
3. (a) 89p
   (b) 24p

**Price List**
| | |
|---|---|
| Can of drink | 55p |
| Packet of crisps | 32p |
| Bar of chocolate | 28p |

4. 25
5. 155 cm
6. 15 g

## Review Exercise 18    Page 160

1. ⬜ 6    ⬜ 12    ⬜ 110
2. 732, 723, 372, 327, 273, 237
   Two are even numbers, 732 and 372.
3. For example: 3, 4, 5: 3 + 4 + 5 = 12,
   which is even.
4.

| | Score | New total |
|---|---|---|
| (a) | 97 | 404 |
| (b) | 100 | 320 |
| (c) | 118 | 183 |

5. (a) 2059   (b) 587   (c) 6462   (d) 241
6. 384 boys
7. 184 cm
8. 79 kg
9. (a) 166   (b) 4
10. 15
11. 1316
12. 75 g
13. 35 cm
14. (a) 68
    (b) 275
    (c) 666
    (d) 46

| | |
|---|---|
| Minibus | 17 |
| Coach | 55 |
| Double-Decker Bus | 74 |

## Chapter 19 — Negative Numbers

## Practice Exercise 19.1    Page 163

1. (a) Warmer   (b) Colder
   (c) Warmer   (d) Colder
2. (a) −4°C   (b) −3°C
3. (a) Less   (b) More   (c) Less   (d) More

4. (a) **Colombo**
   (b) **Moscow**
   (c) **−22°C, −17°C, −7°C, 0°C, 3°C, 15°C, 21°C**

5. (a) −78, −39, −16, −9, 11, 31, 51
   (b) −5, −3, −2, −1, 0, 1, 2, 4, 5
   (c) −103, −63, −19, −3, 5, 52, 99, 104

6. 40, 30, 10, 0, −20, −30, −50
7. −30, −15, −10, 0, 8, 17, 27

## Practice Exercise 19.2    Page 164

1. (a) 1        (b) −2       (c) −2
   (d) −4       (e) −3       (f) −4
3. (a) −3       (b) −2       (c) −3
   (d) −2       (e) −3       (f) −4
   (g) −7       (h) −12      (i) −10
   (j) −7       (k) −21      (l) −1
4. (a) ⬜ 9      (b) ⬜ 1      (c) ⬜ 12
   (d) ⬜ −10    (e) ⬜ 30     (f) ⬜ 15
5. −£75 (£75 overdrawn)
6. 11°C
7. 5°C
8. 17 cm
9. 8 kg
10. (a) −80 m
    (b) −200 m
    (c) 60 m
    (d) 60 m
    (e) 120 m
    (f) 70 m
    (g) 300 m
    (h) 50 m
    (i) 130 m
    (j) 240 m
    (k) 250 m

| | |
|---|---|
| Helicopter | 160 m above |
| Parachute | 100 m above |
| Bird | 50 m above |
| Kite | 30 m above |
| — Sea level — | |
| Jellyfish | 20 m below |
| Diver | 80 m below |
| Treasure chest | 200 m below |

## Practice Exercise 19.3    Page 166

1. (a) 2        (b) 1        (c) −9
   (d) 8        (e) 4        (f) −5
   (g) −7       (h) 7        (i) 1
   (j) −15      (k) −3       (l) −6
2. (a) 13       (b) 6        (c) 7
   (d) 7        (e) 5        (f) −12
   (g) −1       (h) 13       (i) −11
   (j) 11       (k) 9        (l) 0

268

**3.** (a) 5    (b) 3    (c) 3
    (d) −7    (e) −6    (f) −1

**4.** (a) 6    (b) −8    (c) −28
    (d) 0    (e) −35    (f) 19

**5.** (a) 10°C   (b) 10°C   (c) 5°C   (d) 37°C

**6.** −15°C

<hr/>

**Practice** Exercise **19.4**     **Page 167**

**1.** (a) 35    (b) −35   (c) 35    (d) 10
    (e) −10   (f) 10    (g) 1    (h) −24
    (i) −24   (j) −45   (k) 64    (l) −42
    (m) 42   (n) −80   (o) −80   (p) 32

**2.** (a) −4    (b) 4    (c) 5    (d) −5
    (e) −5    (f) 5    (g) 6    (h) −6
    (i) 4    (j) −8    (k) 6    (l) −5

**3.** (a) Ahmed 26,   Bridget 21,   Chris −21,
    Dileep −19,   Evan −3
    (b) Ahmed, Bridget, Evan, Dileep, Chris

<hr/>

**Review** Exercise **19**     **Page 168**

**1.** (a) −28°C,   −13°C,   −3°C,   19°C,   23°C
    (b) −20°C,   −15°C,   −5°C,   0°C,   10°C,
     20°C

**2.** (a) −18
    (b) 4
    (c) 4

**3.** −22°C

**4.** 2°C

**5.** Overdrawn by £34.

**6.** (a) −20
    (b) Naomi.
     Tim: 20 − 10 = 10.
     Naomi: 16 − 5 = 11.

**7.** (a) 13 degrees     (b) −8°C

<hr/>

**Chapter**
**20**   **Decimals**

**Practice** Exercise **20.1**     **Page 170**

**1.** (a)   4.7     = 4 + 0.7
    (b)   5.55    = 5 + 0.5 + 0.05
    (c)   7.62    = 7 + 0.6 + 0.02
    (d) 37.928 = 30 + 7 + 0.9 + 0.02 + 0.008
    (e)   7.541   = 7 + 0.5 + 0.04 + 0.001

**2.** (a) 1.68      (b) 1.09

**3.** (a) Arrow *A*: 3.2
      Arrow *B*: 3.5
      Arrow *C*: 3.9
    (b) Arrow *D*: 0.52
      Arrow *E*: 0.54
      Arrow *F*: 0.59

**4.** (a) (b)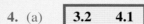

**5.** (a) 3.001,   3.01,   3.1,   3.15,   3.2
    (b) 3.567,   3.576,   3.657,   3.675
    (c) 0.1,   0.15,   0.45,   0.5,   0.55

**6.** 93.07

<hr/>

**Practice** Exercise **20.2**     **Page 171**

**1.** (a) 18.8      (b) 6.4      (c) 18.3
    (d) 33.1     (e) 8.86    (f) 13.1
    (g) 12.38   (h) 17.49   (i) 12.449
    (j) 26.02   (k) 32.36   (l) 18.163

**2.** 7.15 metres

**3.** 36.1 litres

**4.** (a)    **3.2**    **4.1**

    (b)    **1.6**    **0.8**

    (c)    **4.1**    **0.8**

**5.** (a) 6.84     (b) 3.07     (c) 86.33
    (d) 15.781   (e) 16.033   (f) 24.88

**6.** (a)   Team A 148.93s
      Team B 149.53s
      Team C 149.08s

    (b)   Team A
      Team C
      Team B

<hr/>

**Practice** Exercise **20.3**     **Page 173**

**1.** (a) 4.4      (b) 6.23    (c) 4.6
    (d) 14.8    (e) 4.96    (f) 20.8
    (g) 2.14    (h) 5.22    (i) 5.003
    (j) 1.24    (k) 9.04    (l) 1.896

**2.** (a) (i) £3.30    (ii) £1.70
    (b) (i) 83p     (ii) £9.17

**3.** 0.88 m

**4.** 1.55 m

**5.** 0.719 seconds

**6.** (a) 1.2      (b) 8.5      (c) 12.8
    (d) 3.6      (e) 13      (f) 17.6
    (g) 10.8     (h) 30.1     (i) 28.8
    (j) 34.8     (k) 32.1     (l) 0.552

**7.** (a) 5.3      (b) 4.89     (c) 22.35
    (d) 6.328    (e) 17.72    (f) 46.944

**8.** £7.60

**9.** (a) £8.05      (b) £1.95

**10.** (a) £14.95     (b) £5.05

**11.** £6.86

## Practice Exercise 20.4    Page 174

**1.** (a) 1.2      (b) 6.5      (c) 2.25
    (d) 3.6      (e) 62.5     (f) 38.75
    (g) 27.8     (h) 1.75

**2.** (a) 3.14     (b) 1.92     (c) 0.63
    (d) 0.68     (e) 2.6      (f) 0.614
    (g) 0.522    (h) 2.08

**3.** £3.25

**4.** 83.5p

**5.** £1.28

**6.** £1.35

**7.** 21.5

## Practice Exercise 20.5    Page 175

**1.** (a) $\frac{1}{4}$      (b) $\frac{1}{2}$      (c) $\frac{3}{4}$      (d) $\frac{1}{10}$

**2.** (a) $\frac{7}{10}$      (b) $\frac{2}{5}$      (c) $\frac{1}{100}$      (d) $\frac{1}{5}$
    (e) $\frac{1}{20}$      (f) $\frac{3}{20}$      (g) $\frac{13}{25}$      (h) $\frac{7}{100}$
    (i) $\frac{1}{8}$      (j) $\frac{13}{20}$      (k) $\frac{3}{5}$      (l) $\frac{19}{20}$

**3.** (a) $1\frac{7}{10}$     (b) $2\frac{3}{10}$     (c) $1\frac{2}{5}$     (d) $3\frac{1}{4}$
    (e) $4\frac{4}{5}$     (f) $12\frac{1}{10}$    (g) $16\frac{3}{4}$    (h) $5\frac{1}{20}$

## Review Exercise 20    Page 176

**1.** | 0.5 | 0.55 | 0.7 | 0.8 | 0.85 |

**2.** (a) Arrow *A*: 5.6
    Arrow *B*: 6.3
   (b) Arrow *C*: 0.751
    Arrow *D*: 0.755
    Arrow *E*: 0.757

**3.** (a) | 0.07 |      (b) | 0.6 |

**4.** (a) 9.87, 9.78, 8.97, 8.79
   (b) 1.5, 0.15, 0.015, 0.00015

**5.** 4.2 kg

**6.** 40 s

**7.** 2.37 m

**8.** (a) 12.265     (b) 21.33
   (c) 14.074     (d) 35.255

**9.** (a) 5.1      (b) 16.8      (c) £12.60
   (d) 42.25    (e) 4.375

**10.** $\frac{9}{20}$

## Chapter 21   Approximation *and* Estimation

## Practice Exercise 21.1    Page 177

**1.** 4      **3.** 10      **5.** 24
**2.** 5      **4.** 9       **6.** 29      **7.** 7

## Practice Exercise 21.2    Page 179

**1.** (a) 3.96      (b) 4.0

**2.** 4.86    | 4.857142857 |

**3.** 68.8 kg

**4.**

| Number | d.p. | Answer |
|--------|------|--------|
| 2.367 | 1 | 2.4 |
| 0.964 | 2 | 0.96 |
| 0.965 | 2 | 0.97 |
| 15.2806 | 1 | 15.3 |
| 0.056 | 2 | 0.06 |
| 4.991 | 2 | 4.99 |
| 4.996 | 2 | 5.00 |

**5.** (a) (i) 46.1     (ii) 59.7     (iii) 569.4
     (iv) 17.1    (v) 0.7
   (b) (i) 46.14    (ii) 59.70    (iii) 569.43
     (iv) 17.06   (v) 0.66

**6.** (a) 40.9 litres, nearest tenth of a litre.
   (b) £2.37, nearest penny.
   (c) 35.7 cm, nearest millimetre.
   (d) £1.33, nearest penny.
   (e) £20.89, nearest penny.

1. (a) 20     (b) 500     (c) 400
   (d) 2000     (e) 20     (f) 0.08
   (g) 0.09     (h) 0.009     (i) 0.01

2. 500

3. (a) 80 000     (b) 80     (c) 1000
   (d) 0.007     (e) 0.002

4. $472\,m^2$

5. (a) $13.2 \times 11.9 = 157.08$
      Answer $157\,cm^2$, to nearest whole number.
   (b) $99 \times 62 = 6138$
      Answer $6000\,m^2$, to one sig fig.
   (c) $13 \times 16 = 208$
      Answer $200\,m$, to one sig fig.
   (d) $3.65 \times 4.35 = 15.8775$
      Answer $16\,m^2$, to nearest whole number.

1. **£50 + £90 + £60 + £100 = £300**

2. (a) £8000 + £1000 = £9000     (b) £9312

3. (a) (i) $40 \times 20 = 800$
      (ii) $100 \times 20 = 2000$
      (iii) $800 \times 50 = 40\,000$
      (iv) $900 \times 60 = 54\,000$
   (b) (i) $80 \div 20 = 4$
      (ii) $600 \div 30 = 20$
      (iii) $900 \div 60 = 15$
      (iv) $4000 \div 80 = 50$

4. $40 \times 50p = £20$

5. $20 \times 30 = 600$

6. $600 \div 30 = 20$

7. $15\,000 \div 1000 = 15\,km/l$

8. (a) 30 is bigger than 29. 50 is bigger than 48.
      So, $30 \times 50$ is bigger than $29 \times 48$.
   (b) $200 \div 10 = 20$.
      200 is bigger than 18.2
      10 is smaller than 13.
      Actual answer = 14, estimate is bigger.

1. $167.5\,cm$

2. $49.5\,kg$

3. $8.5\,m \leqslant$ height of building $< 9.5\,m$

4. Minimum weight: 835 g
   Maximum weight: 845 g

5. 287.5 g

6. 11.55 seconds

7. 9.35 kg

8. 94 ml

1. 5

2. (a) 28.71     (b) 6.91     (c) 12.40
   (d) 0.04     (e) 0.01

3. (a) 70     (b) 100     (c) 800
   (d) 700     (e) 80     (f) 1000

4. (a) 25.57
   (b) 25.6     | 25.5714285 |
   (c) 30

5. (a) $90 \times 2 = 180$     (b) $2000 \div 50 = 40$

6. $£40 \times 100 = £4000.$

7. 2749

## Chapter 22   Fractions

1. **W**: $\frac{1}{3}$    **X**: $\frac{5}{6}$    **Y**: $\frac{7}{15}$    **Z**: $\frac{6}{25}$

3. (a) $\frac{4}{9}$     (b) $\frac{2}{8} = \frac{1}{4}$
   (c) $\frac{8}{16} = \frac{1}{2}$     (d) $\frac{3}{18} = \frac{1}{6}$

4. (a) $\frac{1}{3}$   (b) $\frac{1}{3}$   (c) $\frac{1}{3}$   (d) $\frac{1}{3}$   (e) $\frac{1}{2}$

5. (a) **P**     (b) **P**     (c) **R**
   (d) **R**     (e) **Q**     (f) **S**

6. (a) (i) Many possible answers.   (ii) $\frac{1}{6}$
   (b) (i) Many possible answers.   (ii) $\frac{1}{12}$

1. (a) 3   (b) 4   (c) 3   (d) 8   (e) 8
   (f) 9   (g) 12   (h) 20   (i) 40   (j) 12

2. (a) 6     (b) 24

3. 56

4. 28

5. £5

6. £7.70

7. £148.40

8. (a) 9     (b) 10     (c) $\frac{5}{24}$

## Practice Exercise 22.3     Page 188

1. $0.5, \frac{1}{2}$;  $0.2, \frac{1}{5}$;  $0.75, \frac{3}{4}$;  $0.7, \frac{7}{10}$;  $0.01, \frac{1}{100}$

2. (a) $\frac{3}{25}$  (b) $\frac{3}{5}$  (c) $\frac{8}{25}$  (d) $\frac{7}{40}$
   (e) $\frac{9}{20}$  (f) $\frac{13}{20}$  (g) $\frac{11}{50}$  (h) $\frac{101}{500}$
   (i) $\frac{7}{25}$  (j) $\frac{111}{200}$  (k) $\frac{5}{8}$  (l) $\frac{21}{25}$

3. (a) (i) 0.1  (ii) 0.3  (iii) 0.7
   (b) (i) 0.25  (ii) 0.5  (iii) 0.75
   (c) (i) 0.15  (ii) 0.35  (iii) 0.95
   (d) (i) 0.16  (ii) 0.36  (iii) 0.92

4. (a) 0.125  (b) 0.625  (c) 0.225  (d) 0.725

5. (a) 0.33  (b) 0.17  (c) 0.43
   (d) 0.45  (e) 0.78

## Review Exercise 22     Page 189

1. (a) $\frac{4}{12} = \frac{1}{3}$  (b) Any 3 squares shaded.

2. (a) $\frac{1}{5}$  (b) 1

3. (a) 18  (b) 15

4. (a) 126  (b) 49

5. (a) 0.375  (b) 0.67

## Chapter 23  Percentages

## Practice Exercise 23.1     Page 191

1. (a) 35%  (b) 54%  (c) 24%  (d) 16%
   (e) 84%  (f) 42%  (g) 5%  (h) 46%

2. (a) (i) 40  (ii) 40%
   (b) (i) 60, shade any 60 squares, 60%.
       (ii) 70, shade any 70 squares, 70%.
       (iii) 45, shade any 45 squares, 45%.
       (iv) 24, shade any 24 squares, 24%.
       (v) 46, shade any 46 squares, 46%.
       (vi) 68, shade any 68 squares, 68%.

3. (a) (b)

| Percentage | Fraction | Decimal |
|---|---|---|
| 10% | $\frac{1}{10}$ | 0.1 |
| 20% | $\frac{1}{5}$ | 0.2 |
| 25% | $\frac{1}{4}$ | 0.25 |
| 50% | $\frac{1}{2}$ | 0.5 |
| 75% | $\frac{3}{4}$ | 0.75 |
| 80% | $\frac{4}{5}$ | 0.8 |

4. (a) $\frac{3}{20}$  (b) $\frac{1}{20}$  (c) $\frac{9}{50}$
   (d) $\frac{13}{25}$  (e) $\frac{23}{100}$  (f) $\frac{1}{8}$

5. (a) 0.15  (b) 0.05  (c) 0.47
   (d) 0.72  (e) 0.875  (f) 1.5

## Practice Exercise 23.2     Page 192

1.

| Fraction | $\frac{3}{10}$ | $\frac{2}{5}$ | $\frac{3}{25}$ | $\frac{7}{20}$ |
|---|---|---|---|---|
| Percentage | 30% | 40% | 12% | 35% |

2.

| Decimal | 0.7 | 0.45 | 0.05 | 1.2 |
|---|---|---|---|---|
| Percentage | 70% | 45% | 5% | 120% |

3. $33\frac{1}{3}\%$

4. (a) 34%  (b) 48%  (c) 15%  (d) 80%
   (e) 27%  (f) 65%  (g) $66\frac{2}{3}\%$  (h) $22\frac{2}{9}\%$

5. (a) 15%  (b) 32%  (c) 12.5%
   (d) 7%  (e) 112%  (f) 1.5%

6. (a) $\frac{2}{5}$,  $\frac{1}{2}$,  0.55,  60%
   (b) 0.42,  43%,  $\frac{11}{25}$,  $\frac{9}{20}$
   (c) 28%,  0.2805,  $\frac{57}{200}$,  $\frac{23}{80}$

7. 80%

8. (a) 90%  (b) 85%  (c) 88%  (d) 80%

9. **B** (A: $62\frac{1}{2}\%$,  **B**: $63\frac{1}{3}\%$.)

10. Team A.
    (A: $72\frac{8}{11}\%$,  B: $71\frac{3}{7}\%$.)

## Practice Exercise 23.3     Page 193

1. (a) 50  (b) 140  (c) 60  (d) 15
   (e) 12  (f) 90  (g) 24  (h) 14

2. (a) £16  (b) £15  (c) £66  (d) 12p

3. 270

4. £42

5. (a) 40  (b) 17  (c) 60
   (d) 64  (e) 24 kg  (f) 280 m
   (g) £11.25  (h) £52.50

6. (a) (i) 60  (ii) 105  (b) 45%

7. £20

8. £2.70

9. £10.50

10. (a) 660  (b) 198

11. 24 g

## Practice Exercise 23.4     Page 195

1. 20%

2. 25%

3. 28%

4. Becky.    Sam's increase = 32%
              Becky's increase = 40%

5. (a) $33\frac{1}{3}\%$      (b) 10.7%, to 1 d.p.
    Rent went up by a greater percentage.

6. Car A 13.8%,   Car B 18.2%.

7. 19.5%

8. 18.4%

## Review Exercise 23     Page 196

1. (a) 70%     (b) Shade any 3 rectangles.

2. 40%  England

3. (a) £16     (b) 45 minutes     (c) £2.56

4. (a) 47%     (b) 35%

5. (a) 18     (b) 20%

6. (a) 360     (b) 65%

7. 20%

8. 15%

9. 19%

## Chapter 24   Time *and* Speed

## Practice Exercise 24.1     Page 198

1. (a) 1030     (b) 2230     (c) 0145
    (d) 1345     (e) 2350

2. (a) 2.15 pm     (b) 5.25 am     (c) 11.20 pm
    (d) 10.05 am     (e) 5.05 pm

3. (a) 7 am
    (b) 0700

4. (a) Start 9 am,
      Finish 3.30 pm
    (b) Start 0900,
      Finish 1530
    (c) 6 hours 30 minutes

5. (a) Start 11.54 am,
      Finish 1.35 pm
    (b) 1 hour 41 minutes

6. (a)

| 1230 | News |
|---|---|
| 1255 | Shortland Street |
| 1320 | Three minutes |
| 1325 | Home and Away |

    (b) 25 minutes

7. (a) 10.13 am     (b) 1 hour 4 minutes

8. (a) 2.32 pm     (b) 292 minutes

9. (a) 1325     (b) 2 hours 15 minutes

10. (a) 7.50 pm     (b) 1950

11. (a) 1235     (b) 12.35 pm

12. (a) 1341     (b) 1.41 pm

## Practice Exercise 24.2     Page 199

1. (a) (i) 33 minutes   (ii) 2.36 pm
    (b) (i) 5 minutes   (ii) 2.44 pm

2. (a) 49 minutes     (b) 1 hour 35 minutes
    (c) 1.42 pm     (d) 0815

3. (a) (i) 15 minutes
       (ii) 5.40 pm
    (b) (i) 1915
       (ii) 11 minutes
    (c) 71 minutes

4. (a) The 1204 from Here.
    (b) The 1201 and 1359 take 46 minutes.

5. (a) 1 hour 9 minutes     (b) 1303
    (c) (i) 1430     (ii) 45 minutes
    (d) The 1731 from Haymarket.

6. (a) (i) 12.41 pm   (ii) 1 hour 43 minutes
    (b) 1815     (c) 13 minutes
    (d) 12.20 am     (e) 6 hours 5 minutes

## Practice Exercise 24.3     Page 203

1. 8 miles per hour

2. 7 km/h

3. 25 metres per minute

4. (a) 20 km/h     (b) 50 km/h     (c) 4 km/h

5. 10 km/h

6. 8 km

7. 30 miles

8. 3 km

9. (a) 150 km     (b) 86 km     (c) 40 km

10. 6 km

11. (a) 60 km/h     (b) 1 hour

12. 11.20 am

1. (a) 300 km     (b) 5 hours     (c) 60 km/h

2. 5 m/s

3. (a) ⎡13.7 km/h⎤

   (b) ⎡1.10 pm⎤

4. 150 m

5. 300 000 000 m/s

6. (a) 8 hours     (b) 111 km/h

7. (a) 4.81 m/s     (b) 17.3 km/h

---

**Review** Exercise **24**    Page 205

1. 10.30 pm

2. (a) 2 hours 16 minutes
   (b) (i)  0737
       (ii) 1 hour 57 minutes
   (c) 1629 (3 hours 40 minutes)
       The 0648 takes 3 hours 47 minutes.

3. 82 miles

4. (a) 1.05 pm
   (b) 0805

5. 64 miles per hour

6. (a) 50 km/h     (b) 7 hours
   (c) No.   Time = $\dfrac{\text{Distance}}{\text{Speed}} = \dfrac{415}{45}$ = 9.2 hours

7. 14 km

8. 80 km/h

9. 34 km/h

10. 3 miles

11. 1315

12. 8 km/h

---

| Chapter | |
|---|---|
| **25** | **Ratio** *and* **Proportion** |

**Practice** Exercise **25.1**    Page 207

1. (a) For every 5 SMILERS
      there are 2 GLUMS.
   (b) The ratio of SMILERS
       to GLUMS is 5 : 2.

2. The ratio of SMILERS to GLUMS is 7 : 3.

3. (a) For every 3 SMILERS there is 1 GLUM.
   (b) The ratio of SMILERS to GLUMS is
       3 : 1.

4. (a) 8 SMILERS and 2 GLUMS
   (b) 3 SMILERS and 9 GLUMS

5. (a) 16          (b) 9
   (c) (i)  84     (ii) 112

6. (a) 14 SMILERS and 6 GLUMS
   (b)  9 SMILERS and 6 GLUMS

7. (a) 1 : 2      (b) 1 : 3      (c) 3 : 4
   (d) 2 : 5      (e) 3 : 4      (f) 2 : 5
   (g) 3 : 7      (h) 9 : 4      (i) 4 : 9
   (j) 7 : 3

8. 2 : 3

9. 5 : 2

10. 1 : 250

11. 1 : 1500

12. (a) 4 : 1      (b) 2 : 25     (c) 11 : 2
    (d) 5 : 2      (e) 4 : 1      (f) 40 : 17
    (g) 9 : 20     (h) 25 : 1     (i) 1 : 15
    (j) 2 : 1

13. 40 : 9

14. 2 : 3

15. 1 : 2

---

**Practice** Exercise **25.2**    Page 209

1. 6

2. 32 kg

3. 140

4. 36

5. (a) $n = 12$     (b) $n = 28$
   (c) $n = 100$    (d) $n = 20$

6. 198 cm

7. 400 g

---

**Practice** Exercise **25.3**    Page 210

1. (a) 16p
   (b) £1.28

2. (a) £7          (b) £70

3. (a) 30p
   (b) £2.40

4. (a) £6.50       (b) £130

5. £2.85

6. £201.60

7. £61

8. £2.85

9. £23.40

10. £89.28

11. £32.41

12. (a) £3.08     (b) 12 minutes

13. (a) 180 g     (b) 637.5 ml     (c) 210 g

14. (a) 12 minutes     (b) 16 miles

15. (a) 12 m²     (b) 12 litres

16. (a) £260     (b) 32

17. (a) 168.75 g     (b) 36     (c) 540 ml

## Review Exercise 25     Page 211

1. (a) 75     (b) 12
   (c) (i) 56     (ii) 140

2. 1 : 3

3. 3 : 4

4. 9

5. 64

6. 8

7. 18 years old

8. (a) 50 g     (b) 720 g

9. (a) 24     (b) 5 : 3

10. 1 : 250

11. £11.50

12. $17\frac{1}{2}$ minutes

13. (a) £27     (b) £58.50

14. 1 : 200 000

15. £1.94

## Chapter 26   Understanding and Using Measures

### Practice Exercise 26.1     Page 214

1. (a) 60 mm     (b) 320 mm     (c) 6320 mm
   (d) 86 mm     (e) 8 mm     (f) 0.8 mm
   (g) 45 mm     (h) 1 mm

2. (a) 9 cm     (b) 21 cm     (c) 350 cm
   (d) 7.35 cm     (e) 0.2 cm     (f) 0.35 cm
   (g) 6 cm     (h) 0.01 cm

3. (a) 2 m     (b) 3.2 m     (c) 45.5 m
   (d) 0.66 m     (e) 0.08 m     (f) 0.098 m
   (g) 15 m     (h) 0.01 m

4. (a) 600 cm     (b) 5600 cm     (c) 760 cm
   (d) 2350 cm     (e) 90 cm     (f) 7 cm
   (g) 150 cm     (h) 10 cm

5. (a) 4 km     (b) 35 km
   (c) 6.5 km     (d) 0.455 km
   (e) 0.075 km     (f) 0.007 km
   (g) 0.2 km     (h) 0.001 km

6. (a) 6000 m     (b) 32 000 m
   (c) 650 000 m     (d) 3310 m
   (e) 350 m     (f) 85 m
   (g) 1500 m     (h) 100 m

7. (a) 142 500 cm²     (b) 14.25 m²

8. (a) 440 cm     (b) 0.96 m²

9. 360 000 cm³

10. (a) 3.57 km     (b) 3570 m

11. 11 576.25 cm³

12. (a) 2000 g     (b) 45 000 g
    (c) 7500 g     (d) 42 500 g
    (e) 600 g     (f) 25 g
    (g) 5600 g     (h) 10 g

13. (a) 3 kg     (b) 32 kg
    (c) 9.3 kg     (d) 0.22 kg
    (e) 0.083 kg     (f) 0.006 kg
    (g) 1.5 kg     (h) 4.95 kg

14. (a) 320 000 ml = 320 l
    (b) 0.32 t = 320 kg = 320 000 g
    (c) 3200 g = 3.2 kg = 0.0032 t
    (d) 320 mm = 32 cm = 0.32 m
    (e) 32 000 cm = 320 m = 0.32 km
    (f) 3.2 km = 3200 m = 320 000 cm

15. (a) 6000 kg     (b) 8 kg
    (c) 0.8 kg     (d) 650 kg

16. (a) 4000 m     (b) 8 m
    (c) 0.086 m     (d) 40 m

17. (a) 2000 ml     (b) 500 ml
    (c) 850 ml     (d) 30 ml

18. **Option A.**
    **Option A:** 18.55 litres.
    **Option B:** 18.2 litres.

19. 1.98 l

20. 50 g

21. 60

1. (a) kilometres     (b) metres
   (c) centimetres    (d) millimetres
   (e) kilograms     (f) grams
   (g) litres         (h) millilitres

2. (a) 12 m,   5.9 m,   5 *l*,   500 m²
   (b) 1200 cm,   5900 mm,   5000 ml,
         500 000 000 mm²

3. (a) A cup holds about 200 ml of tea.
   (b) The height of a car is about 1.5 m.
   (c) The weight of this book is about 700 g.
   (d) The weight of an elephant is about 700 kg.
   (e) The distance from Glasgow to Edinburgh
        is about 80 km.

4. 30 cm

5. 200 ml

6. (a) 40 mm     (b) 100 m     (c) 15 g
   (d) 7 t         (e) 400 ml

7. Between 5.6 m and 6.4 m.
   $3.5 \times 1.6\,m = 5.6\,m$, to nearest 0.1 m.
   $4 \times 1.6\,m = 6.4\,m$, to nearest 0.1 m.

1. (a) **X**: 8.5 cm,   **Y**: 3.2 cm
   (b) **X**: 85 mm,   **Y**: 32 mm

2. (a) **A**: 8.5 cm,   **B**: 4.5 cm,   **C**: 0.5 cm
   (b) **A**: 72 mm,   **B**: 47 mm,   **C**: 88 mm
   (c) **A**: 6.6 m,   **B**: 7.8 m,   **C**: 8.7 m

3. (a) (i) **A**: 1.7 kg,   **B**: 2.6 kg,   **C**: 0.45 kg
   (ii) **A**: 46.6 g,   **B**: 45.8 g,   **C**: 46.25 g
   (iii) **A**: 52.4 kg,   **B**: 51.6 kg,   **C**: 53.3 kg
   (iv) **A**: 300 ml,   **B**: 650 ml,   **C**: 450 ml
   (v) **A**: 45 ml,   **B**: 29 ml,   **C**: 12 ml
   (b) (i) 2.15 kg    (ii) 0.8 kg
   (iii) 1.7 kg    (iv) 350 ml
   (v) 33 ml

4. **A**: 9°C,   **B**: − 8°C,   **C**: 18°C

5. **A**: 23 mph,   **B**: 48 mph,   **C**: 70 mph

1. 263.5 m

2. 31.5 g ≤ weight of necklace < 32.5 g

3. Minimum 1.55 m, maximum 1.65 m

4. 4.75 km

5. 645 g ≤ weight of block < 655 g

6. 12.625 seconds

1. 8 kg and 8000 g

2. 0.5 km

3. 200

4. 8 full glasses

5. 50 ml

6. 20

7. 250 g

8. (a) 0.04 m²
   (b) 400 cm²

9. 3.765 kg

10. 4.736 m³

11. (a) 48 litres
    (b) 15 litres
    (c) 33 litres

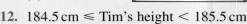

12. 184.5 cm ≤ Tim's height < 185.5 cm

13. 135 tonnes

## Chapter 27 Interpreting Graphs

1. (a) 4 inches     (b) 25 centimetres
   (c) 40 centimetres   (d) 40 inches

2. (a) 12.80 dollars   (b) £6.25

3. (a) 5.6 km      (b) 3.1 miles

4. (a) 8.8 pounds    (b) 6.8 kg

5. (a) 10°C       (b) 167°F

1. (a) 80
   (b) 40
   (c) 1200, 1400
   (d) 1315 and 1400
   (e) 140

2. (a) 4 kg     (b) 6.5 cm

3. (a) 25 m
   (b) 100 m
   (c) 2 minutes
       20 seconds

4. (a) Brian     (b) Afzal
   (c) 600 m    (d) Afzal

1. (a) 10   (b) 3   (c) 4   (d) $\frac{7}{10}$   (e) 75%

2. (a) Brett
   (b) Trent
   (c) 5 marks
   (d) 13 marks
   (e) (i) Trent (40 marks)
       (ii) Dexter (26 marks)

3. (a) 12     (b) 6     (c) Flu
   (d) For example: Boys are more likely to be absent with lesser ailments, such as coughs and colds, than girls.
   Girls suffer more from flu.
   Girls visit the dentist more than boys.

4. (a) 5
   (b) 7
   (c) 7
   (d) $33\frac{1}{3}$%
   (e) 35%
   (f) 4
   (g) 5
   (h) For example: Boys have higher mode and larger range.

1. (a) 5     (b) 4     (c) 5     (d) 5

2. (a) 6
   (b) 5
   (c) 4
   (d) 5.38.
   No shoe of this size.

3. (a) Range 6p, mode 55p
   (b) Median 54p, mean 54.1p

1.

| | | | | | | | 1 | 0 means 10 litres |
|---|---|---|---|---|---|---|---|---|
| 1 | 0 | 2 | 6 | 6 | 7 | 9 | | |
| 2 | 3 | 3 | 4 | 5 | 5 | 6 | 7 | 9 |
| 3 | 1 | 3 | 5 | 5 | | | | |
| 4 | 1 | 2 | | | | | | |

2. (a) 12     (b) 23 pence     (c) 79 pence

3. (a) 9
   (b) 50
   (c) 17
   (d) For example: Highest mark scored by a boy. Lowest mark scored by a girl. Boys have a greater range of marks.

4. (a) 4.2 cm     (b) 3.45 cm

1. (a) 8     (b) Jan, Feb, June
   (c) No information given about when cars are sold during the month.

2. (a) 82 kg     (b) 82 kg
   (c) 5 kg     (d) Week 4

3. (a) 15°C
   (b) Temperature variations during each day are not known. Line only indicates trend in midday temperatures.

4. (a) £118 - £119
   (b) Money was withdrawn.

1. (a) £140     (b) 35 km     (c) £60

2. (a) 7 hours
   (b) 5 hours
   (c) 3
   (d) (i) 20     (ii) 20%
   (e) For example:
   Boys have higher mode and larger range.

3. (b) (i) 154 cm     (ii) 15 years 4 months

4. (a) 9     (b) 9     (c) 30     (d) 8.5

5. (a) 0915     (b) 60 miles
   (c) 2     (d) 30 miles per hour

6. (a) 60     (b) 50     (c) 45.5
   (d) 37     (e) 23

## Chapter 28   Making Decisions

1. (a) 4p per pint
   (b) 9p per pint

2. Small: 5.2 g per penny.
   Large: 5.1 g per penny.
   Small tin is better buy.

3. Small: 8.7 g per penny.
   Large: 8.5 g per penny.
   Small pot is better buy.

4. 460 g gives 7.08 g per penny.
   700 g gives 7.14 g per penny.
   700 g at 98p is better value for money.

5. Large: 2.3 g per penny.
   Small: 2.2 g per penny.
   Large pot is better buy.

**6.** 120 g gives 1.41 g per penny.
250 g gives 1.61 g per penny.
1 kg gives 1.66 g per penny.
1 kg is best value for money.

**7.** Small:     7.5 g per penny.
Medium: 7.6 g per penny.
Medium is better buy.

**8.** Small:     0.882 ml per penny.
Medium: 0.862 ml per penny.
Large:     0.878 ml per penny.
Small size is best value for money.

## Practice Exercise 28.2          Page 237

**1.** (a) £500          (b) £41.67

**2.** (a) £93.92
(b) No.   Would cost £96.17.

**3.** (a) 395 units
(b) 407.64 therms
(c) £248.93
(d) Yes.   395 × 59p = £233.05

Start          End

**4.** (a) £8.59          (b) £6892.80

**5.** COMPANY A
Buildings: £383.40
Contents: £154
Total: £537.40
COMPANY B
Buildings + Contents: £529.55
George should choose COMPANY B.

**6.** (a) £1.70          (b) 21p

**7.** £1660

## Practice Exercise 28.3          Page 240

**1.** (a) 8          (b) 16          (c) 20
(d) 40          (e) 50%

**2.** (a) 14
(b) 20
(c) 70%
(d) 80%
(e) Disprove.   80% is greater than 70%.

**3.** Disprove.
Boys $\frac{3}{21} = \frac{1}{7}$,   Girls $\frac{2}{14} = \frac{1}{7}$,   same proportion.

**4.** (a)

| Taller? | Men | Women |
|---------|-----|-------|
| Yes     | 47  | 18    |
| No      | 11  | 24    |

(b) Yes.   Taller: $\frac{47}{58} \times 100 = 81\%$

## Practice Exercise 28.4          Page 241

**1.** Bars not equal width.

**2.** Pass rate not given.
Advert implies you "pass" after 8 lessons.

**3.** 10% increase in price, disproportionate
increase in diagram size.

**4.** Horizontal axis does not begin at zero and is
not a uniform scale.

**5.** Vertical scale not uniform.
Size of diagrams disproportionate to increase
in sales.

## Practice Exercise 28.5          Page 243

**1.** (a) $\frac{52}{100} = 0.52$   $\frac{102}{200} = 0.51$   $\frac{141}{300} = 0.47$
(b) 0.47
(c) Less likely, as probability of taking a red
counter from the bag is less than 0.5.

**2.** (a) June to October.
(b) January.
(c) Probability of good conditions
on the slopes is very low.

(d) January, February and December.

**3.** P(at least 1 picture card) $= \frac{1201}{5525} = 0.217$,
to 3 d.p.

**4.** (a)

| Score | Relative frequency |
|-------|--------------------|
| 1     | 0.16               |
| 2     | 0.18               |
| 3     | 0.16               |
| 4     | 0.17               |
| 5     | 0.16               |
| 6     | 0.17               |

(b) The probability of obtaining each number
$= \frac{1}{6} = 0.17$, to 2 d.p.   So, the dice is fair.

(c)

| Score | Relative frequency |
|-------|--------------------|
| 1     | 0.15               |
| 2     | 0.16               |
| 3     | 0.16               |
| 4     | 0.16               |
| 5     | 0.16               |
| 6     | 0.21               |

The dice is not fair.
Relative frequency of obtaining a 6 much
higher than calculated probability of 0.17.

## Review Exercise 28 — Page 244

1. (a) £9656.40    (b) £2156.40

2. 1.5 litre bottle gives 16.7 ml per penny.
   2 litre bottle gives 15.4 ml per penny.
   1.5 litre bottle is better value for money.

3. (a) 20
   (b) 5
   (c) No.
   Smaller proportion of females got less than 11 spellings correct.
   Males: $\frac{4}{15} = 26.7\%$,   Females: $\frac{5}{20} = 25\%$

4. Horizontal scale not uniform.
   Vertical scale not calibrated.

5. Do not support.
   Women 75%, Men 75%, same proportion.

6. (a)

| Score | 1 | 2 | 3 | 4 | 5 |
|---|---|---|---|---|---|
| Frequency | 5 | 10 | 5 | 4 | 6 |

   (b)

| Score | Relative frequency |
|---|---|
| 1 | 0.17 |
| 2 | 0.33 |
| 3 | 0.17 |
| 4 | 0.13 |
| 5 | 0.20 |

   (c) Probably not, as 2 occurs twice as many times as other numbers.

## Section Review — Numeracy

### Non-calculator section — Page 246

1. (a) −4°C    (b) 15 degrees Celsius
   (c) 2.67°C

2. −15, −4, 3, 39, 120

3. (a) £3.64    (b) £6.36

4. (a) $\frac{2}{3}$    (b) Shade any 4 squares.

5. (a) £20    (b) £145.04

6. (a) 2.25 pm    (b) 32 minutes

7. (a) $\frac{1}{10}$    (b) £5

8. (a) 87    (b) 86.7    (c) 86.74

9. (a) 12 000 cm²    (b) 1.2 m²

10. 4.4 cm

11. (a) 31 cm    (b) 15    (c) 18 cm    (d) 26 cm

---

12. (a) kilometre    (b) tonne
    (c) metre    (d) square metre

13. (a) (i) 2.5 miles
       (ii) 6.4 kilometres
    (b) 5 miles = 8km,   20 × 8 km = 160 km

14. 217.5 litres ≤ capacity < 222.5 litres

15. $\frac{4}{5}$

16. 6

17. (a) 6    (b) 21    (c) Football

18. 1600 kg

19. (a) 11 degrees Celsius
    (b) −2°C

20. (a) 5    (b) 8    (c) 10    (d) 8

21. 100 × 8 = 800

22. $\frac{60}{20-5} = 4$

23. (a) 50%    (b) 0.4
    (c) $\frac{2}{5}, \frac{1}{2}, \frac{2}{3}, \frac{3}{4}$
    (d) 27    (e) $\frac{3}{4}$

24. (a) $\frac{7}{9}$    (b) $\frac{6}{25}$
    (c) Can swim: girls 0.76, boys 0.8.
    Not true. 0.8 > 0.76

25. (a) 75%    (b) $\frac{3}{10}$

## Section Review — Numeracy

### Calculator section — Page 249

26. 2 : 5

27. 39p

28. (a) 230 cm    (b) 40 gallons

29. 90

30. 36 miles per hour.

31. 8

32. 2500

33. (a) 5    (b) $\frac{1}{2}$    (c) 6

34. (a) 86.5 m    (b) 87.5 m

35. 6

36. £48

37. 31.6%

# INDEX